Introduction to LITERATURE
pearson custom library

Pearson Learning Solutions

New York   Boston   San Francisco
London   Toronto   Sydney   Tokyo   Singapore   Madrid
Mexico City   Munich   Paris   Cape Town   Hong Kong   Montreal

Senior Vice President, Editorial and Marketing: Patrick F. Boles
Senior Sponsoring Editor: Natalie Danner
Development Editor: Mary Kate Paris
Assistant Editor: Jill Johnson
Operations Manager: Eric M. Kenney
Production Manager: Jennifer Berry
Rights Manager: Jillian Santos
Art Director and Cover Designer: Renée Sartell

Cover Art: Photography by Chris Beaudoin.

Please visit our website at *www.pearsoncustom.com.*

Attention bookstores: For permission to return any unsold stock, contact
us at *pe-uscustomreturns@pearson.com.*

Pearson Learning Solutions, 501 Boylston Street, Suite 900, Boston, MA 02116
A Pearson Education Company
www.pearsoned.com

ISBN 10: 1-256-17821-7
ISBN 13: 978-1-256-17821-7

Introduction to
LITERATURE
pearson custom library

Acknowledgements

A project as broad, far-reaching, challenging, and path-breaking as *The Pearson Custom Library: Introduction to Literature* could not be undertaken or accomplished without the support and participation of many colleagues. For their contributions, research, ideas, and suggestions, the editors particularly wish to thank David L.G. Arnold, University of Wisconsin, Stevens Point; Lydia M. Barovero, Providence College; Lisa Bickmore, Salt Lake City Community College; Claire Connolly, University of Wales–Cardiff; Allison Fernley, Salt Lake City Community College; Lisa Fluet, Boston College; Clint Gardner, Salt Lake City Community College; Curtis Gruenler, Hope College; Hilary Justice, Illinois State University; Martin Kevorkian, University of Texas, Austin; Lynn Kilpatrick, University of Utah; Susanne Liaw; Mark Lovely, Merrimack College; James J. Lu, California Baptist University; Sarah McKibben, University of Notre Dame; Cristanne Miller, University of Buffalo, The State University of New York; Jim Miracky, College of the Holy Cross; Bill Morgan, Illinois State University; Mark Morrison, Pennsylvania State University; John Mulrooney, College of the Holy Cross; Jamil Mustafa, Lewis University; Lisa Perdigao, Florida Institute of Technology; Jason Pickavance, Salt Lake City Community College; Robin Schulze, Pennsylvania State University; Mary Trotter, University of Wisconsin–Madison; Steve Vineberg, College of the Holy Cross; Helen Whall, College of the Holy Cross; Mario Pereira, Brown University; and Janice Wiggins.

Your *Introduction to Literature* purchase includes access to online resources designed to complement your readings. This Companion Website is located at the following URL:

http://www.pearsoncustom.com/dbintrolit/introlit/student

When prompted, enter the User Name: **ilstudent** and Password: **illearn**

(*Note:* The User Name and Password are case-sensitive, so be sure to use upper and lower case characters exactly as shown above.)

Once logged in, you will have access to the following resources:

Link Library. A collection of vetted web links organized by key terms and literary figures which offer you background and context for many of the selections you'll be reading.

The Writing Process. Advice that can aid you during the writing process. Included are guidelines and suggestions for each phase of writing, from start to finish.

Plagiarism. Suggestions to help you maintain academic honesty, with illustrative examples.

Grammar Guide. Spells out some of the rules and conventions of standard written English.

MLA Style. A brief guide to help you follow MLA style in citing your sources. The Modern Language Association style is widely used for papers in English composition, literature, and foreign languages.

We invite you to explore!

Contents

Part 1: Short Stories

Francine Prose
[1947–   ]

FRANCINE PROSE *was born in New York, the child of two physicians. She received her bachelor's degree from Radcliffe College, and her master's from Harvard University. After completing her master's, she spent a year in India, searching for a new way to relate to the world through her writing. Her first novel,* Judah the Pious *(1973), was written during this period; set in seventeenth-century Poland, and unfolding through a series of tales within tales,* Judah the Pious *received the Jewish Book Council Award. Prose followed this novel, during the next five years, with three more novels,* The Glorious Ones *(1974),* Marie Laveau *(1977), and* Animal Magnetism *(1978), plus a collection of short stories for children,* Stories from Our Living Past *(1974). Prose first achieved wide popular recognition, however, with her novel* Household Saints *(1981), which explores mid-twentieth century Italian-American culture in compelling detail. Since that time, Prose has published seven more novels, including* Blue Angel *(2000), which was nominated for the National Book Award, and, most recently,* A Changed Man *(2005). She has also published three collections of short stories and novellas, four children's books, and five volumes of non-fiction, including* The Lives of the Muses: Nine Women and the Artists They Inspired *(2002) and* Caravaggio: Painter of Miracles *(2005).* Reading Like a Writer *(2006) brings together Prose's experiences as an author, a student, and a teacher, in an exploration of the primary way that writers learned to write before creative writing programs came into existence— by reading.*

"Close Reading"
from Reading Like a Writer

FRANCINE PROSE

Can Creative Writing be Taught?

It's a reasonable question, but no matter how often I've been asked it, I never know quite what to say. Because if what people mean is: Can the love of language be taught? Can a gift for storytelling be taught? then the answer is no. Which may be why the question is so often asked in a skeptical tone implying that, unlike the multiplication tables or the principles of auto mechanics, creativity can't be transmitted from teacher to student. Imagine Milton enrolling in a graduate program for help with *Paradise Lost*, or Kafka enduring the seminar in which his classmates inform him that, frankly, they just don't believe the part about the guy waking up one morning to find he's a giant bug.

What confuses me is not the sensibleness of the question but the fact that it's being asked of a writer who has taught writing, on and off, for almost twenty years. What would it say about me, my students, and the hours we'd spent in the classroom if I said that any attempt to teach the writing of fiction was a complete waste of time? Probably, I should just go ahead and admit that I've been committing criminal fraud.

Instead I answer by recalling my own most valuable experience, not as a teacher but as a student in one of the few fiction workshops I took. This was in the 1970s, during my brief career as a graduate student in medieval English literature, when I was allowed the indulgence of taking one fiction class. Its generous teacher showed me, among other things, how to line edit my work. For any writer, the ability to look at a sentence and see what's superfluous, what can be altered, revised, expanded, and, especially, cut, is essential. It's satisfying to see that sentence shrink, snap into place, and ultimately emerge in a more polished form: clear, economical, sharp.

Meanwhile, my classmates were providing me with my first real audience. In that prehistory, before mass photocopying enabled students to distribute manuscripts in advance, we read our work aloud. That year, I was beginning what would become my first novel. And what made an important difference to me was the attention I felt in the room as the others listened. I was encouraged by their eagerness to hear more.

That's the experience I describe, the answer I give to people who ask about teaching creative writing: A workshop can be useful. A good teacher can show you how to edit your work. The right class can form the basis of a community that will help and sustain you.

But that class, as helpful as it was, was not where I learned to write.

Like most—maybe all—writers, I learned to write by writing and, by example, by reading books.

Long before the idea of a writer's conference was a glimmer in anyone's eye, writers learned by reading the work of their predecessors. They studied meter with Ovid, plot construction with Homer, comedy with Aristophanes; they honed their prose style by absorbing the lucid sentences of Montaigne and Samuel Johnson. And who could have asked for better teachers: generous, uncritical, blessed with wisdom and genius, as endlessly forgiving as only the dead can be?

Though writers have learned from the masters in a formal, methodical way—Harry Crews has described taking apart a Graham Greene novel to see how many chapters it contained, how much time it covered, how Greene handled pacing, tone, and point of view—the truth is that this sort of education more often involves a kind of osmosis. After I've written an essay in which I've quoted at length from great writers, so that I've had to copy out long passages of their work, I've noticed that my own work becomes, however briefly, just a little more fluent.

In the ongoing process of becoming a writer, I read and reread the authors I most loved. I read for pleasure, first, but also more analytically, conscious of style, of diction, of how sentences were formed and information was being conveyed, how the writer was structuring a plot, creating characters, employing detail and dialogue. And as I wrote, I discovered that writing, like reading, was done one word at a time, one punctuation mark at a time. It required what a friend calls "putting every word on trial for its life": changing an adjective, cutting a phrase, removing a comma, and putting the comma back in.

I read closely, word by word, sentence by sentence, pondering each deceptively minor decision the writer had made. And though it's impossible to recall every source of inspiration and instruction, I can remember the novels and stories that seemed to me revelations: wells of beauty and pleasure that were also textbooks, private lessons in the art of fiction.

This book is intended partly as a response to that unavoidable question about how writers learn to do something that cannot be taught. What writers know is that, ultimately, we learn to write by practice, hard work, by repeated trial and error, success and failure, and from the books we admire. And so the book that follows represents an effort to recall my own education as a novelist and to help the passionate reader and would-be writer understand how a writer reads.

When I was a high school junior, our English teacher assigned a term paper on the theme of blindness in *Oedipus Rex* and *King Lear*. We were supposed to go through the two tragedies and circle every reference to eyes, light, darkness, and vision, then draw some conclusion on which we would base our final essay.

It all seemed so dull, so mechanical. We felt we were way beyond it. Without this tedious, time-consuming exercise, all of us knew that blindness played a starring role in both dramas.

Still, we liked our English teacher, and we wanted to please him. And searching for every relevant word turned out to have an enjoyable treasure-hunt aspect, a *Where's Waldo* detective thrill. Once we started looking for eyes, we found them everywhere, glinting at us, winking from every page.

Long before the blinding of Oedipus or Gloucester, the language of vision and its opposite was preparing us, consciously or unconsciously, for those violent mutilations. It asked us to consider what it meant to be clear-sighted or obtuse, shortsighted or prescient, to heed the signs and warnings, to see or deny what was right in front of one's eyes. Teiresias, Oedipus, Goneril, Kent— all of them could be defined by the sincerity or falseness with which they mused or ranted on the subject of literal or metaphorical blindness.

It was fun to trace those patterns and to make those connections. It was like cracking a code that the playwright had embedded in the text, a riddle that existed just for me to decipher. I felt as if I were engaged in some intimate communication with the writer, as if the ghosts of Sophocles and Shakespeare had been waiting patiently all those centuries for a bookish sixteen-year-old to come along and find them.

I believed that I was learning to read in a whole new way. But this was only partly true. Because in fact I was merely relearning to read in an old way that I had learned, but forgotten.

We all begin as close readers. Even before we learn to read, the process of being read aloud to, and of listening, is one in which we are taking in one word after another, one phrase at a time, in which we are paying attention to whatever each word or phrase is transmitting. Word by word is how we learn to hear and then read, which seems only fitting, because it is how the books we are reading were written in the first place.

The more we read, the faster we can perform that magic trick of seeing how the letters have been combined into words that have meaning. The more we read, the more we comprehend, the more likely we are to discover new ways to read, each one tailored to the reason why we are reading a particular book.

At first, the thrill of our own brand-new expertise is all we ask or expect from Dick and Jane. But soon we begin to ask what else those marks on the page can give us. We begin to want information, entertainment, invention, even truth and beauty. We concentrate, we skim, we skip words, put down the book and daydream, start over, and reread. We finish a book and return to it years later to see what we might have missed, or the ways in which time and age have affected our understanding.

As a child, I was drawn to the works of the great escapist children's writers. I liked trading my familiar world for the London of the four children whose nanny parachuted into their lives with her umbrella and who turned the most routine shopping trip into a magical outing. I would gladly have followed the White Rabbit down into the rabbit hole and had tea with the Mad Hatter. I loved novels in which children stepped through portals—a garden door, a wardrobe—into an alternate universe.

Children love the imagination, with its kaleidoscopic possibilities and its protest against the way that children are always being told exactly what's true and what's false, what's real and what's illusion. Perhaps my taste in reading had something to do with the limitations I was discovering, day by day: the brick walls of time and space, science and probability, to say nothing of whatever messages I was picking up from the culture. I liked novels with plucky heroines like Pippi Longstocking, the astringent Jane Eyre, and the daughters in *Little Women,* girls whose resourcefulness and intelligence don't automatically exclude them from the pleasures of male attention.

Each word of these novels was a yellow brick in the road to Oz. There were chapters I read and reread so as to repeat the dependable, out-of-body sensation of being *somewhere else.* I read addictively, constantly. On one family vacation, my father pleaded with me to close my book long enough to look at the Grand Canyon. I borrowed stacks of books from the public library: novels, biographies, history, anything that looked even remotely engaging.

Along with pre-adolescence came a more pressing desire for escape. I read more widely, more indiscriminately, and mostly with an interest in how far a book could take me from my life and how long it could keep me there: *Gone With the Wind,* Pearl Buck, Edna Ferber, fat bestsellers by James Michener, with a dash of history sprinkled in to cool down the steamy love scenes between the Hawaiian girls and the missionaries, the geishas and the GIs. I also appreciated these books for the often misleading nuggets of information they provided about sex in that innocent era, the 1950s. I turned the pages of these page-turners as fast as I could. Reading was like eating alone, with that same element of bingeing.

I was fortunate to have good teachers, and friends who were also readers. The books I read became more challenging, better written, more substantial: Steinbeck, Camus, Hemingway, Fitzgerald, Twain, Salinger, Anne Frank. My friends and

I, little beatniks, were passionate fans of Jack Kerouac, Allen Ginsberg, Lawrence Ferlinghetti. We read Truman Capote, Carson McCullers, and the proto-hippie classics of Herman Hesse, Carlos Castaneda—*Mary Poppins* for people who thought they'd outgrown the flying nanny. I must have been vaguely aware of the power of language, but only dimly, and only as it applied to whatever effect the book was having on me.

All of that that changed with every mark I made on the pages of *King Lear* and *Oedipus Rex.* I still have my old copy of Sophocles, heavily underlined, covered with sweet, embarrassing notes-to-self ("irony?" "recognition of fate?") written in my rounded, heartbreakingly neat schoolgirl print. Like seeing a photograph of yourself as a child, encountering handwriting that you know was once yours but that now seems only dimly familiar can inspire a confrontation with the mystery of time.

Focusing on language proved to be a practical skill, useful the way sight-reading with ease can come in handy for a musician. My high school English teacher had only recently graduated from a college where his own English professors taught what was called New Criticism, a school of thought that favored reading what was on the page with only passing reference to the biography of the writer or the period in which the text was written. Luckily for me, that approach to literature was still in fashion when I graduated and went on to college. At my university there was a well-known professor and critic whose belief in close reading trickled down and influenced the entire humanities program. In French class, we spent an hour each Friday afternoon working our way from *The Song of Roland* to Sartre, paragraph by paragraph, focusing on small sections for what was called the *explication de texte.*

Of course, there were many occasions on which I had to skim as rapidly as I could to get through those survey courses that gave us two weeks to finish *Don Quixote,* ten days for *War and Peace*—courses designed to produce college graduates who could say they'd read the classics. By then I knew enough to regret having to read those books that way. And I promised myself that I would revisit them as soon as I could give them the time and attention they deserved.

Only once did my passion for reading steer me in the wrong direction, and that was when I let it persuade me to go to graduate school. There, I soon realized that my love for books was unshared by many of my classmates and professors. I found it hard to understand what they *did* love, exactly, and this gave me an anxious shiver that would later seem like a warning about what would happen to the teaching of literature over the decade or so after I dropped out of my Ph.D. program. That was when literary academia split into warring camps of deconstructionists, Marxists, feminists, and so forth, all battling for the right to tell students that they were reading "texts" in which ideas and politics trumped what the writer had actually written.

I left graduate school and became a writer. I wrote my first novel in India, in Bombay, where I read as omnivorously as I had as a child, rereading classics that I borrowed from the old-fashioned, musty, beautiful university library that seemed to have acquired almost nothing written after 1920. Afraid of running out of books, I decided to slow myself down by reading Proust in French.

Reading a masterpiece in a language for which you need a dictionary is in itself a course in reading word by word. And as I puzzled out the gorgeous, labyrinthine sentences, I discovered how reading a book can make you want to write one.

A work of art can start you thinking about some aesthetic or philosophical problem; it can suggest some new method, some fresh approach to fiction. But the relationship between reading and writing is rarely so clear-cut, and in fact my first novel could hardly have been less Proustian.

More often the connection has to do with whatever mysterious promptings make you want to write. It's like watching someone dance and then secretly, in your own room, trying out a few steps. I often think of learning to write by reading as something like the way I first began to read. I had a few picture books I'd memorized and pretended I could read, as a sort of party trick that I did repeatedly for my parents, who were also pretending—in their case, to be amused. I never knew exactly when I crossed the line from pretending to actually being able, but that was how it happened.

Not long ago, a friend told me that her students had complained that reading masterpieces made them feel stupid. But I've always found that the better the book I'm reading, the smarter I feel, or, at least, the more able I am to imagine that I might, someday, *become* smarter. I've also heard fellow writers say that they cannot read while working on a book of their own, for fear that Tolstoy or Shakespeare might influence them. I've always *hoped* they would influence me, and I wonder if I would have taken so happily to being a writer if it had meant that I couldn't read during the years it might take to complete a novel.

To be truthful, some writers stop you dead in your tracks by making you see your own work in the most unflattering light. Each of us will meet a different harbinger of personal failure, some innocent genius chosen by us for reasons having to do with what we see as our own inadequacies. The only remedy to this I have found is to read a writer whose work is entirely different from another, though not necessarily more like your own—a difference that will remind you of how many rooms there are in the house of art.

After my novels began to be published, I started to teach, taking a succession of jobs as a visiting writer at a series of colleges and universities. Usually, I would teach one creative writing workshop each semester, together with a literature class entitled something like "The Modern Short Story"—a course designed for undergraduates who weren't planning to major in literature or go on to graduate school and so would not be damaged by my inability to teach literary theory. Alternately, I would conduct a reading seminar for MFA students who wanted to be writers rather than scholars, which meant that it was all right for us to fritter away our time talking about books rather than politics or ideas.

I enjoyed the reading classes, and the opportunity to function as a sort of cheerleader for literature. I liked my students, who were often so eager, bright, and enthusiastic that it took me years to notice how much trouble they had in reading a fairly simple short story. Almost simultaneously, I was struck by how little attention they had been taught to pay to the language, to the actual words and sentences that a writer had used. Instead, they had been encouraged to form strong, critical, and often negative opinions of geniuses who had been read with delight for centuries before they were born. They had been instructed to prosecute or defend these authors, as if in a court of law, on charges having to do with the writers' origins, their racial, cultural, and class backgrounds. They had been encouraged to rewrite the classics into the more acceptable forms that the authors might have discovered had they only shared their young critics' level of insight, tolerance, and awareness.

No wonder my students found it so stressful to read! And possibly because of the harsh judgments they felt required to make about fictional characters and their creators, they didn't seem to *like* reading, which also made me worry for them and wonder why they wanted to become writers. I asked myself how they planned to learn to write, since I had always thought that others learned, as I had, from reading.

Responding to what my students seemed to need, I began to change the way I taught. No more general discussions of this character or that plot turn. No more attempts to talk about how it *felt* to read Borges or Poe or to describe the experience of navigating the fantastic fictional worlds they created. It was a pity, because I'd often enjoyed these wide-ranging discussions, during which my students said things I would always remember. I recall one student saying that reading the stories of Bruno Schulz was like being a child again, hiding behind the door, eavesdropping on the adults, understanding a fraction of what they were saying and inventing the rest. But I assumed that I would still hear such things even if I organized classes around the more pedestrian, halting method of beginning at the beginning, lingering over every word, every phrase, every image, considering how it enhanced and contributed to the story as a whole. In this way, the students and I would get through as much of the text as possible—sometimes three or four, sometimes as many as ten, pages—in a two-hour class.

This remains the way I prefer to teach, partly because it's a method from which I benefit nearly as much as my students. And there are many stories that I have taught for years and from which I learn more each time I read them, word by word.

I've always thought that a close-reading course should at least be a companion, if not an alternative, to the writing workshop. Though it also doles out praise, the workshop most often focuses on what a writer has done wrong, what needs to be fixed, cut, or augmented. Whereas reading a masterpiece can inspire us by showing us how a writer does something brilliantly.

Occasionally, while I was teaching a reading course and simultaneously working on a novel, and when I had reached an impasse in my own work, I began to notice that whatever story I taught that week somehow helped me get past the obstacle that had been in my way. Once, for example, I was struggling with a party scene and happened to be teaching James Joyce's "The Dead," which taught me something about how to orchestrate the voices of the party guests into a chorus from which the principal players step forward, in turn, to take their solos.

On another occasion, I was writing a story that I knew was going to end in an eruption of horrific violence, and I was having trouble getting it to sound natural and inevitable rather than forced and melodramatic. Fortunately, I was teaching the stories of Isaac Babel, whose work so often explores the nature, the causes, and the aftermath of violence. What I noticed, close-reading along with my students, was that frequently in Babel's fiction, a moment of violence is directly preceded by a passage of intense lyricism. It's characteristic of Babel to offer the reader a lovely glimpse of the crescent moon just before all hell breaks loose. I tried it—first the poetry, then the horror—and suddenly everything came together, the pacing seemed right, and the incident I had been struggling with appeared, at least to me, to be plausible and convincing.

Close reading helped me figure out, as I hoped it did for my students, a way to approach a difficult aspect of writing, which is nearly always difficult. Readers of this book will notice that there are writers to whom I keep returning: Chekhov, Joyce, Austen, George Eliot, Kafka, Tolstoy, Flannery O'Connor, Katherine Mansfield, Nabokov, Heinrich von Kleist, Raymond Carver, Jane Bowles, James Baldwin, Alice Munro, Mavis Gallant—the list goes on and on. They are the teachers to whom I go, the authorities I consult, the models that still help to inspire me with the energy and courage it takes to sit down at a desk each day and resume the process of learning, anew, to write.

QUESTIONS

FRANCINE PROSE, *"Close Reading"*
from Reading Like a Writer

1. How does Prose use her own history as a reader and a writer to convey to her audience how they might use their reading to help them learn how to write?

2. What aspects of writing does Prose claim can be taught? What aspects cannot? What are the relative levels of importance of those different aspects of writing?

3. Why does Prose claim that graduate school was a bad choice for her? What was Prose looking for, as a reader and writer, that graduate school couldn't provide?

4. Prose tells us that some writers of her acquaintance stop reading while they're writing, fearing the influence of other writers on their own work, and that she, by contrast, longs for that influence. What kinds of influence does she suggest that other authors have had on her writing? What kinds of influence might be positive, and what kinds of influence might be more worrisome?

5. How do Prose's students surprise her with their approaches to reading? Why does she change her style of teaching? How might the "close reading" style she adopts help her students?

6. Select a short story that you have already read—perhaps during this course—and return to it, re-reading it as Prose suggests: slowly, closely, line by line. What do you notice in the story that you hadn't uncovered previously? How does the author create his or her story's meaning?

Edgar Allan Poe

[1809–1849]

The son of traveling actors, **EDGAR ALLAN POE** *was probably abandoned by his father shortly after his birth. In any case, his father died in 1810, and his mother continued to act, moving frequently with her children until 1811, when she too died, leaving Poe and his siblings destitute. Poe was adopted by the family of John and Frances Allan, and at his baptism assumed his benefactor's name. Despite this early gesture of connectedness, Poe's relationship with the Allans was fractious, especially after Poe began attending the University of Virginia in 1836. Here Poe was known both for his writing and also for his gambling and drinking. His repeated, abusive pleas for money caused John Allan to cut him off periodically. After one such incident Poe left the university and joined the army. During his service he published his first book of poetry,* Tamerlane and Other Poems *(1827). His second,* Al Aaraaf, *was published in 1829. In 1830, through Allan's influence, Poe was awarded an appointment to West Point, but he was soon expelled. Among cadets the legend still circulates that he forced this himself by showing up naked for morning formation, but it is more likely that drinking and gambling lay at the heart of the matter. In any event, this disgrace seems to have been fortuitous, because at this time Poe began to devote himself to writing, publishing several stories and winning a fiction contest in 1832.*

In 1833 he became editor of the Southern Literary Messenger, *one of several important literary posts he would fill in his life. In 1839 he became editor of* Burton's Gentleman's Magazine; *in 1840 editor of* Graham's; *and in 1845 editor of the* Broadway Journal. *He published a great deal of his own poetry and fiction in these journals, as well as numerous reviews (many of them quite strident), and in this way had a significant impact on literary trends and tastes. However, despite the fact that he continued to be awarded editorial positions, the same kind of behavior that resulted in his dismissal from West Point—drinking, gambling, and a disinclination to bow to authority—led him regularly into conflict with his employers. And although he published his work regularly, he was never far from poverty. He also had a tendency to pick literary fights, and was most famously dismissive of the New England transcendentalists. Some speculate that this kind of controversy may have been a ploy to sell magazines.*

Although his writing career was relatively brief and his habits were self-destructive, Poe managed to amass an impressive canon before his death in 1849. In addition to such works as "Ligeia" (1838); "The Fall of the House of Usher" (1839); Tales of the Grotesque and Arabesque *(1840); and the popular "The Raven" (1844); Poe is credited with the invention of the detective story. His character C. Auguste Dupin from "The Murders in the Rue Morgue"; "The Mystery of Marie Roget"; and "The Purloined Letter" served as type for Sherlock Holmes and countless other detectives. In these and other stories Poe demonstrates an obsession with the dark side of human psychology. Many of his tales explore a concept he labeled "the spirit of perverseness . . . the unfathomable longing of the soul to vex itself." This phenomenon can be seen in stories such as "The Black Cat" and "The Tell-Tale Heart," in which seemingly rational characters are drawn to commit ghastly crimes for reasons they cannot explain. While his last years were clouded by the death of his wife from tuberculosis in 1846, he seemed on the road to recovery when, in 1849, he stopped in Baltimore on his way to Philadelphia and was found on the street four days later, unconscious and near death. The exact cause of his death on October 7 remains a mystery.*

—David L. G. Arnold, *University of Wisconsin, Stevens Point*

The Tell-Tale Heart

EDGAR ALLAN POE

Read

TRUE!—NERVOUS—VERY, VERY dreadfully nervous I had been and am; but why *will* you say that I am mad? The disease had sharpened my senses—not destroyed—not dulled them. Above all was the sense of hearing acute. I heard all things in the heaven and in the earth. I heard many things in hell. How, then, am I mad? Hearken! and observe how healthily—how calmly I can tell you the whole story.

It is impossible to say how first the idea entered my brain; but once conceived, it haunted me day and night. Object there was none. Passion there was none. I loved the old man. He had never wronged me. He had never given me insult. For his gold I had no desire. I think it was his eye! yes, it was this! He had the eye of a vulture—a pale blue eye, with a film over it. Whenever it fell upon me, my blood ran cold; and so by degrees—very gradually—I made up my mind to take the life of the old man, and thus rid myself of the eye forever.

Now this is the point. You fancy me mad. Madmen know nothing. But you should have seen *me*. You should have seen how wisely I proceeded—with what caution—with what foresight—with what dissimulation[1] I went to work! I was never kinder to the old man than during the whole week before I killed him. And every night, about midnight, I turned the latch of his door and opened it—oh so gently! And then, when I had made an opening sufficient for my head, I put in a dark lantern,[2] all closed, closed, so that no light shone out, and then I thrust in my head. Oh, you would have laughed to see how cunningly I thrust it in! I moved it slowly—very, very slowly, so that I might not disturb the old man's sleep. It took me an hour to place my whole head within the opening so far that I could see him he lay upon his bed. Ha!—would a madman have been so wise as this? And then, when my head was well in the room, I undid the lantern cautiously—oh, so cautiously—cautiously (for the hinges creaked)—I undid it just so much that a single thin ray fell upon the vulture eye. And this I did for seven long nights—every night just at

[1]Deception

[2]A lantern with a sliding or perforated cover that limits the beam of light.

First published in *The Pioneer* in January, 1843.

midnight—but I found the eye always closed; and so it was impossible to do the work; for it was not the old man who vexed me, but his Evil Eye. And every morning, when the day broke, I went boldly into the chamber, and spoke courageously to him, calling him by name in a hearty tone and inquiring how he had passed the night. So you see he would have been a very profound old man, indeed, to suspect that every night, just at twelve, I looked in upon him while he slept.

Upon the eighth night I was more than usually cautious in opening the door. A watch's minute hand moves more quickly than did mine. Never, before that night, had I *felt* the extent of my own powers—of my sagacity. I could scarcely contain my feelings of triumph. To think that there I was, opening the door, little by little, and he not even to dream of my secret deeds or thoughts. I fairly chuckled at the idea; and perhaps he heard me; for he moved on the bed suddenly, as if startled. Now you may think that I drew back—but no. His room was as black as pitch with the thick darkness, (for the shutters were close fastened, through fear of robbers,) and so I knew that he could not see the opening of the door, and I kept pushing it on steadily, steadily.

I had my head in, and was about to open the lantern, when my thumb slipped upon the tin fastening, and the old man sprang up in bed, crying out—"Who's there?"

I kept quite still and said nothing. For a whole hour I did not move a muscle, and in the meantime I did not hear him lie down. He was still sitting up in the bed listening;—just as I have done, night after night, hearkening to the death watches[3] in the wall.

Presently I heard a slight groan, and I knew it was the groan of mortal terror. It was not a groan of pain or of grief—oh, no!—it was the low stifled sound that arises from the bottom of the soul when overcharged with awe. I knew the sound well. Many a night, just at midnight, when all the world slept, it had welled up from my own bosom, deepening, with its dreadful echo, the terrors that distracted me. I say I knew it well. I knew what the old man felt, and pitied him, although I chuckled at heart. I knew that he had been lying awake ever since the first slight noise, when he had turned in the bed. His fears had been ever since growing upon him. He had been trying to fancy them causeless, but could not. He had been saying to himself—"It is nothing but the wind in the chimney—it is only a mouse crossing the floor," or "it is merely a cricket which has made a single chirp." Yes, he had been trying to comfort himself with these suppositions: but he had found all in vain. *All in vain*; because Death, in approaching him, had stalked with his black shadow before him, and enveloped the victim. And it was the mournful influence of the perceived

---

[3]Small wood-beetles whose ticking noises were thought to predict a death.

shadow that caused him to feel—although he neither saw nor heard—to *feel* the presence of my head within the room.

When I had waited a long time, very patiently, without hearing him lie down, I resolved to open a little—a very, very little crevice in the lantern. So I opened it—you cannot imagine how stealthily, stealthily—until, at length, a single dim ray, like the thread of the spider, shot from out the crevice and fell full upon the vulture eye.

It was open—wide, wide open—and I grew furious as I gazed upon it. I saw it with perfect distinctness—all a dull blue, with a hideous veil over it that chilled the very marrow in my bones; but I could see nothing else of the old man's face or person: for I had directed the ray as if by instinct, precisely upon the damned spot.

And have I not told you that what you mistake for madness is but over acuteness of the senses?—now, I say, there came to my ears a low, dull quick sound, such as a watch makes when enveloped in cotton. I knew *that* sound well, too. It was the beating of the old man's heart. It increased my fury, as the beating of a drum stimulates the soldier into courage.

But even yet I refrained and kept still. I scarcely breathed. I held the lantern motionless. I tried how steadily I could maintain the ray upon the eye. Meantime the hellish tattoo[4] of the heart increased. It grew quicker and quicker, and louder and louder every instant. The old man's terror *must* have been extreme! It grew louder, I say, louder every moment!—do you mark me well? I have told you that I am nervous: so I am. And now at the dead hour of the night, amid the dreadful silence of that old house, so strange a noise as this excited me to uncontrollable terror. Yet, for some minutes longer I refrained and stood still. But the beating grew louder, louder! I thought the he heart must burst. And now a new anxiety seized me—the sound would be heard by a neighbour! The old man's hour had come! With a loud yell, I threw open the lantern and leaped into the room. He shrieked once—once only. In an instant I dragged him to the floor, and pulled the heavy bed[5] over him. I then smiled gaily, to find the deed so far done. But, for many minutes, the heart beat on with a muffled sound. This, however, did not vex me; it would not be heard through the wall. At length it ceased. The old man was dead. I removed the bed and examined the corpse. Yes, he was stone, stone dead. I placed my hand upon the heart and held it there many minutes. There was no pulsation. He was stone dead. His eye would trouble me no more.

If still you think me mad, you will think so no longer when I describe the wise precautions I took for the concealment of the body. The night waned,

---

[4]In this sense, a "tattoo" is a rhythmic beat.

[5]Down comforter sometimes used as a mattress.

and I worked hastily, but in silence. First of all I dismembered the corpse. I cut off the head and the arms and the legs.

I then took up three planks from the flooring of the chamber, and deposited all between the scantlings.[6] I then replaced the boards so cleverly, so cunningly, that no human eye—not even *his*—could have detected anything wrong. There was nothing to wash out—no stain of any kind—no blood-spot whatever. I had been too wary for that. A tub had caught all—ha! ha!

When I had made an end of these labors, it was four o'clock—still dark as midnight. As the bell sounded the hour, there came a knocking at the street door. I went down to open it with a light heart,—for what had I *now* to fear? There entered three men, who introduced themselves, with perfect suavity, as officers of the police. A shriek had been heard by a neighbour during the night; suspicion of foul play had been aroused; information had been lodged at the police office, and they (the officers) had been deputed to search the premises.

I smiled,—for *what* had I to fear? I bade the gentlemen welcome. The shriek, I said, was my own in a dream. The old man, I mentioned, was absent in the country. I took my visitors all over the house. I bade them search—search *well*. I led them, at length, to *his* chamber. I showed them his treasures, secure, undisturbed. In the enthusiasm of my confidence, I brought chairs into the room and desired them *here* to rest from their fatigues, while I myself, in the wild audacity of my perfect triumph, placed my own seat upon the very spot beneath which reposed the corpse of the victim.

The officers were satisfied. My *manner* had convinced them. I was singularly at ease. They sat, and while I answered cheerily, they chatted of familiar things. But, ere long, I felt myself getting pale and wished them gone. My head ached, and I fancied a ringing in my ears: but still they sat and still they chatted. The ringing became more distinct:—it continued and became more distinct: I talked more freely to get rid of the feeling: but it continued and gained definiteness—until, at length, I found that the noise was *not* within my ears.

No doubt I now grew *very* pale;—but I talked more fluently, and with a heightened voice. Yet the sound increased—and what could I do? It was *a low, dull, quick sound—much such a sound as a watch makes when enveloped in cotton.* I gasped for breath—and yet the officers heard it not. I talked more quickly—more vehemently; but the noise steadily increased. I arose and argued about trifles, in a high key and with violent gesticulations; but the noise steadily increased. Why *would* they not be gone? I paced the floor to and fro with heavy strides, as if excited to fury by the observations of the men—but the noise steadily increased. Oh God! what *could* I do? I foamed—I raved—I swore! I

---

[6]Beams

swung the chair upon which I had been sitting, and grated it upon the boards, but the noise arose over all and continually increased. It grew louder—louder—*louder!* And still the men chatted pleasantly, and smiled. Was it possible they heard not? Almighty God!—no, no! They heard!—they suspected!—they *knew!*—they were making a mockery of my horror!—this I thought, and this I think. But anything was better than this agony! Anything was more tolerable than this derision! I could bear those hypocritical smiles no longer! I felt that I must scream or die! and now—again!—hark! louder! louder! louder! *louder!*

"Villains!" I shrieked, "dissemble no more! I admit the deed!—tear up the planks! here, here!—it is the beating of his hideous heart!"

[1843]

QUESTIONS

EDGAR ALLAN POE, *The Tell-Tale Heart*

1. Describe the "dramatic situation" of this story. Who tells the story? What are the circumstances of his narration?

2. Speculate about the narrator's motives for killing his neighbor. Why does the old man's eye bother the narrator? What does the eye suggest or symbolize?

3. How does the narrator murder and dispose of his neighbor? What is the effect of this revelation on the reader?

4. What is symbolized by the act of dismemberment? How does the image of the dismembered human body speak to questions of identity and selfhood?

5. Consider the role of the police in "The Tell Tale-Heart." To what extent do they participate in the solution of the crime?

6. Why does the narrator confess to the murder? How does this confession direct our attention to inner, subjective life as opposed to an objective, social reality?

7. Research and write an essay about "The Tell-Tale Heart" as Poe's commentary on urban experience in America. What peculiar dangers does the city present in this story? How does the failure of the police detectives reflect Poe's opinion of contemporary social institutions?

8. With his short story, "The Murders in the Rue Morgue" (1841), Poe invented the modern detective story. Is "The Tell-Tale Heart" another example of the mystery genre? Review one of Poe's detective stories and write an essay about the ways in which "The Tell-Tale Heart" complements and/or revises the literary form to which Poe so heavily contributed.

The Black Cat

EDGAR ALLAN POE

FOR THE MOST WILD, yet most homely narrative which I am about to pen, I neither expect nor solicit belief. Mad indeed would I be to expect it, in a case where my very senses reject their own evidence. Yet, mad am I not—and very surely do I not dream. But to-morrow I die, and to-day I would unburthen my soul. My immediate purpose is to place before the world, plainly, succinctly, and without comment, a series of mere household events. In their consequences, these events have terrified—have tortured—have destroyed me. Yet I will not attempt to expound them. To me, they have presented little but Horror—to many they will seem less terrible than *baroques*.[1] Hereafter, perhaps, some intellect may be found which will reduce my phantasm to the common-place—some intellect more calm, more logical, and far less excitable than my own, which will perceive, in the circumstances I detail with awe, nothing more than an ordinary succession of very natural causes and effects.

From my infancy I was noted for the docility and humanity of my disposition. My tenderness of heart was even so conspicuous as to make me the jest of my companions. I was especially fond of animals, and was indulged by my parents with a great variety of pets. With these I spent most of my time, and never was so happy as when feeding and caressing them. This peculiarity of character grew with my growth, and, in my manhood, I derived from it one of my principal sources of pleasure. To those who have cherished an affection for a faithful and sagacious dog, I need hardly be at the trouble of explaining the nature or the intensity of the gratification thus derivable. There is something in the unselfish and self-sacrificing love of a brute, which goes directly to the heart of him who has had frequent occasion to test the paltry friendship and gossamer fidelity of mere *Man*.

I married early, and was happy to find in my wife a disposition not uncongenial with my own. Observing my partiality for domestic pets, she lost

[1]Grotesque, bizarre

First published in the *United States Saturday Post* on August 19, 1843. Collected in *Tales of Edgar A. Poe* in 1845.

no opportunity of procuring those of the most agreeable kind. We had birds, gold fish, a fine dog, rabbits, a small monkey, and *a cat.*

This latter was a remarkably large and beautiful animal, entirely black, and sagacious to an astonishing degree. In speaking of his intelligence, my wife, who at heart was not a little tinctured with superstition, made frequent allusion to the ancient popular notion, which regarded all black cats as witches in disguise. Not that she was ever *serious* upon this point—and I mention the matter at all for no better reason than that it happens, just now, to be remembered.

Pluto[2]—this was the cat's name—was my favorite pet and playmate. I alone fed him, and he attended me wherever I went about the house. It was even with difficulty that I could prevent him from following me through the streets.

Our friendship lasted, in this manner, for several years, during which my general temperament and character—through the instrumentality of the Fiend Intemperance[3]—had (I blush to confess it) experienced a radical alteration for the worse. I grew, day by day, more moody, more irritable, more regardless of the feelings of others. I suffered myself to use intemperate language to my wife. At length, I even offered her personal violence. My pets, of course, were made to feel the change in my disposition. I not only neglected, but ill-used them. For Pluto, however, I still retained sufficient regard to restrain me from maltreating him, as I made no scruple of maltreating the rabbits, the monkey, or even the dog, when by accident, or through affection, they came in my way. But my disease grew upon me—for what disease is like Alcohol!—and at length even Pluto, who was now becoming old, and consequently somewhat peevish—even Pluto began to experience the effects of my ill temper.

One night, returning home, much intoxicated, from one of my haunts about town, I fancied that the cat avoided my presence. I seized him; when, in his fright at my violence, he inflicted a slight wound upon my hand with his teeth. The fury of a demon instantly possessed me. I knew myself no longer. My original soul seemed, at once, to take its flight from my body; and a more than fiendish malevolence, gin-nurtured, thrilled every fibre of my frame. I took from my waistcoat-pocket a penknife, opened it, grasped the poor beast by the throat, and deliberately cut one of its eyes from the socket! I blush, I burn, I shudder, while I pen the damnable atrocity.

When reason returned with the morning—when I had slept off the fumes of the night's debauch—I experienced a sentiment half of horror, half of remorse, for the crime of which I had been guilty, but it was, at best, a feeble

---

[2]Roman god of the dead.

[3]Alcoholism

and equivocal feeling, and the soul remained untouched. I again plunged into excess, and soon drowned in wine all memory of the deed.

In the meantime the cat slowly recovered. The socket of the lost eye presented, it is true, a frightful appearance, but he no longer appeared to suffer any pain. He went about the house as usual, but, as might be expected, fled in extreme terror at my approach. I had so much of my old heart left, as to be at first grieved by this evident dislike on the part of a creature which had once so loved me. But this feeling soon gave place to irritation. And then came, as if to my final and irrevocable overthrow, the spirit of PERVERSENESS. Of this spirit philosophy takes no account. Yet I am not more sure that my soul lives, than I am that perverseness is one of the primitive impulses of the human heart— one of the indivisible primary faculties, or sentiments, which give direction to the character of Man. Who has not, a hundred times, found himself committing a vile or a silly action, for no other reason than because he knows he should *not*? Have we not a perpetual inclination, in the teeth of our best judgment, to violate that which is *Law*, merely because we understand it to be such? This spirit of perverseness, I say, came to my final overthrow. It was this unfathomable longing of the soul to *vex itself*—to offer violence to its own nature—to do wrong for the wrong's sake only—that urged me to continue and finally to consummate the injury I had inflicted upon the unoffending brute. One morning, in cool blood, I slipped a noose about its neck and hung it to the limb of a tree;—hung it with the tears streaming from my eyes, and with the bitterest remorse at my heart;—hung it *because* I knew that it had loved me, and *because* I felt it had given me no reason of offence;—hung it *because* I knew that in so doing I was committing a sin—a deadly sin that would so jeopardize my immortal soul as to place it—if such a thing were possible—even beyond the reach of the infinite mercy of the Most Merciful and Most Terrible God.

On the night of the day on which this cruel deed was done, I was aroused from sleep by the cry of fire. The curtains of my bed were in flames. The whole house was blazing. It was with great difficulty that my wife, a servant, and myself, made our escape from the conflagration. The destruction was complete. My entire worldly wealth was swallowed up, and I resigned myself thenceforward to despair.

I am above the weakness of seeking to establish a sequence of cause and effect, between the disaster and the atrocity. But I am detailing a chain of facts—and wish not to leave even a possible link imperfect. On the day succeeding the fire, I visited the ruins. The walls, with one exception, had fallen in. This exception was found in a compartment wall, not very thick, which stood about the middle of the house, and against which had rested the head of my bed. The plastering had here, in great measure, resisted the action of the fire—a fact which I attributed to its having been recently spread. About this wall a dense crowd were collected, and many persons seemed to be examining a particular portion of it with very minute and eager attention. The words "strange!" "singular!" and other similar expressions, excited my curiosity. I approached and saw, as if graven in *bas relief* upon the white surface, the figure of a gigantic *cat*. The impression was given with an accuracy truly marvellous. There was a rope about the animal's neck.

When I first beheld this apparition—for I could scarcely regard it as less—my wonder and my terror were extreme. But at length reflection came to my aid. The cat, I remembered, had been hung in a garden adjacent to the house. Upon the alarm of fire, this garden had been immediately filled by the crowd—by some one of whom the animal must have been cut from the tree and thrown, through an open window, into my chamber. This had probably been done with the view of arousing me from sleep. The falling of other walls had compressed the victim of my cruelty into the substance of the freshly-spread plaster; the lime of which, with the flames, and the *ammonia* from the carcass, had then accomplished the portraiture as I saw it.

Although I thus readily accounted to my reason, if not altogether to my conscience, for the startling fact just detailed, it did not the less fail to make a deep impression upon my fancy. For months I could not rid myself of the phantasm[4] of the cat; and, during this period, there came back into my spirit a half-sentiment that seemed, but was not, remorse. I went so far as to regret the loss of the animal, and to look about me, among the vile haunts which I now habitually frequented, for another pet of the same species, and of somewhat similar appearance, with which to supply its place.

One night as I sat, half stupefied, in a den of more than infamy, my attention was suddenly drawn to some black object, reposing upon the head of one of the immense hogsheads[5] of Gin, or of Rum, which constituted the chief furniture of the apartment. I had been looking steadily at the top of this hogshead for some minutes, and what now caused me surprise was the fact that I had not sooner perceived the object thereupon. I approached it, and touched it with my hand. It was a black cat—a very large one—fully as large as Pluto, and closely resembling him in every respect but one. Pluto had not a white hair upon any portion of his body; but this cat had a large, although indefinite splotch of white, covering nearly the whole region of the breast.

Upon my touching him, he immediately arose, purred loudly, rubbed against my hand, and appeared delighted with my notice. This, then, was the very creature of which I was in search. I at once offered to purchase it of the

---

[4]Terrifying vision

[5]Large barrel or cask.

landlord; but this person made no claim to it—knew nothing of it—had never seen it before.

I continued my caresses, and, when I prepared to go home, the animal evinced a disposition to accompany me. I permitted it to do so; occasionally stooping and patting it as I proceeded. When it reached the house it domesticated itself at once, and became immediately a great favorite with my wife.

For my own part, I soon found a dislike to it arising within me. This was just the reverse of what I had anticipated; but I know not how or why it was— its evident fondness for myself rather disgusted and annoyed. By slow degrees, these feelings of disgust and annoyance rose into the bitterness of hatred. I avoided the creature; a certain sense of shame, and the remembrance of my former deed of cruelty, preventing me from physically abusing it. I did not, for some weeks, strike, or otherwise violently ill use it; but gradually—very gradually—I came to look upon it with unutterable loathing, and to flee silently from its odious presence, as from the breath of a pestilence.

What added, no doubt, to my hatred of the beast, was the discovery, on the morning after I brought it home, that, like Pluto, it also had been deprived of one of its eyes. This circumstance, however, only endeared it to my wife, who, as I have already said, possessed, in a high degree, that humanity of feeling which had once been my distinguishing trait, and the source of many of my simplest and purest pleasures.

With my aversion to this cat, however, its partiality for myself seemed to increase. It followed my footsteps with a pertinacity which it would be difficult to make the reader comprehend. Whenever I sat, it would crouch beneath my chair, or spring upon my knees, covering me with its loathsome caresses. If I arose to walk it would get between my feet and thus nearly throw me down, or, fastening its long and sharp claws in my dress, clamber, in this manner, to my breast. At such times, although I longed to destroy it with a blow, I was yet withheld from so doing, partly by a memory of my former crime, but chiefly—let me confess it at once—by absolute *dread* of the beast.

This dread was not exactly a dread of physical evil—and yet I should be at a loss how otherwise to define it. I am almost ashamed to own—yes, even in this felon's cell, I am almost ashamed to own—that the terror and horror with which the animal inspired me, had been heightened by one of the merest chimæras[6] it would be possible to conceive. My wife had called my attention, more than once, to the character of the mark of white hair, of which I have spoken, and which constituted the sole visible difference between the strange beast and the one I had destroyed. The reader will remember that this

---

[6]In Greek mythology, this fire-breathing monster has a lion's head, a goat's body, and a serpent's tail. The word has come to signify any horrible vision or phantasm.

mark, although large, had been originally very indefinite; but, by slow degrees—degrees nearly imperceptible, and which for a long time my Reason struggled to reject as fanciful—it had, at length, assumed a rigorous distinctness of outline. It was now the representation of an object that I shudder to name—and for this, above all, I loathed, and dreaded, and would have rid myself of the monster *had I dared*—it was now, I say, the image of a hideous—of a ghastly thing—of the GALLOWS!—oh, mournful and terrible engine of Horror and of Crime—of Agony and of Death!

And now was I indeed wretched beyond the wretchedness of mere Humanity. And *a brute beast*—whose fellow I had contemptuously destroyed—*a brute beast* to work out for *me*—for me a man, fashioned in the image of the High God—so much of insufferable wo! Alas! neither by day nor by night knew I the blessing of Rest any more! During the former the creature left me no moment alone; and, in the latter, I started, hourly, from dreams of unutterable fear, to find the hot breath of *the thing* upon my face, and its vast weight—an incarnate Night-Mare that I had no power to shake off—incumbent eternally upon my *heart!*

Beneath the pressure of torments such as these, the feeble remnant of the good within me succumbed. Evil thoughts became my sole intimates—the darkest and most evil of thoughts. The moodiness of my usual temper increased to hatred of all things and of all mankind; while, from the sudden, frequent, and ungovernable outbursts of a fury to which I now blindly abandoned myself, my uncomplaining wife, alas! was the most usual and the most patient of sufferers.

One day she accompanied me, upon some household errand, into the cellar of the old building which our poverty compelled us to inhabit. The cat followed me down the steep stairs, and, nearly throwing me headlong, exasperated me to madness. Uplifting an axe, and forgetting, in my wrath, the childish dread which had hitherto stayed my hand, I aimed a blow at the animal which, of course, would have proved instantly fatal had it descended as I wished. But this blow was arrested by the hand of my wife. Goaded, by the interference, into a rage more than demoniacal, I withdrew my arm from her grasp and buried the axe in her brain. She fell dead upon the spot, without a groan.

This hideous murder accomplished, I set myself forthwith, and with entire deliberation, to the task of concealing the body. I knew that I could not remove it from the house, either by day or by night, without the risk of being observed by the neighbors. Many projects entered my mind. At one period I thought of cutting the corpse into minute fragments, and destroying them by fire. At another, I resolved to dig a grave for it in the floor of the cellar. Again, I deliberated about casting it in the well in the yard—about packing it in a box, as if merchandize, with the usual arrangements, and so getting a porter to take it from the house. Finally I hit upon what I considered a far better expedient than either of these. I determined to wall it up in the cellar—as the monks of the middle ages are recorded to have walled up their victims.

For a purpose such as this the cellar was well adapted. Its walls were loosely constructed, and had lately been plastered throughout with a rough plaster, which the dampness of the atmosphere had prevented from hardening. Moreover, in one of the walls was a projection, caused by a false chimney, or fireplace, that had been filled up, and made to resemble the rest of the cellar. I made no doubt that I could readily displace the bricks at this point, insert the corpse, and wall the whole up as before, so that no eye could detect anything suspicious.

And in this calculation I was not deceived. By means of a crow-bar I easily dislodged the bricks, and, having carefully deposited the body against the inner wall, I propped it in that position, while, with little trouble, I re-laid the whole structure as it originally stood. Having procured mortar, sand, and hair, with every possible precaution, I prepared a plaster which could not be distinguished from the old, and with this I very carefully went over the new brick-work. When I had finished, I felt satisfied that all was right. The wall did not present the slightest appearance of having been disturbed. The rubbish on the floor was picked up with the minutest care. I looked around triumphantly, and said to myself—"Here at least, then, my labor has not been in vain."

My next step was to look for the beast which had been the cause of so much wretchedness; for I had, at length, firmly resolved to put it to death. Had I been able to meet with it, at the moment, there could have been no doubt of its fate; but it appeared that the crafty animal had been alarmed at the violence of my previous anger, and forebore to present itself in my present mood. It is impossible to describe, or to imagine, the deep, the blissful sense of relief which the absence of the detested creature occasioned in my bosom. It did not make its appearance during the night—and thus for one night at least, since its introduction into the house, I soundly and tranquilly slept; aye, *slept* even with the burden of murder upon my soul!

The second and the third day passed, and still my tormentor came not. Once again I breathed as a freeman. The monster, in terror, had fled the premises forever! I should behold it no more! My happiness was supreme! The guilt of my dark deed disturbed me but little. Some few inquiries had been made, but these had been readily answered. Even a search had been instituted—but of course nothing was to be discovered. I looked upon my future felicity as secured.

Upon the fourth day of the assassination, a party of police came, very unexpectedly, into the house, and proceeded again to make rigorous investigation of the premises. Secure, however, in the inscrutability of my place of concealment, I felt no embarrassment whatever. The officers bade me accompany them in their search. They left no nook or corner unexplored. At length, for the third or fourth time, they descended into the cellar. I quivered not in a muscle. My heart beat calmly as that of one who slumbers in innocence. I walked the cellar from end to end. I folded my arms upon my bosom, and roamed easily to and fro. The police were thoroughly satisfied and prepared to depart. The glee at my heart was too strong to be restrained. I burned to say if but one word, by way of triumph, and to render doubly sure their assurance of my guiltlessness.

"Gentlemen," I said at last, as the party ascended the steps, "I delight to have allayed your suspicions. I wish you all health, and a little more courtesy. By the bye, gentlemen, this—this is a very well constructed house." [In the rabid desire to say something easily, I scarcely knew what I uttered at all.]—"I may say an *excellently* well constructed house. These walls—are you going, gentlemen?—these walls are solidly put together;" and here, through the mere phrenzy of bravado, I rapped heavily, with a cane which I held in my hand, upon that very portion of the brick-work behind which stood the corpse of the wife of my bosom.

But may God shield and deliver me from the fangs of the Arch-Fiend! No sooner had the reverberation of my blows sunk into silence, than I was answered by a voice from within the tomb!—by a cry, at first muffled and broken, like the sobbing of a child, and then quickly swelling into one long, loud, and continuous scream, utterly anomalous and inhuman—a howl!—a wailing shriek, half of horror and half of triumph, such as might have arisen only out of hell, conjointly from the throats of the damned in their agony and of the demons that exult in the damnation.

Of my own thoughts it is folly to speak. Swooning, I staggered to the opposite wall. For one instant the party upon the stairs remained motionless, through extremity of terror and of awe. In the next, a dozen stout arms were toiling at the wall. It fell bodily. The corpse, already greatly decayed and clotted with gore, stood erect before the eyes of the spectators. Upon its head, with red extended mouth and solitary eye of fire, sat the hideous beast whose craft had seduced me into murder, and whose informing voice had consigned me to the hangman. I had walled the monster up within the tomb!

[1843]

QUESTIONS

1. Describe your experience of reading this story. What do you find interesting, surprising, or even shocking about the tale?

2. Why does the narrator maim his cat? With what weapon does he perpetrate this crime? Discuss the ways in which this instrument symbolizes the broader themes and character transformations of the story.

3. How does the narrator come to murder his wife? In what way does he attempt to hide her body? How does this central movement of the story reflect Poe's vision of domestic life?

4. What imagination of human identity emerges from "The Black Cat"? Is the narrator a powerful figure? Is he capable of self-knowledge and control?

5. Compare the narrator's tone with his actions. What emerges from the clash between these two aspects of his character?

6. Discuss the narrative frame of "The Black Cat." What is the immediate setting of the story? What is the context of the narrator's confession?

7. In "The Tell-Tale Heart," Poe confronts us with a narrator murderously obsessed by his one-eyed neighbor; the same may be said of "The Black Cat." Write an essay about "ocular" imagery in these two stories. What is significant about eyes—blind or seeing—in these two fictions?

8. With his short story "The Murders in the Rue Morgue" (1841), Poe invented the modern detective story; he elaborated the form with tales such as "The Purloined Letter" and "The Gold Bug." Is "The Black Cat" yet another example of the mystery genre? Review one of Poe's detective stories and write an essay about the ways in which "The Black Cat" complements and/or revises Poe's detective fiction.

The Cask of Amontillado

EDGAR ALLAN POE

THE THOUSAND INJURIES OF Fortunato I had borne as I best could; but when he ventured upon insult, I vowed revenge. You, who so well know the nature of my soul, will not suppose, however, that I gave utterance to a threat. *At length* I would be avenged; this was a point definitely settled—but the very definitiveness with which it was resolved, precluded the idea of risk. I must not only punish, but punish with impunity. A wrong is unredressed when retribution overtakes its redresser. It is equally unredressed when the avenger fails to make himself felt as such to him who has done the wrong.

It must be understood, that neither by word nor deed had I given Fortunato cause to doubt my good-will. I continued, as was my wont, to smile in his face, and he did not perceive that my smile *now* was at the thought of his immolation.

He had a weak point—this Fortunato—although in other regards he was a man to be respected and even feared. He prided himself on his connoisseurship in wine. Few Italians have the true virtuoso[1] spirit. For the most part their enthusiasm is adopted to suit the time and opportunity—to practice imposture upon the British and Austrian *millionaires*. In painting and gemmary, Fortunato, like his countrymen, was quack[2]—but in the matter of old wines he was sincere. In this respect I did not differ from him materially: I was skilful in the Italian vintages myself, and bought largely whenever I could.

It was about dusk, one evening during the supreme madness of the carnival season, that I encountered my friend. He accosted me with excessive warmth, for he had been drinking much. The man wore motley[3]. He had on a tight-fitting parti-striped dress, and his head was surmounted by the conical cap and bells. I was so pleased to see him, that I thought I should never have done wringing his hand.

---

[1] A learned devotee

[2] An imposter, poseur

[3] A multi-colored costume, particularly that worn by a jester.

First published in 1846.

I said to him: "My dear Fortunato, you are luckily met. How remarkably well you are looking to-day! But I have received a pipe[4] of what passes for Amontillado[5], and I have my doubts."

"How?" said he. "Amontillado? A pipe? Impossible! And in the middle of the carnival!"

"I have my doubts," I replied; "and I was silly enough to pay the full Amontillado price without consulting you in the matter. You were not to be found, and I was fearful of losing a bargain."

"Amontillado!"

"I have my doubts."

"Amontillado!"

"And I must satisfy them."

"Amontillado!"

"As you are engaged, I am on my way to Luchesi. If any one has a critical turn it is he: He will tell me—"

"Luchesi cannot tell Amontillado from Sherry."

"And yet some fools will have it that his taste is a match for your own."

"Come, let us go."

"Whither?"

"To your vaults."

"My friend, no; I will not impose upon your good nature. I perceive you have an engagement. Luchesi—"

"I have no engagement;—come."

"My friend, no. It is not the engagement, but the severe cold with which I perceive you are afflicted. The vaults are insufferably damp. They are encrusted with nitre."[6]

"Let us go, nevertheless. The cold is merely nothing. Amontillado! You have been imposed upon. And as for Luchesi, he cannot distinguish Sherry from Amontillado."

Thus speaking, Fortunato possessed himself of my arm. Putting on a mask of black silk, and drawing a *roquelaire*[7] closely about my person, I suffered him to hurry me to my palazzo.

There were no attendants at home; they had absconded to make merry in honor of the time. I had told them that I should not return until the morning, and had given them explicit orders not to stir from the house. These orders

---

[4] A wine cask.

[5] A light sherry produced in the Spanish town of Montilla.

[6] Salt peter (potassium nitrate).

[7] A knee-length cloak.

were sufficient, I well knew, to insure their immediate disappearance, one and all, as soon as my back was turned.

I took from their sconces two flambeaux[8], and giving one to Fortunato, bowed him through several suites of rooms to the archway that led into the vaults. I passed down a long and winding staircase, requesting him to be cautious as he followed. We came at length to the foot of the descent, and stood together upon the damp ground of the catacombs of the Montresors.

The gait of my friend was unsteady, and the bells upon his cap jingled as he strode.

"The pipe?" said he.

"It is farther on," said I; "but observe the white web-work which gleams from these cavern walls."

He turned towards me, and looked into my eyes with two filmy orbs that distilled the rheum of intoxication.

"Nitre?" he asked, at length.

"Nitre," I replied. "How long have you had that cough?"

"Ugh! ugh! ugh!—ugh! ugh! ugh!—ugh! ugh! ugh!—ugh! ugh! ugh!— ugh! ugh! ugh!"

My poor friend found it impossible to reply for many minutes.

"It is nothing," he said, at last.

"Come," I said, with decision, "we will go back; your health is precious. You are rich, respected, admired, beloved; you are happy, as once I was. You are a man to be missed. For me it is no matter. We will go back; you will be ill, and I cannot be responsible. Besides there is Luchesi—"

"Enough," he said; "the cough is a mere nothing; it will not kill me. I shall not die of a cough."

"True—true," I replied; "and, indeed, I had no intention of alarming you unnecessarily; but you should use all proper caution. A draught of this Medoc[9] will defend us from the damps."

Here I knocked off the neck of a bottle which I drew from a long row of its fellows that lay upon the mould.

"Drink," I said, presenting him the wine.

He raised it to his lips with a leer. He paused and nodded to me familiarly, while his bells jingled.

"I drink," he said, "to the buried that repose around us."

"And I to your long life."

He again took my arm, and we proceeded.

---

[8]Torches

[9]A red wine named for the French region of its origin.

"These vaults," he said, "are extensive."

"The Montresors," I replied, "were a great and numerous family."

"I forget your arms."

"A huge human foot d'or, in a field azure; the foot crushes a serpent rampant whose fangs are imbedded in the heel."

"And the motto?"

"*Nemo me impune lacessit.*"[10]

"Good!" he said.

The wine sparkled in his eyes and the bells jingled. My own fancy grew warm with the Medoc. We had passed through long walls of piled bones, with casks and puncheons intermingling, into the inmost recesses of the catacombs. I paused again, and this time I made bold to seize Fortunato by an arm above the elbow.

"The nitre!" I said; "see, it increases. It hangs like moss upon the vaults. We are below the river's bed. The drops of moisture trickle among the bones. Come, we will go back ere it is too late. Your cough—"

"It is nothing," he said; "let us go on. But first, another draught of the Medoc."

I broke and reached him a flagon[11] of De Grâve[12]. He emptied it at a breath. His eyes flashed with a fierce light. He laughed and threw the bottle upward with a gesticulation I did not understand.

I looked at him in surprise. He repeated the movement—a grotesque one.

"You do not comprehend?" he said.

"Not I," I replied.

"Then you are not of the brotherhood."

"How?"

"You are not of the masons."

"Yes, yes," I said; "yes, yes."

"You? Impossible! A mason?"

"A mason," I replied.

"A sign," he said.

"It is this," I answered, producing a trowel from beneath the folds of my *roquelaire.*

"You jest," he exclaimed, recoiling a few paces. "But let us proceed to the Amontillado."

---

[10]Latin: "No one insults me with impunity." Such mottos are often inscribed in the coat of arms (symbol originally borne on a shield or clothing) of European aristocratic families.

[11]A large wine bottle.

[12]A white wine from Bordeaux.

"Be it so," I said, replacing the tool beneath the cloak, and again offering him my arm. He leaned upon it heavily. We continued our route in search of the Amontillado. We passed through a range of low arches, descended, passed on, and descending again, arrived at a deep crypt, in which the foulness of the air caused our flambeaux rather to glow than flame.

At the most remote end of the crypt there appeared another less spacious. Its walls had been lined with human remains, piled to the vault overhead, in the fashion of the great catacombs of Paris. Three sides of this interior crypt were still ornamented in this manner. From the fourth the bones had been thrown down, and lay promiscuously upon the earth, forming at one point a mound of some size. Within the wall thus exposed by the displacing of the bones, we perceived a still interior recess, in depth about four feet, in width three, in height six or seven. It seemed to have been constructed for no especial use within itself, but formed merely the interval between two of the colossal supports of the roof of the catacombs, and was backed by one of their circumscribing walls of solid granite.

It was in vain that Fortunato, uplifting his dull torch, endeavored to pry into the depth of the recess. Its termination the feeble light did not enable us to see.

"Proceed," I said; "herein is the Amontillado. As for Luchesi—"

"He is an ignoramus," interrupted my friend, as he stepped unsteadily forward, while I followed immediately at his heels. In an instant he had reached the extremity of the niche, and finding his progress arrested by the rock, stood stupidly bewildered. A moment more and I had fettered him to the granite. In its surface were two iron staples, distant from each other about two feet, horizontally. From one of these depended a short chain, from the other a padlock. Throwing the links about his waist, it was but the work of a few seconds to secure it. He was too much astounded to resist. Withdrawing the key I stepped back from the recess.

"Pass your hand," I said, "over the wall; you cannot help feeling the nitre. Indeed, it is *very* damp. Once more let me *implore* you to return. No? Then I must positively leave you. But I must first render you all the little attentions in my power."

"The Amontillado!" ejaculated my friend, not yet recovered from his astonishment.

"True," I replied; "the Amontillado."

As I said these words I busied myself among the pile of bones of which I have before spoken. Throwing them aside, I soon uncovered a quantity of building stone and mortar. With these materials and with the aid of my trowel, I began vigorously to wall up the entrance of the niche.

I had scarcely laid the first tier of the masonry when I discovered that the intoxication of Fortunato had in a great measure worn off. The earliest indication I had of this was a low moaning cry from the depths of the recess. It was *not* the cry of a drunken man. There was then a long and obstinate silence. I laid the second tier, and the third, and the fourth; and then I heard the furious vibrations of the chain. The noise lasted for several minutes, during which, that I might hearken to it with the more satisfaction, I ceased my labors and sat down upon the bones. When at last the clanking subsided, I resumed the trowel, and finished without interruption the fifth, the sixth, and the seventh tier. The wall was now nearly upon a level with my breast. I again paused, and holding the flambeaux over the mason-work, threw a few feeble rays upon the figure within.

A succession of loud and shrill screams, bursting suddenly from the throat of the chained form, seemed to thrust me violently back. For a brief moment I hesitated—I trembled. Unsheathing my rapier, I began to grope with it about the recess; but the thought of an instant reassured me. I placed my hand upon the solid fabric of the catacombs, and felt satisfied. I reapproached the wall. I replied to the yells of him who clamoured. I re-echoed—I aided—I surpassed them in volume and in strength. I did this, and the clamourer grew still.

It was now midnight, and my task was drawing to a close. I had completed the eighth, the ninth and the tenth tier. I had finished a portion of the last and the eleventh; there remained but a single stone to be fitted and plastered in. I struggled with its weight; I placed it partially in its destined position. But now there came from out the niche a low laugh that erected the hairs upon my head. It was succeeded by a sad voice, which I had difficulty in recognizing as that of the noble Fortunato. The voice said—

"Ha! ha! ha!—he! he!—a very good joke indeed—an excellent jest. We will have many a rich laugh about it at the palazzo—he! he! he!—over our wine—he! he! he!"

"The Amontillado!" I said.

"He! ha! he!—he! he! he!—yes, the Amontillado. But is it not getting late? Will not they be awaiting us at the palazzo, the Lady Fortunato and the rest? Let us be gone."

"Yes," I said, "let us be gone."

"For the love of God, Montresor!"

"Yes," I said, "for the love of God."

But to these words I hearkened in vain for a reply. I grew impatient. I called aloud:

"Fortunato!"

No answer. I called again:

"Fortunato!"

No answer still. I thrust a torch through the remaining aperture and let it fall within. There came forth in return only a tingling of the bells. My heart grew sick—on account of the dampness of the catacombs. I hastened to make an end of my labour. I forced the last stone into its position; I plastered it up. Against the new masonry I reerected the old rampart of bones. For the half of a century no mortal has disturbed them. *In pace requiescat!*[13]

[1850]

---

[13]Latin: "Rest in peace."

QUESTIONS

EDGAR ALLAN POE, *The Cask of Amontillado*

1. Why does the Montresor dislike Fortunato? What drives him to commit murder?

2. What is the frame of this story? That is, how much time has elapsed since the events described in the tale? To whom might Montresor be speaking?

3. Montresor means "my treasure" in French. The name Fortunato obviously suggests someone who enjoys good fortune. To what extent do these names illuminate larger themes and motifs in "The Cask of Amontillado"?

4. What celebration takes place during the course of the story? How does this event reflect, enable, or somehow authorize Montresor's plot against Fortunato?

5. Why does Montresor use a story about fine wine as a means of luring Fortunato? Discuss the ways in which the ruse illuminates Fortunato's personality and social position.

6. Consider the physical settings of "The Cask of Amontillado." What is the significance of the transition from street to catacombs?

7. As the Montresor and Fortunato descend into the catacombs, they at one point discuss the latter's membership in the secret society of the Freemasons. Describe this phase of the story and comment on its significance to the story as a whole. Who are the Masons? What social or political tensions surround this exchange between Montresor and Fortunato?

8. Montresor refers to his family and to his own happiness in the past tense. What does this tendency say about his personal situation and about his motives for committing the murder?

9. Review "The Cask of Amontillado" along with Poe's "The Gold Bug"; "The Murders in the Rue Morgue"; and/or "The Purloined Letter." Consider the ways in which Poe represents aristocratic characters. Why does Poe, living in the democratic society of early nineteenth century America, devote so much attention to European noblemen? Argue for your findings in an essay.

Guy de Maupassant
[1850–1893]

GUY DE MAUPASSANT *came from Château de Miromesniel, Dieppe. His youth was varied, moving from the study of law in Paris around 1869 but giving that up to serve in the army during the Franco-Prussian War. Later, around 1872, he became a civil servant, working for the ministry of maritime affairs and then at the ministry of education. He left the public employ in 1880. His poetry first appeared that year with Des Vers (1880), and his fiction with "Boule De Suif" (or "Ball of Fat" in the anthology Soirées de Medan edited by Emile Zola. During the next ten years, de Maupassant wrote over three hundred short stories, as well as six novels.*

De Maupassant created a rich irony in his work, often characterized by a kind of humor that creates both amusement and discomfort at the same time. He was a "Naturalist," who showed life as it was for the middle class and poor who surrounded him in his life. The stories ring true because they reflect human foibles and frailties that do not change with time and place. De Maupassant helps the reader sees humans as they are and hope that they are not. He also wrote about the sadness of a life of toil in A Woman's Life, 1883, and family struggles and conflicts in Peter and John, 1888.

De Maupassant became a victim of syphilis when he was in his twenties, a condition that eventually led to madness and death, but not before it first led to stories of horror and distress. The later stories resemble those of the American writer Poe, showing the dark side of human life and the nightmarish qualities that can haunt an author in distress. His quite unpleasant story "The Horror" (1887) displays his movement toward madness and death.

In 1892 de Maupassant attempted suicide. He spent the final year of his life in a mental institution in Paris and died there at the end of the following year.

The Necklace

GUY DE MAUPASSANT

SHE WAS ONE OF THOSE PRETTY and charming girls, born by a blunder of destiny in a family of employees. She had no dowry, no expectations, no means of being known, understood, loved, married by a man rich and distinguished; and she let them make a match for her with a little clerk in the Department of Education.

She was simple since she could not be adorned; but she was unhappy as though kept out of her own class; for women have no caste and no descent, their beauty, their grace, and their charm serving them instead of birth and fortune. Their native keenness, their instinctive elegance, their flexibility of mind, are their only hierarchy; and these make the daughters of the people the equals of the most lofty dames.

She suffered intensely, feeling herself born for every delicacy and every luxury. She suffered from the poverty of her dwelling, from the worn walls, the abraded chairs, the ugliness of the stuffs. All these things, which another woman of her caste would not even have noticed, tortured her and made her indignant. The sight of the little girl from Brittany who did her humble housework awoke in her desolated regrets and distracted dreams. She let her mind dwell on the quiet vestibules, hung with Oriental tapestries, lighted by tall lamps of bronze, and on the two tall footmen in knee breeches who dozed in the large armchairs, made drowsy by the heat of the furnace. She let her mind dwell on the large parlors, decked with old silk, with their delicate furniture, supporting precious bric-a-brac, and on the coquettish little rooms, perfumed, prepared for the five o'clock chat with the most intimate friends, men well known and sought after, whose attentions all women envied and desired.

When she sat down to dine, before a tablecloth three days old, in front of her husband, who lifted the cover of the tureen, declaring with an air of satisfaction, "Ah, the good *pot-au-feu*. I don't know anything better than that," she was thinking of delicate repasts, with glittering silver, with tapestries peopling the walls with ancient figures and with strange birds in a fairy-like forest; she was thinking of exquisite dishes, served in marvelous platters, of compliment whispered and heard with a sphinx-like smile, while she was eating the rosy flesh of a trout or the wings of a quail.

She had no dresses, no jewelry, nothing. And she loved nothing else; she felt herself made for that only. She would so much have liked to please, to be envied, to be seductive and sought after.

She had a rich friend, a comrade of her convent days, whom she did not want to go and see any more, so much did she suffer as she came away. And she wept all day long, from chagrin, from regret, from despair, and from distress.

But one evening her husband came in with a proud air, holding in his hand a large envelope.

"There," said he, "there's something for you."

She quickly tore the paper and took out of it a printed card which bore these words:—

"The Minister of Education and Mme. Georges Rampouneau beg M. and Mme. Loisel to do them the honor to pass the evening with them at the palace of the Ministry, on Monday, January 18."

Instead of being delighted, as her husband hoped, she threw the invitation on the table with annoyance, murmuring—

"What do you want me to do with that?"

"But, my dear, I thought you would be pleased. You never go out, and here's a chance, a fine one. I had the hardest work to get it. Everybody is after them; they are greatly sought for and not many are given to the clerks. You will see there all the official world."

She looked at him with an irritated eye and she declared with impatience:—

"What do you want me to put on my back to go there?"

He had not thought of that; he hesitated:—

"But the dress in which you go to the theater. That looks very well to me—"

He shut up, astonished and distracted at seeing that his wife was weeping. Two big tears were descending slowly from the corners of the eyes to the corners of the mouth. He stuttered:—

What's the matter? What's the matter?"

But by a violent effort she had conquered her trouble, and she replied in a calm voice as she wiped her damp cheeks:—

"Nothing. Only I have no clothes, and in consequence I cannot go to this party. Give your card to some colleague whose wife has a better outfit than I."

He was disconsolate. He began again:—

"See here, Mathilde, how much would this cost, a proper dress, which would do on other occasions; something very simple?"

She reflected a few seconds, going over her calculations, and thinking also of the sum which she might ask without meeting an immediate refusal and a frightened exclamation from the frugal clerk.

"At last, she answered hesitatingly:—

"I don't know exactly, but it seems to me that with four hundred francs I might do it."

He grew a little pale, for he was reserving just that sum to buy a gun and treat himself to a little shooting, the next summer, on the plain of Nanterre, with some friends who used to shoot larks there on Sundays.

But he said:—

"All right. I will give you four hundred francs. But take care to have a pretty dress."

The day of the party drew near, and Mme. Loisel seemed sad, restless, anxious. Yet her dress was ready. One evening her husband said to her:—

"What's the matter? Come, now, you have been quite queer these last three days."

And she answered:—

"It annoys me not to have a jewel, not a single stone, to put on. I shall look like distress.

I would almost rather not go to this party."

He answered:—

"You will wear some natural flowers. They are very stylish this time of the year. For ten francs you will have two or three magnificent roses."

But she was not convinced.

"No; there's nothing more humiliating than to look poor among a lot of rich women."

But her husband cried:—

"What a goose you are! Go find your friend, Mme. Forester, and ask her to lend you some jewelry. You know her well enough to do that."

She gave a cry of joy:—

"That's true. I had not thought of it."

The next day she went to her friend's and told her about her distress.

Mme. Forester went to her mirrored wardrobe, took out a large casket, brought it, opened it, and said to Mme. Loisel:—

"Choose, my dear."

She saw at first bracelets, then a necklace of pearls, then a Venetian cross of gold set with precious stones of an admirable workmanship. She tried on the ornaments before the glass, hesitated, and could not decide to take them off and to give them up. She kept on asking:—

"You haven't anything else?"

"Yes, yes. Look. I do not know what will happen to please you."

All at once she discovered, in a box of black satin, a superb necklace of diamonds, and her heart began to beat with boundless desire. Her hands trembled in taking it up. She fastened it round her throat, on her high dress, and remained in ecstasy before herself.

Then, she asked, hesitating, full of anxiety:—

"Can you lend me this, only this?"

"Yes, yes, certainly."

She sprang to her friend's neck, kissed her with ardor, and then escaped with her treasure.

The day of the party arrived. Mme. Loisel was a success. She was the prettiest of them all, elegant, gracious, smiling, and mad with joy. All the men were looking at her, inquiring her name, asking to be introduced. All the attaches of the Cabinet wanted to dance with her. The Minister took notice of her. She danced with delight, with passion, intoxicated with pleasure, thinking of nothing, in the triumph of her beauty, in the glory of her success, in a sort of cloud of happiness made up of all these tributes, of all the admirations, of all these awakened desires, of this victory so complete and so sweet to a woman's heart.

She went away about four in the morning. Since midnight—her husband has been dozing in a little anteroom with three other men whose wives were having a good time.

He threw over her shoulders the wraps he had brought to go home in, modest garments of every-day life, the poverty of which was out of keeping with the elegance of the ball dress. She felt this, and wanted to fly so as not to be noticed by the other women, who were wrapping themselves up in rich furs. Loisel kept her back—

"Wait a minute; you will catch cold outside; I'll call a cab."

But she did not listen to him, and went downstairs rapidly. When they were in the street, they could not find a carriage, and they set out in search of one, hailing the drivers whom they saw passing in the distance.

They went down toward the Seine, disgusted, shivering. Finally, they found on the Quai one of those old night-hawk cabs which one sees in Paris only after night has fallen, as though they are ashamed of their misery in the daytime.

It brought them to their door, rue des Martyrs; and they went up their own stairs sadly. For her it was finished. And he was thinking that he would have to be at the Ministry at ten o'clock.

She took off the wraps with which she had covered her shoulders, before the mirror, so as to see herself once more in her glory. But suddenly she gave a cry. She no longer had the necklace around her throat!

Her husband, half undressed already, asked—

"What is the matter with you?"

She turned to him, terror-stricken:—

"I—I—I have not Mme. Forester's diamond necklace!"

He jumped up, frightened—

"What? How? It is not possible!"

And they searched in the folds of the dress, in the folds of the wrap, in the pockets, everywhere. They did not find it.

He asked:—

"Are you sure you still had it when you left the ball?"

"Yes, I touched it in the vestibule of the Ministry."

"But if you had lost it in the street, we should have heard it fall. It must be in the cab."

"Yes. That is probable. Did you take the number?"

"No. And you—you did not even look at it?"

"No."

They gazed at each other, crushed. At last Loisel dressed himself again.

"I'm going," he said, "back the whole distance we came on foot, to see if I cannot find it."

And he went out. She stayed there, in her ball dress, without strength to go to bed, overwhelmed, on a chair, without a fire, without a thought.

Her husband came back about seven o'clock. He had found nothing.

Then he went to police headquarters, to the newspapers to offer a reward, to the cab company; he did everything, in fact, that a trace of hope could urge him to.

She waited all day, in the same dazed state in face of this horrible disaster. Loisel came back in the evening, with his face worn and white; he had discovered nothing.

"You must write to your friend," he said, "that you have broken the clasp of her necklace and that you are having it repaired. That will give us time to turn around."

She wrote as he dictated.

At the end of a week they had lost all hope. And Loisel, aged by five years, declared:—

"We must see how we can replace those jewels."

The next day they took the case which had held them to the jeweler whose name was in the cover. He consulted his books.

"It was not I, madam, who sold this necklace. I only supplied the case."

Then they went from jeweler to jeweler, looking for a necklace like the other, consulting their memory,—sick both of them with grief and anxiety.

In a shop in the Palais Royal, they found a diamond necklace that seemed to them absolutely like the one they were seeking. It was priced forty thousand francs. They could have it for thirty-six.

They begged the jeweler not to sell it for three days. And they made a bargain that he should take it back for thirty-four thousand, if the first was found before the end of February.

Loisel possessed eighteen thousand francs which his father had left him. He had to borrow the remainder.

He borrowed, asking a thousand francs from one, five hundred from another, five here, three louis there. He gave promissory notes, made ruinous agreements, dealt with usurers, with all kinds of lenders. He compromised the end of his life, risked his signature without even knowing whether it could be honored; and, frightened by all the anguish of the future, by the black misery which was about to settle down on him, by the perspective of all sorts of physical deprivations and of all sorts of moral tortures, he went to buy the new diamond necklace, laying down on the jeweler's counter thirty-six thousand francs.

When Mme. Loisel took back the necklace to Mme. Forester, the latter said, with an irritated air:—

"You ought to have brought it back sooner, for I might have needed it."

She did not open the case, which her friend had been fearing. If she had noticed the substitution, what would she have thought? What would she have said? Might she not have been taken for a thief?

Mme. Loisel learned the horrible life of the needy. She made the best of it, moreover, frankly, heroically. The frightful debt must be paid. She would pay it. They dismissed the servant; they changed their rooms; they took an attic under the roof.

She learned the rough work of the household, the odious labors of the kitchen. She washed the dishes, wearing out her pink nails on the greasy pots and the bottoms of the pans. She washed the dirty linen, the shirts and the towels, which she dried on a rope; she carried down the garbage to the street every morning, and she carried up the water, pausing for breath on every floor. And, dressed like a woman of the people, she went to the fruiterer, the grocer, the butcher, a basket on her arm, bargaining, insulted, fighting for her wretched money, sou by sou.

Every month they had to pay notes, to renew others to gain time. The husband worked in the evening keeping up the books of a shopkeeper, and at night often he did copying at five sous the page.

And this life lasted ten years.

At the end of ten years they had paid everything back, everything, with the rates of usury and all the accumulation of heaped-up interest.

Mme. Loisel seemed aged now. She had become the robust woman, hard and rough, of a poor household. Badly combed, with her skirts awry and her hands red, her voice was loud, and she washed the floor with splashing water.

But sometimes, when her husband was at the office, she sat down by the window and she thought of that evening long ago, of that ball, where she had been so beautiful and so admired.

What would have happened if she had not lost that necklace? Who knows? Who knows? How singular life is, how changeable! What a little thing it takes to save you or to lose you.

Then, one Sunday, as she was taking a turn in the Champs Elysées, as a recreation after the labors of the week, she perceived suddenly a woman walking with a child. It was Mme. Forester, still young, still beautiful, still seductive.

Mme. Loisel felt moved. Should she speak to her? Yes, certainly. And now that she had paid up, she would tell her all. Why not?

She drew near.

"Good morning, Jeanne."

The other did not recognize her, astonished to be hailed thus familiarly by this woman of the people. She hesitated—

"But—madam—I don't know—are you not making a mistake?"

"No. I am Mathilde Loisel."

Her friend gave a cry—

"Oh!—My poor Mathilde, how you are changed."

"Yes, I have had hard days since I saw you, and many troubles,—and that because of you."

"Of me?—How so?"

"You remember that diamond necklace that you lent me to go to the ball at the Ministry?"

"Yes. And then?"

"Well, I lost it."

"How can that be?—since you brought it back to me?"

"I brought you back another just like it. And now for ten years we have been paying for it. You will understand that it was not easy for us, who had nothing. At last, it is done, and I am mighty glad."

Mme. Forester had guessed.

"You say that you bought a diamond necklace to replace mine?"

"Yes. You did not notice it, even, did you? They were exactly alike?"

And she smiled with proud and naïve joy.

Mme. Forester, much moved, took her by both hands:—

"Oh, my poor Mathilde. But mine were false. At most they were worth five hundred francs!"

[1907]

Translated by Brander Matthews (1852–1929)

QUESTIONS

GUY DE MAUPASSANT, *The Necklace*

1. Mme. Loisel is proud and will not go to a ball without a proper necklace, though her husband has struggled to get an invitation for them. Mme. Loisel borrows a necklace from her friend Mme. Foster to wear to the ball. What happens to the necklace?

2. In order to replace the necklace, what do the Loisels do? What happens to their lives? What happens to Mme. Loisel's pride and vanity?

3. What does Mme. Loisel find out about the necklace at the end of the story?

4. What are the consequences of trying to live above one's income? Why do we suffer when we overuse credit cards and other kinds of credit?

5. Social pressures can force us to do truly silly things. Why do we let ourselves be drawn in by fashion and style, even when we cannot afford new clothes?

6. How does irony of the kind we see in this story affect the reader? What is the feeling when the irony becomes clear? Does it caution the reader to be careful?

7. Why does the beginning of the story say that Mme. Loisel was born into a working class family by a "blunder of destiny"? What kind of family would Mme. Loisel have preferred?

8. How does the husband's indulgence lead to the problems in the story? Is he to blame for being so willing to please his wife at all costs? Is he likely still so indulgent after she has worked so hard at the end of the story?

9. In what ways does the final twist of the story reflect on what has gone before? Why does such an ending make such a story so memorable?

10. What kinds of people drive the entertainment industry? How do they dress, and what expectations do they set up in the young? Pick a particular entertainer, and write about how that person influences those who admire her or him.

11. Have you ever borrowed something from someone else or lent something to someone and have it go wrong? Write about the experience and its effect on your relationship.

12. Have you ever spent far too much for something that later did not mean much to you? How did you feel about your mistake? What did you learn from the experience?

The Horla
Or Modern Ghosts

GUY DE MAUPASSANT

May 8. what a lovely day! I have spent all the morning lying in the grass in front of my house, under the enormous plane[1] tree that shades the whole of it. I like this part of the country and I like to live here because I am attached to it by old associations, by those deep and delicate roots which attach a man to the soil on which his ancestors were born and died, which attach him to the ideas and usages of the place as well as to the food, to local expressions, to the peculiar twang of the peasants, to the smell of the soil, of the villages and of the atmosphere itself.

I love my house in which I grew up. From my windows I can see the Seine[2] which flows alongside my garden, on the other side of the high road, almost through my grounds, the great and wide Seine, which goes to Rouen[3] and Havre,[4] and is covered with boats passing to and fro.

On the left, down yonder, lies Rouen, that large town, with its blue roofs, under its pointed Gothic towers. These are innumerable, slender or broad, dominated by the spire of the cathedral, and full of bells which sound through the blue air on fine mornings, sending their sweet and distant iron clang even as far as my home; that song of the metal, which the breeze wafts in my direction, now stronger and now weaker, according as the wind is stronger or lighter.

What a delicious morning it was!

About eleven o'clock, a long line of boats drawn by a steam tug as big as a fly, and which scarcely puffed while emitting its thick smoke, passed my gate.

---

[1]plane tree: plantain tree.

[2]Seine: a major river and commercial waterway in France.

[3]Rouen: a city in Northern France, the historical capitol city of Normandy, located on the River Seine.

[4]Havre: a city in northwestern France.

Reprinted from *The Works of Guy de Maupassant: The Horla, Miss Harriet, LIttle Louise Roque, and Other Stories* (1911).

After two English schooners, whose red flag fluttered in space, there came a magnificent Brazilian three-master; it was perfectly white, and wonderfully clean and shining. I saluted it, I hardly knew why, except that the sight of the vessel gave me great pleasure.

May 12. I have had a slight feverish attack for the last few days, and I feel ill, or rather I feel low-spirited.

Whence come those mysterious influences which change our happiness into discouragement, and our self-confidence into diffidence? One might almost say that the air, the invisible air, is full of unknowable Powers whose mysterious presence we have to endure. I wake up in the best spirits, with an inclination to sing. Why? I go down to the edge of the water, and suddenly, after walking a short distance, I return home wretched, as if some misfortune were awaiting me there. Why? Is it a cold shiver which, passing over my skin, has upset my nerves and given me low spirits? Is it the form of the clouds, the color of the sky, or the color of the surrounding objects which is so changeable, that has troubled my thoughts as they passed before my eyes? Who can tell? Everything that surrounds us, everything that we see, without looking at it, everything that we touch, without knowing it, everything that we handle, without feeling it, all that we meet, without clearly distinguishing it, has a rapid, surprising and inexplicable effect upon us and upon our senses, and, through them, on our ideas and on our heart itself.

How profound that mystery of the Invisible is! We cannot fathom it with our miserable senses, with our eyes which are unable to perceive what is either too small or too great, too near to us, or too far from us—neither the inhabitants of a star nor of a drop of water; nor with our ears that deceive us, for they transmit to us the vibrations of the air in sonorous notes. They are fairies who work the miracle of changing these vibrations into sound, and by that metamorphosis give birth to music, which makes the silent motion of nature musical . . . with our sense of smell which is less keen than that of a dog . . . with our sense of taste which can scarcely distinguish the age of a wine!

Oh! If we only had other organs which would work other miracles in our favor, what a number of fresh things we might discover around us!

May 16. I am ill, decidedly! I was so well last month! I am feverish, horribly feverish, or rather I am in a state of feverish enervation, which makes my mind suffer as much as my body. I have, continually, that horrible sensation of some impending danger, that apprehension of some coming misfortune, or of approaching death; that presentiment which is, no doubt, an attack of some illness which is still unknown, which germinates in the flesh and in the blood.

May 17. I have just come from consulting my physician, for I could no longer get any sleep. He said my pulse was rapid, my eyes dilated, my nerves highly strung, but there were no alarming symptoms. I must take a course of shower baths and of bromide of potassium.[5]

May 25. No change! My condition is really very peculiar. As the evening comes on, an incomprehensible feeling of disquietude seizes me, just as if night concealed some threatening disaster. I dine hurriedly, and then try to read, but I do not understand the words, and can scarcely distinguish the letters. Then I walk up and down my drawing-room, oppressed by a feeling of confused and irresistible fear, the fear of sleep and fear of my bed.

About ten o'clock I go up to my room. As soon as I enter it I double-lock and bolt the door; I am afraid . . . of what? Up to the present time I have been afraid of nothing . . . I open my cupboards, and look under my bed; I listen . . . to what? How strange it is that a simple feeling of discomfort, impeded or heightened circulation, perhaps the irritation of a nerve filament, a slight congestion, a small disturbance in the imperfect delicate functioning of our living machinery, may turn the most light-hearted of men into a melancholy one, and make a coward of the bravest? Then, I go to bed, and wait for sleep as a man might wait for the executioner. I wait for its coming with dread, and my heart beats and my legs tremble, while my whole body shivers beneath the warmth of the bedclothes, until all at once I fall asleep, as though one should plunge into a pool of stagnant water in order to drown. I do not feel it coming on as I did formerly, this perfidious sleep which is close to me and watching me, which is going to seize me by the head, to close my eyes and annihilate me.

I sleep—a long time—two or three hours perhaps—then a dream—no—a nightmare lays hold on me. I feel that I am in bed and asleep . . . I feel it and I know it . . . and I feel also that somebody is coming close to me, is looking at me, touching me, is getting on to my bed, is kneeling on my chest, is taking my neck between his hands and squeezing it . . . squeezing it with all his might in order to strangle me.

I struggle, bound by that terrible sense of powerlessness which paralyzes us in our dreams; I try to cry out—but I cannot; I want to move—I cannot do so; I try, with the most violent efforts and breathing hard, to turn over and throw off this being who is crushing and suffocating me—I cannot!

And then, suddenly, I wake up, trembling and bathed in perspiration; I light a candle and find that I am alone, and after that crisis, which occurs every night, I at length fall asleep and slumber tranquilly till morning.

June 2. My condition has grown worse. What is the matter with me? The bromide does me no good, and the shower baths have no effect. Sometimes, in order to tire myself thoroughly, though I am fatigued enough already, I go for a walk in the forest of Roumare. I used to think at first that the fresh light

---

[5]A salt used as an anti-convulsant and sedative in the late nineteenth and early twentieth century.

and soft air, impregnated with the odor of herbs and leaves, would instill new blood into my veins and impart fresh energy to my heart. I turned into a broad hunting road, and then turned toward La Bouille, through a narrow path, between two rows of exceedingly tall trees, which placed a thick green, almost black, roof between the sky and me.

A sudden shiver ran through me, not a cold shiver, but a strange shiver of agony, and I hastened my steps, uneasy at being alone in the forest, afraid, stupidly and without reason, of the profound solitude. Suddenly it seemed to me as if I were being followed, that somebody was walking at my heels, close, quite close to me, near enough to touch me.

I turned round suddenly, but I was alone. I saw nothing behind me except the straight, broad path, empty and bordered by high trees, horribly empty; before me it also extended until it was lost in the distance, and looked just the same, terrible.

I closed my eyes. Why? And then I began to turn round on one heel very quickly, just like a top. I nearly fell down, and opened my eyes; the trees were dancing round me and the earth heaved; I was obliged to sit down. Then, ah! I no longer remembered how I had come! What a strange idea! What a strange, strange idea! I did not the least know. I started off to the right, and got back into the avenue which had led me into the middle of the forest.

June 3. I have had a terrible night. I shall go away for a few weeks, for no doubt a journey will set me up again.

July 2. I have come back, quite cured, and have had a most delightful trip into the bargain. I have been to Mont Saint-Michel,[6] which I had not seen before.

What a sight, when one arrives as I did, at Avranches[7] toward the end of the day! The town stands on a hill, and I was taken into the public garden at the extremity of the town. I uttered a cry of astonishment. An extraordinarily large bay lay extended before me, as far as my eyes could reach, between two hills which were lost to sight in the mist; and in the middle of this immense yellow bay, uinder a clear, golden sky, a peculiar hill rose up, sombre and pointed in the midst of the sand. The sun had just disappeared, and under the still flaming sky appeared the outline of that fantastic rock which bears on its summit a fantastic monument.

At daybreak I went out to it. The tide was low, as it had been the night before, and I saw that wonderful abbey rise up before me as I approached it. After several hours' walking. I reached the enormous mass of rocks which sup-

---

[6]Mont Saint-Michel: a rocky tidal island in Northern France.

[7]Avranches: a commune in Northwestern France.

ports the little town, dominated by the great church. Having climbed the steep and narrow street, I entered the most wonderful Gothic building that has ever been built to God on earth, as large as a town, full of low rooms which seem buried beneath vaulted roofs, and lofty galleries supported by delicate columns.

I entered this gigantic granite gem, which is as light as a bit of lace, covered with towers, with slender belfries with spiral staircases, which raise their strange heads that bristle with chimeras,[8] with devils, with fantastic animals, with monstrous flowers, to the blue sky by day, and to the black sky by night, and are connected by finely carved arches.

When I had reached the summit I said to the monk who accompanied me: "Father, how happy you must be here!" And he replied: "It is very windy here, monsieur"; and so we began to talk while watching the rising tide, which ran over the sand and covered it as with a steel cuirass.

And then the monk told me stories, all the old stories belonging to the place, legends, nothing but legends.

One of them struck me forcibly. The country people, those belonging to the Mount, declare that at night one can hear voices talking on the sands, and then that one hears two goats bleating, one with a strong, the other with a weak voice. Incredulous people declare that it is nothing but the cry of the sea birds, which occasionally resembles bleatings, and occasionally, human lamentations; but belated fishermen swear that they have met an old shepherd wandering between tides on the sands around the little town. His head is completely concealed by his cloak and he is followed by a billy goat with a man's face, and a nanny goat with a woman's face, both having long, white hair and talking incessantly and quarreling in an unknown tongue. Then suddenly they cease and begin to bleat with all their might.

"Do you believe it?" I asked the monk. "I scarcely know," he replied, and I continued: "If there are other beings besides ourselves on this earth, how comes it that we have not known it long since, or why have *you* not seen them? How is it that *I* have not seen them?" He replied: "Do we see the hundred-thousandth part of what exists? Look here; there is the wind, which is the strongest force in nature, which knocks down men, and blows down buildings, uproots trees, raises the sea into mountains of water, destroys cliffs and casts great ships on the rocks; the wind which kills, which whistles, which sighs, which roars—have you ever seen it, and can you see it? It exists for all that, however."

I was silent before this simple reasoning. That man was a philosopher, or perhaps a fool; I could not say which exactly, so I held my tongue. What he had said had often been in my own thoughts.

---

[8]chimera: in Greek Mythology, a female monster with features of a lion, serpent, and goat.

July 3. I have slept badly; certainly there is some feverish influence here, for my coachman is suffering in the same way as I am. When I went back home yesterday, I noticed his singular paleness, and I asked him: "What is the matter with you, Jean?" "The matter is that I never get any rest, and my nights devour my days. Since your departure, monsieur, there has been a spell over me."

However, the other servants are all well, but I am very much afraid of having another attack myself.

July 4. I am decidedly ill again; for my old nightmares have returned. Last night I felt somebody leaning on me and sucking my life from between my lips. Yes, he was sucking it out of my throat, like a leech. Then he got up, satiated, and I woke up, so exhausted, crushed and weak that I could not move. If this continues for a few days, I shall certainly go away again.

July 5. Have I lost my reason? What happened last night is so strange that my head wanders when I think of it!

I had locked my door, as I do now every evening, and then, being thirsty, I drank half a glass of water, and accidentally noticed that the water bottle was full up to the cut-glass stopper.

Then I went to bed and fell into one of my terrible sleeps, from which I was aroused in about two hours by a still more frightful shock.

Picture to yourself a sleeping man who is being murdered and who wakes up with a knife in his lung, and whose breath rattles, who is covered with blood, and who can no longer breathe and is about to die, and does not understand—there you have it.

Having recovered my senses, I was thirsty again, so I lit a candle and went to the table on which stood my water bottle. I lifted it up and tilted it over my glass, but nothing came out. It was empty! It was completely empty! At first I could not understand it at all, and then suddenly I was seized by such a terrible feeling that I had to sit down, or rather I fell into a chair! Then I sprang up suddenly to look about me; then I sat down again, overcome by astonishment and fear, in front of the transparent glass bottle! I looked at it with fixed eyes, trying to conjecture, and my hands trembled! Somebody had drunk the water, but who? I? I without any doubt. It could surely only be I. In that case I was a somnambulist;[9] I lived, without knowing it, that mysterious double life which makes us doubt whether there are not two beings in us, or whether a strange, unknowable and invisible being does not at such moments, when our soul is in a state of torpor, animate our captive body, which obeys this other being, as it obeys us, and more than it obeys ourselves.

Oh! Who will understand my horrible agony? Who will understand the emotion of a man who is sound in mind, wide awake, full of common sense,

---

[9]somnambulist: a sleepwalker.

who looks in horror through the glass of a water bottle for a little water that disappeared while he was asleep? I remained thus until it was daylight, without venturing to go to bed again.

July 6. I am going mad. Again all the contents of my water bottle have been drunk during the night—or rather, I have drunk it!

But is it I? Is it I? Who could it be? Who? Oh! God! Am I going mad? Who will save me?

July 10. I have just been through some surprising ordeals. Decidedly I am mad! And yet! . . .

On July 6, before going to bed, I put some wine, milk, water, bread and strawberries on my table. Somebody drank—I drank—all the water and a little of the milk, but neither the wine, bread, nor the strawberries were touched.

On the seventh of July I renewed the same experiment, with the same results, and on July 8, I left out the water and the milk, and nothing was touched.

Lastly, on July 9, I put only water and milk on my table, taking care to wrap up the bottles in white muslin and to tie down the stoppers. Then I rubbed my lips, my beard and my hands with pencil lead, and went to bed.

Irresistible sleep seized me, which was soon followed by a terrible awakening. I had not moved, and there was no mark of lead on the sheets. I rushed to the table. The muslin round the bottles remained intact; I undid the string, trembling with fear. All the water had been drunk, and so had the milk! Ah! Great God! . . .

I must start for Paris immediately.

July 12. Paris. I must have lost my head during the last few days! I must be the plaything of my enervated imagination, unless I am really a somnambulist, or that I have been under the power of one of those hitherto unexplained influences which are called suggestions. In any case, my mental state bordered on madness, and twenty-four hours of Paris sufficed to restore my equilibrium.

Yesterday, after doing some business and paying some visits which instilled fresh and invigorating air into my soul, I wound up the evening at the *Théâtre-Français*. A play by Alexandre Dumas the younger[10] was being acted, and his active and powerful imagination completed my cure. Certainly solitude is dangerous for active minds. We require around us men who can think and talk. When we are alone for a long time, we people space with phantoms.

I returned along the boulevards to my hotel in excellent spirits. Amid the jostling of the crowd I thought, not without irony, of my terrors and surmises

---

[10]Alexander Dumas the younger (1824–95): a French dramatist, the illegitimate son of the novelist Alexandre Dumas (1802–70).

of the previous week, because I had believed—yes, I had believed—that an invisible being lived beneath my roof. How weak our brains are, and how quickly they are terrified and led into error by a small incomprehensible fact.

Instead of saying simply: "I do not understand because I do not know the cause," we immediately imagine terrible mysteries and supernatural powers.

July 14. Fête of the Republic.[11] I walked through the streets, amused as a child at the firecrackers and flags. Still it is very foolish to be merry on a fixed date, by Government decree. The populace is an imbecile flock of sheep, now stupidly patient, and now in ferocious revolt. Say to it: "Amuse yourself," and it amuses itself. Say to it: "Go and fight with your neighbor," and it goes and fights. Say to it: "Vote for the Emperor," and it votes for the Emperor, and then say to it: "Vote for the Republic," and it votes for the Republic.

Those who direct it are also stupid; only, instead of obeying men, they obey principles which can only be stupid, sterile, and false, for the very reason that they are principles, that is to say, ideas which are considered as certain and unchangeable, in this world where one is certain of nothing, since light is an illusion and noise is an illusion.

July 16. I saw some things yesterday that troubled me very much.

I was dining at the house of my cousin, Madame Sablé, whose husband is colonel of the 76th Chasseurs at Limoges.[12] There were two young women there, one of whom had married a medical man, Dr. Parent, who devotes much attention to nervous diseases and to the remarkable manifestations taking place at this moment under the influence of hypnotism and suggestion.

He related to us at some length the wonderful results obtained by English scientists and by the doctors of the Nancy school; and the facts which he adduced appeared to me so strange that I declared that I was altogether incredulous.

"We are," he declared, "on the point of discovering one of the most important secrets of nature; I mean to say, one of its most important secrets on this earth, for there are certainly others of a different kind of importance up in the stars, yonder. Ever since man has thought, ever since he has been able to express and write down his thoughts, he has felt himself close to a mystery which is impenetrable to his gross and imperfect senses, and he endeavors to supplement through his intellect the inefficiency of his senses. As long as that intellect remained in its elementary stage, these apparitions of invisible spirits assumed forms that were commonplace, though terrifying. Thence sprang the popular belief in the supernatural, the legends of wandering spirits, of fairies, of gnomes, ghosts, I might even say the legend of God; for our conceptions of

---

[11]French national holiday celebrating the storming of the Bastille on July 14, 1789; also known as Bastille Day.

[12]Chasseurs at Limoges: French army unit stationed at the capital of the Limousin region in France.

the workman-creator, from whatever religion they may have come down to us, are certainly the most mediocre, the most stupid and the most incredible inventions that ever sprang from the terrified brain of any human beings. Nothing is truer than what Voltaire[13] says: 'God made man in His own image, but man has certainly paid Him back in his own coin.'

"However, for rather more than a century men seem to have had a presentiment of something new. Mesmer and some others have put us on an unexpected track, and, especially within the last two or three years, we have arrived at really surprising results."

My cousin, who is also very incredulous, smiled, and Dr. Parent said to her: "Would you like me to try and send you to sleep, madame?" "Yes, certainly."

She sat down in an easy chair, and he began to look at her fixedly, so as to fascinate her. I suddenly felt myself growing uncomfortable, my heart beating rapidly and a choking sensation in my throat. I saw Madame Sablé's eyes becoming heavy, her mouth twitching and her bosom heaving, and at the end of ten minutes she was asleep.

"Go behind her," the doctor said to me, and I took a seat behind her. He put a visiting card into her hands, and said to her: "This is a looking-glass; what do you see in it?" And she replied: "I see my cousin." "What is he doing?" "He is twisting his mustache." "And now?" "He is taking a photograph out of his pocket." "Whose photograph is it?" "His own."

That was true, and the photograph had been given me that same evening at the hotel.

"What is his attitude in this portrait?" "He is standing up with his hat in his hand."

She saw, therefore, on that card, on that piece of white pasteboard, as if she had seen it in a mirror.

The young women were frightened, and exclaimed: "That is enough! Quite, quite enough!"

But the doctor said to Madame Sablé authoritatively: "You will rise at eight o'clock to-morrow morning; then you will go and call on your cousin at his hotel and ask him to lend you five thousand francs which your husband demands of you, and which he will ask for when he sets out on his coming journey."

Then he woke her up.

On returning to my hotel, I thought over this curious séance, and I was assailed by doubts, not as to my cousin's absolute and undoubted good faith,

---

[13]Voltaire: the pen name of French Enlightenment writer and philosopher Francois-Marie Arouet (1694–1778).

for I had known her as well as if she were my own sister ever since she was a child, but as to a possible trick on the doctor's part. Had he not, perhaps, kept a glass hidden in his hand, which he showed to the young woman in her sleep, at the same time as he did the card? Professional conjurors do things that are just as singular.

So I went home and to bed, and this morning, at about half-past eight, I was awakened by my valet, who said to me: "Madame Sablé has asked to see you immediately, monsieur." I dressed hastily and went to her.

She sat down in some agitation, with her eyes on the floor, and without raising her veil she said to me: "My dear cousin, I am going to ask a great favor of you." "What is it, cousin?" "I do not like to tell you, and yet I must. I am in absolute need of five thousand francs." "What, you?" "Yes, I, or rather my husband, who has asked me to procure them for him."

I was so thunderstruck that I stammered out my answers. I asked myself whether she had not really been making fun of me with Dr. Parent, if it was not merely a very well-acted farce which had been rehearsed beforehand. On looking at her attentively, however, all my doubts disappeared. She was trembling with grief, so painful was this step to her, and I was convinced that her throat was full of sobs.

I knew that she was very rich and I continued: "What! Has not your husband five thousand francs at his disposal? Come, think. Are you sure that he commissioned you to ask me for them?"

She hesitated for a few seconds, as if she were making a great effort to search her memory, and then she replied: "Yes . . . yes, I am quite sure of it." "He has written to you?"

She hesitated again and reflected, and I guessed the torture of her thoughts. She did not know. She only knew that she was to borrow five thousand francs of me for her husband. So she told a lie. "Yes, he has written to me." "When, pray? You did not mention it to me yesterday." "I received his letter this morning." "Can you show it me?" "No; no . . . no . . . it contained private matters . . . things too personal to ourselves. . . . I burned it." "So your husband runs into debt?"

She hesitated again, and then murmured: "I do not know." Thereupon I said bluntly: "I have not five thousand francs at my disposal at this moment, my dear cousin."

She uttered a kind of cry as if she were in pain and said: "Oh! oh! I beseech you, I beseech you to get them for me. . . ."

She got excited and clasped her hands as if she were praying to me! I heard her voice change its tone; she wept and stammered, harassed and dominated by the irresistible order that she had received.

"Oh! oh! I beg you to . . . if you knew what I am suffering . . . I want them to-day."

I had pity on her: "You shall have them by and by, I swear to you." "Oh! thank you! thank you! How kind you are."

I continued: "Do you remember what took place at your house last night?" "Yes." "Do you remember that Dr. Parent sent you to sleep?" "Yes." "Oh! Very well, then; he ordered you to come to me this morning to borrow five thousand francs, and at this moment you are obeying that suggestion."

She considered for a few moments, and then replied: "But as it is my husband who wants them——"

For a whole hour I tried to convince her, but could not succeed, and when she had gone I went to the doctor. He was just going out, and he listened to me with a smile, and said: "Do you believe now?" "Yes, I cannot help it." "Let us go to your cousin's."

She was already half asleep on a reclining chair, overcome with fatigue. The doctor felt her pulse, looked at her for some time with one hand raised toward her eyes, which she closed by degrees under the irresistible power of this magnetic influence, and when she was asleep, he said:

"Your husband does not require the five thousand francs any longer! You must, therefore, forget that you asked your cousin to lend them to you, and, if he speaks to you about it, you will not understand him."

Then he woke her up, and I took out a pocket book and said: "Here is what you asked me for this morning, my dear cousin." But she was so surprised that I did not venture to persist; nevertheless, I tried to recall the circumstance to her, but she denied it vigorously, thought I was making fun of her, and, in the end, very nearly lost her temper.

* * *

THERE! I HAVE JUST come back, and I have not been able to eat any lunch, for this experiment has altogether upset me.

July 19. Many people to whom I told the adventure laughed at me. I no longer know what to think. The wise man says: "It may be!"

July 21. I dined at Bougival, and then I spent the evening at a boatmen's ball. Decidedly everything depends on place and surroundings. It would be the height of folly to believe in the supernatural on the Ile de la Grenouillière . . . but on the top of Mont Saint-Michel? . . . and in India? We are terribly influenced by our surroundings. I shall return home next week.

July 30. I came back to my own house yesterday. Everything is going on well.

August 2. Nothing new; it is splendid weather, and I spend my days in watching the Seine flowing past.

August 4. Quarrels among my servants. They declare that the glasses are broken in the cupboards at night. The footman accuses the cook, who accuses the seamstress, who accuses the other two. Who is the culprit? It is a clever person who can tell.

August 6. This time I am not mad. I have seen . . . I have seen . . . I have seen! . . . I can doubt no longer . . . I have seen it! . . .

I was walking at two o'clock among my rose trees, in the full sunlight . . . in the walk bordered by autumn roses which are beginning to fall. As I stopped to look at a Géant de Bataille, which had three splendid blossoms, I distinctly saw the stalk of one of the roses near me bend, as if an invisible hand had bent it, and then break, as if that hand had picked it! Then the flower raised itself, following the curve which a hand would have described in carrying it toward a mouth, and it remained suspended in the transparent air, all alone and motionless, a terrible red spot, three yards from my eyes. In desperation I rushed at it to take it! I found nothing; it had disappeared. Then I was seized with furious rage against myself, for a reasonable and serious man should not have such hallucinations.

But was it an hallucination? I turned round to look for the stalk, and I found it at once, on the bush, freshly broken, between two other roses which remained on the branch. I returned home then, my mind greatly disturbed; for I am certain now, as certain as I am of the alternation of day and night, that there exists close to me an invisible being that lives on milk and water, that can touch objects, take them and change their places; that is, consequently, endowed with a material nature, although it is imperceptible to our senses, and that lives as I do, under my roof—

August 7. I slept tranquilly. He drank the water out of my decanter, but did not disturb my sleep.

I wonder if I am mad. As I was walking just now in the sun by the river side, doubts as to my sanity arose in me; not vague doubts such as I have had hitherto, but definite, absolute doubts. I have seen mad people, and I have known some who have been quite intelligent, lucid, even clear-sighted in every concern of life, except on one point. They spoke clearly, readily, profoundly on everything, when suddenly their mind struck upon the shoals of their madness and broke to pieces there, and scattered and floundered in that furious and terrible sea, full of rolling waves, fogs and squalls, which is called *madness*.

I certainly should think that I was mad, absolutely mad, if I were not conscious, did not perfectly know my condition, did not fathom it by analyzing it with the most complete lucidity. I should, in fact, be only a rational man who was laboring under an hallucination. Some unknown disturbance must have arisen in my brain, one of those disturbances which physiologists of the present day try to note and to verify; and that disturbance must have caused a deep gap in my mind and in the sequence and logic of my ideas. Similar phenomena occur in dreams which lead us among the most unlikely phantasmagoria, without causing us any surprise, because our verifying apparatus and our organ of control are asleep, while our imaginative faculty is awake and active. Is it not possible that one of the imperceptible notes of the cerebral keyboard has been paralyzed in me? Some men lose the recollection of proper names, of verbs, or of numbers, or merely of dates, in consequence of an accident. The localization of all the variations of thought has been established nowadays; why, then, should it be surprising if my faculty of controlling the unreality of certain hallucinations were dormant in me for the time being?

I thought of all this as I walked by the side of the water. The sun shone brightly on the river and made earth delightful, while it filled me with a love for life, for the swallows, whose agility always delights my eye, for the plants by the river side, the rustle of whose leaves is a pleasure to my ears.

By degrees, however, an inexplicable feeling of discomfort seized me. It seemed as if some unknown force were numbing and stopping me, were preventing me from going further, and were calling me back. I felt that painful wish to return which oppresses you when you have left a beloved invalid at home, and when you are seized with a presentiment that he is worse.

I, therefore, returned in spite of myself, feeling certain that I should find some bad news awaiting me, a letter or a telegram. There was nothing, however, and I was more surprised and uneasy than if I had had another fantastic vision.

August 8. I spent a terrible evening yesterday. He does not show himself any more, but I feel that he is near me, watching me, looking at me, penetrating me, dominating me, and more redoubtable when he hides himself thus than if he were to manifest his constant and invisible presence by supernatural phenomena. However, I slept.

August 9. Nothing, but I am afraid.

August 10. Nothing; what will happen to-morrow?

August 11. Still nothing; I cannot stop at home with this fear hanging over me and these thoughts in my mind; I shall go away.

August 12. Ten o'clock at night. All day long I have been trying to get away, and have not been able. I wished to accomplish this simple and easy act of freedom—to go out—to get into my carriage in order to go to Rouen—and I have not been able to do it. What is the reason?

August 13. When one is attacked by certain maladies, all the springs of our physical being appear to be broken, all our energies destroyed, all our muscles relaxed; our bones, too, have become as soft as flesh, and our blood as liquid as water. I am experiencing these sensations in my moral being in a strange and distressing manner. I have no longer any strength, any courage, any self-control, not even any power to set my own will in motion. I have no power left to will anything; but some one does it for me and I obey.

August 14. I am lost! Somebody possesses my soul and dominates it. Somebody orders all my acts, all my movements, all my thoughts. I am no longer anything in myself, nothing except an enslaved and terrified spectator of all the things I do. I wish to go out; I cannot. He does not wish to, and so I remain, trembling and distracted, in the armchair in which he keeps me sitting. I merely wish to get up and to rouse myself; I cannot! I am riveted to my chair, and my chair adheres to the ground in such a manner that no power could move us.

Then, suddenly, I must, I must go to the bottom of my garden to pick some strawberries and eat them, and I go there. I pick the strawberries and eat them! Oh, my God! My God! Is there a God? If there be one, deliver me! Save me! Succor me! Pardon! Pity! Mercy! Save me! Oh, what sufferings! What torture! What horror!

August 15. This is certainly the way in which my poor cousin was possessed and controlled when she came to borrow five thousand francs of me. She was under the power of a strange will which had entered into her, like another soul, like another parasitic and dominating soul. Is the world coming to an end?

But who is he, this invisible being that rules me? This unknowable being, this rover of a supernatural race?

Invisible beings exist, then! How is it, then, that since the beginning of the world they have never manifested themselves precisely as they do to me? I have never read of anything that resembles what goes on in my house. Oh, if I could only leave it, if I could only go away, escape, and never return! I should be saved, but I cannot.

August 16. I managed to escape to-day for two hours, like a prisoner who finds the door of his dungeon accidentally open. I suddenly felt that I was free and that he was far away, and so I gave orders to harness the horses as quickly as possible, and I drove to Rouen. Oh, how delightful to be able to say to a man who obeys you: "Go to Rouen!"

I made him pull up before the library, and I begged them to lend me Dr. Herrmann Herestauss' treatise on the unknown inhabitants of the ancient and modern world.

Then, as I was getting into my carriage, I intended to say: "To the railway station!" but instead of this I shouted—I did not say, but I shouted—in such a loud voice that all the passers-by turned round: "Home!" and I fell back on the cushion of my carriage, overcome by mental agony. He had found me again and regained possession of me.

August 17. Oh, what a night! What a night! And yet it seems to me that I ought to rejoice. I read until one o'clock in the morning! Herestauss, doctor of philosophy and theogony, wrote the history of the manifestation of all those invisible beings which hover around man, or of whom he dreams. He describes their origin, their domain, their power; but none of them resembles the one which haunts me. One might say that man, ever since he began to think, has had a foreboding fear of a new being, stronger than himself, his successor in this world, and that, feeling his presence, and not being able to foresee the nature of that master, he has, in his terror, created the whole race of occult beings, of vague phantoms born of fear.

Having, therefore, read until one o'clock in the morning, I went and sat down at the open window, in order to cool my forehead and my thoughts, in the calm night air. It was very pleasant and warm! How I should have enjoyed such a night formerly!

There was no moon, but the stars darted out their rays in the dark heavens. Who inhabits those worlds? What forms, what living beings, what animals are there yonder? What do the thinkers in those distant worlds know more than we do? What can they do more than we can? What do they see which we do not know? Will not one of them, some day or other, traversing space, appear on our earth to conquer it, just as the Norsemen formerly crossed the sea in order to subjugate nations more feeble than themselves?

We are so weak, so defenseless, so ignorant, so small, we who live on this particle of mud which revolves in a drop of water.

I fell asleep, dreaming thus in the cool night air, and when I had slept for about three-quarters of an hour, I opened my eyes without moving, awakened by I know not what confused and strange sensation. At first I saw nothing, and then suddenly it appeared to me as if a page of a book which had remained open on my table turned over of its own accord. Not a breath of air had come in at my window, and I was surprised, and waited. In about four minutes, I saw, I saw, yes, I saw with my own eyes, another page lift itself up and fall down on the others, as if a finger had turned it over. My armchair was empty, appeared empty, but I knew that he was there, he, and sitting in my place, and that he was reading. With a furious bound, the bound of an enraged wild beast that springs at its tamer, I crossed my room to seize him, to strangle him, to kill him! But before I could reach it, the chair fell over as if somebody had run away from me—my table rocked, my lamp fell and went out, and my window closed as if some thief had been surprised and had fled out into the night, shutting it behind him.

So he had run away; he had been afraid; he, afraid of me!

But—but—to-morrow—or later—some day or other—I should be able to hold him in my clutches and crush him against the ground! Do not dogs occasionally bite and strangle their masters?

August 18. I have been thinking the whole day long. Oh, yes, I will obey him, follow his impulses, fulfill all his wishes, show myself humble, submissive, a coward. He is the stronger; but the hour will come——

August 19. I know—I know—I know all! I have just read the following in the *Revue du Monde Scientifique*: "A curious piece of news comes to us from

Rio de Janeiro. Madness, an epidemic of madness, which may be compared to that contagious madness which attacked the people of Europe in the Middle Ages, is at this moment raging in the Province of San-Paolo. The terrified inhabitants are leaving their houses, saying that they are pursued, possessed, dominated like human cattle by invisible, though tangible beings, a species of vampire, which feed on their life while they are asleep, and who, besides, drink water and milk without appearing to touch any other nourishment.

"Professor Don Pedro Henriques, accompanied by several medical savants, has gone to the Province of San-Paolo, in order to study the origin and the manifestations of this surprising madness on the spot, and to propose such measures to the Emperor as may appear to him to be most fitted to restore the mad population to reason."

Ah! Ah! I remember now that fine Brazilian three-master which passed in front of my windows as it was going up the Seine, on the 8th day of last May! I thought it looked so pretty, so white and bright! That Being was on board of her, coming from there, where its race originated. And it saw me! It saw my house which was also white, and it sprang from the ship on to the land. Oh, merciful heaven!

Now I know, I can divine. The reign of man is over, and he has come. He who was feared by primitive man; whom disquieted priests exorcised; whom sorcerers evoked on dark nights, without having seen him appear, to whom the imagination of the transient masters of the world lent all the monstrous or graceful forms of gnomes, spirits, genii, fairies and familiar spirits. After the coarse conceptions of primitive fear, more clear-sighted men foresaw it more clearly. Mesmer divined it, and ten years ago physicians accurately discovered the nature of his power, even before he exercised it himself. They played with this new weapon of the Lord, the sway of a mysterious will over the human soul, which had become a slave. They called it magnetism, hypnotism, suggestion—what do I know? I have seen them amusing themselves like rash children with this horrible power! Woe to us! Woe to man! He has come, the—the—what does he call himself—the—I fancy that he is shouting out his name to me and I do not hear him—the—yes—he is shouting it out—I am listening—I cannot—he repeats it—the—Horla—I hear—the Horla—it is he—the Horla—he has come!

Ah! the vulture has eaten the pigeon; the wolf has eaten the lamb; the lion has devoured the sharp-horned buffalo; man has killed the lion with an arrow, with a sword, with gunpowder; but the Horla will make of man what we have made of the horse and of the ox; his chattel, his slave and his food, by the mere power of his will. Woe to us!

But, nevertheless, the animal sometimes revolts and kills the man who has subjugated it. I should also like—I shall be able to—but I must know him, touch him, see him! Scientists say that animals' eyes, being different from ours, do not distinguish objects as ours do. And my eye cannot distinguish this newcomer who is oppressing me.

Why? Oh, now I remember the words of the monk at Mont Saint-Michel: "Can we see the hundred-thousandth part of what exists? See here; there is the wind, which is the strongest force in nature, which knocks men, and blows down buildings, uproots trees, raises the sea into mountains of water, destroys cliffs and casts great ships on the breakers; the wind which kills, which whistles, which sighs, which roars—have you ever seen it, and can you see it? It exists for all that, however!"

And I went on thinking; my eyes are so weak, so imperfect, that they do not even distinguish hard bodies, if they are as transparent as glass! If a glass without tinfoil behind it were to bar my way, I should run into it, just as a bird which has flown into a room breaks its head against the window-panes. A thousand things, moreover, deceive man and lead him astray. Why should it then be surprising that he cannot perceive an unknown body through which the light passes?

A new being! Why not? It was assuredly bound to come! Why should we be the last? We do not distinguish it any more than all the others created before us! The reason is, that its nature is more perfect, its body finer and more finished than ours, that ours is so weak, so awkwardly constructed, encumbered with organs that are always tired, always on the strain like machinery that is too complicated, which lives like a plant and like a beast, nourishing itself with difficulty on air, herbs and flesh, an animal machine which is a prey to maladies, to malformations, to decay; broken-winded, badly regulated, simple and eccentric, ingeniously badly made, at once a coarse and a delicate piece of workmanship, the rough sketch of a being that might become intelligent and grand.

We are only a few, so few in this world, from the oyster up to man. Why should there not be one more, once that period is passed which separates the successive apparitions from all the different species?

Why not one more? Why not, also, other trees with immense, splendid flowers, perfuming whole regions? Why not other elements besides fire, air, earth and water? There are four, only four, those nursing fathers of various beings! What a pity! Why are there not forty, four hundred, four thousand? How poor everything is, how mean and wretched! grudgingly produced, roughly constructed, clumsily made! Ah, the elephant and the hippopotamus, what grace! And the camel, what elegance!

But the butterfly, you will say, a flying flower! I dream of one that should be as large as a hundred worlds, with wings whose shape, beauty, colors and motion I cannot even express. But I see it—it flutters from star to star, refreshing them and perfuming them with the light and harmonious breath of its flight! And the people up there look at it as it passes in an ecstasy of delight!

* * *

WHAT IS THE MATTER with me? It is he, the Horla, who haunts me, and who makes me think of these foolish things! He is within me, he is becoming my soul; I shall kill him!

August 19. I shall kill him. I have seen him! Yesterday I sat down at my table and pretended to write very assiduously. I knew quite well that he would come prowling round me, quite close to me, so close that I might perhaps be able to touch him, to seize him. And then—then I should have the strength of desperation; I should have my hands, my knees, my chest, my forehead, my teeth to strangle him, to crush him, to bite him, to tear him to pieces. And I watched for him with all my over-excited senses.

I had lighted my two lamps and the eight wax candles on my mantelpiece, as if with this light I could discover him.

My bedstead, my old oak post bedstead, stood opposite to me; on my right was the fireplace; on my left, the door which was carefully closed, after I had left it open for some time in order to attract him; behind me was a very high wardrobe with a looking-glass in it, before which I stood to shave and dress every day, and in which I was in the habit of glancing at myself from head to foot every time I passed it.

I pretended to be writing in order to deceive him, for he also was watching me, and suddenly I felt—I was certain that he was reading over my shoulder, that he was there, touching my ear.

I got up, my hands extended, and turned round so quickly that I almost fell. Eh! well? It was as bright as at midday, but I did not see my reflection in the mirror! It was empty, clear, profound, full of light! But my figure was not reflected in it—and I, I was opposite to it! I saw the large, clear glass from top to bottom, and I looked at it with unsteady eyes; and I did not dare to advance; I did not venture to make a movement, feeling that he was there, but that he would escape me again, he whose imperceptible body had absorbed my reflection.

How frightened I was! And then, suddenly, I began to see myself in a mist in the depths of the looking-glass, in a mist as it were a sheet of water; and it seemed to me as if this water were flowing clearer every moment. It was like the end of an eclipse. Whatever it was that hid me did not appear to possess any clearly defined outlines, but a sort of opaque transparency which gradually grew clearer.

At last I was able to distinguish myself completely, as I do every day when I look at myself.

I had seen it! And the horror of it remained with me, and makes me shudder even now.

August 20. How could I kill it, as I could not get hold of it? Poison? But it would see me mix it with the water; and then, would our poisons have any effect on its impalpable body? No—no—no doubt about the matter—Then—then?—

August 21. I sent for a blacksmith from Rouen, and ordered iron shutters for my room, such as some private hotels in Paris have on the ground floor, for fear of burglars, and he is going to make me an iron door as well. I have made myself out a coward, but I do not care about that!

* * *

September 10.—Rouen, hotel Continental. It is done—it is done—but is he dead? My mind is thoroughly upset by what I have seen.

Well then, yesterday, the locksmith having put on the iron shutters and door, I left everything open until midnight, although it was getting cold.

Suddenly I felt that he was there, and joy, mad joy, took possession of me. I got up softly, and walked up and down for some time, so that he might not suspect anything; then I took off my boots and put on my slippers carelessly; then I fastened the iron shutters, and, going back to the door, quickly double-locked it with a padlock, putting the key into my pocket.

Suddenly I noticed that he was moving restlessly round me, that in his turn he was frightened and was ordering me to let him out. I nearly yielded; I did not, however, but, putting my back to the door, I half opened it, just enough to allow me to go out backward, and as I am very tall my head touched the casing. I was sure that he had not been able to escape, and I shut him up quite alone, quite alone. What happiness! I had him fast. Then I ran downstairs; in the drawing-room, which was under my bedroom, I took the two lamps and I poured all the oil on the carpet, the furniture, everywhere; then I set fire to it and made my escape, after having carefully double-locked the door.

I went and hid myself at the bottom of the garden, in a clump of laurel bushes. How long it seemed! How long it seemed! Everything was dark, silent, motionless, not a breath of air and not a star, but heavy banks of clouds which one could not see, but which weighed, oh, so heavily on my soul.

I looked at my house and waited. How long it was! I already began to think that the fire had gone out of its own accord, or that he had extinguished it, when one of the lower windows gave way under the violence of the flames, and a long, soft, caressing sheet of red flame mounted up the white wall, and enveloped it as far as the roof. The light fell on the trees, the branches, and the leaves, and a shiver of fear pervaded them also! The birds awoke, a dog began to howl, and it seemed to me as if the day were breaking! Almost immediately two other windows flew into fragments, and I saw that the whole of the lower part of my house was nothing but a terrible furnace. But a cry, a horrible, shrill, heartrending cry, a woman's cry, sounded through the night, and two garret windows were opened! I had forgotten the servants! I saw their terror-stricken faces, and their arms waving frantically.

Then, overwhelmed with horror, I set off to run to the village, shouting: "Help! help! fire! fire!" I met some people who were already coming to the scene, and I returned with them.

By this time the house was nothing but a horrible and magnificent funeral pile, a monstrous funeral pile which lit up the whole country, a funeral pile where men were burning, and where he was burning also, He, He, my prisoner, that new Being, the new master, the Horla!

Suddenly the whole roof fell in between the walls, and a volcano of flames darted up to the sky. Through all the windows which opened on that furnace, I saw the flames darting, and I thought that he was there, in that kiln, dead.

Dead? Perhaps?——His body? Was not his body, which was transparent, indestructible by such means as would kill ours?

If he were not dead?——Perhaps time alone has power over that Invisible and Redoubtable Being. Why this transparent, unrecognizable body, this body belonging to a spirit, if it also has to fear ills, infirmities and premature destruction?

Premature destruction? All human terror springs from that! After man, the Horla. After him who can die every day, at any hour, at any moment, by any accident, came the one who would die only at his own proper hour, day, and minute, because he had touched the limits of his existence!

No—no—without any doubt—he is not dead——Then—then—I suppose I must kill myself! . . .

[1911]

QUESTIONS

GUY DE MAUPASSANT, *The Horla*

1. Provide a brief description of the character who narrates "The Horla." How does he spend his time, and what sort of person is he?

2. How does the narrator first notice and then narrate the changes in his demeanor? Could there be reasons for the changes other than his encounter with the Horla?

3. Why does the narrator assume that the Horla arrived on the Brazilian three-mast? What might this reveal about the narrator's sense of the relationship between Europe and South America?

4. Is it possible that the narrator is not being "haunted" by the Horla, but is instead going mad? Is he imagining the Horla? If so, what evidence do we see of his deterioration?

5. Compare the Horla to other vampiric monsters in literature, film, or television. Consider Bram Stoker's novel *Dracula* (1897) or its film adaptations, *Nosferatu* (Murnau, 1922) and *Dracula* (Browning, 1931). Discuss the ways in which Maupassant approaches Gothic conventions that would inform these later texts.

Anton Chekhov
[1860–1904]

The Russian playwright and short story writer **ANTON CHEKHOV** *grew up in poverty. His grandfather was a serf who purchased his own freedom, and eventually acquired enough wealth to buy an estate; however, his father squandered much of the wealth. Chekhov himself studied medicine, and practiced as a physician for much of his life. He was also a prolific fiction writer; by 1896, he had published more than three hundred short stories.*

During the 1880s, Chekhov wrote short dramatic sketches and one-act plays, such as The Bear *(1880) and* The Marriage Proposal *(1888), satirizing middle class norms and pretensions. His full-length theatrical works were not immediately successful. An early version of* Uncle Vanya, *titled* The Wood Demon *(1889), was a failure. However, his later plays—*The Seagull *(1896),* Uncle Vanya *(1899),* Three Sisters *(1901), and* The Cherry Orchard *(1903), his last play—found great success.*

In part, this later achievement was due to Chekov's collaboration with the Moscow Art Theater. Founded in 1898, this experimental theater company read The Seagull *as a work that reflected the theater's interest in realistically presenting individual psychology on stage. The Russian director and actor Konstantin Stanislavsky and playwright Vladimir Nemirovich-Danchenko co-founded this company, which used ensemble acting and advocated a restrained acting method that stressed the psychology of dramatic characters. In their hands, Chekhov's* The Seagull *was an enormous hit.*

Chekhov's restrained realism was at odds with the colorful foreign melodramas that Russian audiences embraced. Like his short stories, his plays offer plots that slowly unfold focusing on local detail. The dialogue, while clear and direct, sometimes seems meaningless or trivial, and the action slow-paced. He nonetheless touched on important social changes in Russia, particularly the genteel poverty of the landed aristocracy and the decline of rural culture. Chekhov also focused on individual psychology. In Uncle Vanya, *for instance, the eponymous protagonist discovers he has wasted his life supporting a bombastic professor. When he tries to shoot the professor, he fails. The drama rests not in the gunshot, but instead in the struggle of this character to come to terms with his misguided past.*

Toward the end of his life, Chekhov achieved great fame and public support for his drama, in part due to his fortuitous association with the Moscow Art Theater. He died of tuberculosis in 1904, shortly after this association was forged.

A Marriage Proposal

ANTON CHEKHOV
TRANSLATED BY BAUKHAGE & BARRETT H. CLARK

PERSONS IN THE PLAY

STEPAN STEPANOVITCH TSCHUBUKOV	A country farmer
NATALIA STEPANOVNA	His daughter (aged 25)
IVAN VASSILIYITCH LOMOV	Tschubukov's neighbor

SCENE: *Reception-room in* TSCHUBUKOV'S *country home, Russia.*

TIME: *The present.*

TSCHUBUKOV *discovered as the curtain rises.*

Enter LOMOV, *wearing a dress-suit.*

TSCHUB (*Going toward him and greeting him*). Who is this I see? My dear fellow! Ivan Vassiliyitch! I'm so glad to see you! (*Shakes hands*) But this is a surprise! How are you?

LOMOV. Thank you! And how are you?

TSCHUB. Oh, so-so, my friend. Please sit down. It isn't right to forget one's neighbor. But tell me, why all this ceremony? Dress clothes, white gloves and all? Are you on your way to some engagement, my good fellow?

LOMOV. No, I have no engagement except with you, Stepan Stepanovitch.

TSCHUB. But why in evening clothes, my friend? This isn't New Year's!

LOMOV. You see, it's simply this, that—(*Composing himself*) I have come to you, Stepan Stepanovitch, to trouble you with a request. It is not the first time I have had the honor of turning to you for assistance, and you have always, that is—I beg your pardon, I am a bit excited! I'll take a drink of water first, dear Stepan Stepanovitch. (*He drinks*)

TSCHUB (*Aside*). He's come to borrow money! I won't give him any! (*To* LOMOV) What is it, then, dear Lomov?

LOMOV. You see—dear—Stepanovitch, pardon me, Stepan—Stepan—dearvitch—I mean—I am terribly nervous, as you will be so good as to see—! What I mean to say—you are the only one who can help me, though I don't deserve it, and—and I have no right whatever to make this request of you.

TSCHUB. Oh, don't beat about the bush, my dear fellow. Tell me!

LOMOV. Immediately—in a moment. Here it is, then: I have come to ask for the hand of your daughter, Natalia Stepanovna.

TSCHUB (*Joyfully*). Angel! Ivan Vassiliyitch! Say that once again! I didn't quite hear it!

LOMOV. I have the honor to beg——

TSCHUB (*Interrupting*). My dear, dear man! I am so happy that everything is so—everything! (*Embraces and kisses him*) I have wanted this to happen for so long. It has been my dearest wish! (*He represses a tear*) And I have always loved you, my dear fellow, as my own son! May God give you His blessings and His grace and—I always wanted it to happen. But why am I standing here like a blockhead? I am completely dumbfounded with pleasure, completely dumbfounded. My whole being—! I'll call Natalia——

LOMOV. Dear Stepan Stepanovitch, what do you think? May I hope for Natalia Stepanovna's acceptance?

TSCHUB. Really! A fine boy like you—and you think she won't accept on the minute? Love-sick as a cat and all that—! (*He goes out, right*)

LOMOV. I'm cold. My whole body is trembling as though I was going to take my examination! But the chief thing is to settle matters! If a person meditates too much, or hesitates, or talks about it, waits for an ideal or for true love, he never gets it. Brrr! It's cold! Natalia is an excellent house-keeper, not at all bad-looking, well educated—what more could I ask? I'm so excited my ears are roaring! (*He drinks water*) And not to marry, that won't do! In the first place, I'm thirty-five—a critical age, you might say. In the second place, I must live a well-regulated life. I have a weak heart, continual palpitation, and I am very sensitive and always getting excited. My lips begin to tremble and the pulse in my right temple throbs terribly. But the worst of all is sleep! I hardly lie down and begin to doze before something in my left side begins to pull and tug, and something begins to hammer in my left shoulder—and in my head, too! I jump up like a madman, walk about a little, lie down again, but the moment I fall asleep I have a terrible cramp in the side. And so it is all night long!

(*Enter* NATALIA STEPANOVNA.)

NATALIA. Ah! It's you. Papa said to go in: there was a dealer in there who'd come to buy something. Good afternoon, Ivan Vassiliyitch.

LOMOV. Good day, my dear Natalia Stepanovna.

NATALIA. You must pardon me for wearing my apron and this old dress: we are working to-day. Why haven't you come to see us oftener? You've not been here for so long! Sit down. (*They sit down*) Won't you have something to eat?

LOMOV. Thank you, I have just had lunch.

NATALIA. Smoke, do, there are the matches. To-day it is beautiful and only yesterday it rained so hard that the workmen couldn't do a stroke of work.
How many bricks have you cut? Think of it! I was so anxious that I had
the whole field mowed, and now I'm sorry I did it, because I'm afraid the
hay will rot. It would have been better if I had waited. But what on earth
is this? You are in evening clothes! The latest cut! Are you on your way to
a ball? And you seem to be looking better, too—really. Why are you
dressed up so gorgeously?

LOMOV (*Excited*) You see, my dear Natalia Stepanovna—it's simply this: I
have decided to ask you to listen to me—of course it will be a surprise,
and indeed you'll be angry, but I—(*aside*) How fearfully cold it is!

NATALIA. What is it? (*A pause*) Well?

LOMOV. I'll try to be brief. My dear Natalia Stepanovna, as you know, for
many years, since my childhood, I have had the honor to know your family. My poor aunt and her husband, from whom, as you know, I inherited
the estate, always had the greatest respect for your father and your poor
mother. The Lomovs and the Tschubukovs have been for decades on the
friendliest, indeed the closest, terms with each other, and furthermore my
property, as you know, adjoins your own. If you will be so good as to
remember, my meadows touch your birch woods.

NATALIA. Pardon the interruption. You said "my meadows"—but are they
yours?

LOMOV. Yes, they belong to me.

NATALIA. What nonsense! The meadows belong to us—not to you!

LOMOV. No, to me! Now, my dear Natalia Stepanovna!

NATALIA. Well, that is certainly news to me. How do they belong to you?

LOMOV. How? I am speaking of the meadows lying between your birch
woods and my brick-earth.

NATALIA. Yes, exactly. They belong to us.

LOMOV. No, you are mistaken, my dear Natalia Stepanovna, they belong to me.

NATALIA. Try to remember exactly, Ivan Vassiliyitch. Is it so long ago that you
inherited them?

LOMOV. Long ago! As far back as I can remember they have always belonged
to us.

NATALIA. But that isn't true! You'll pardon my saying so.

LOMOV. It is all a matter of record, my dear Natalia Stepanovna. It is true that
at one time the title to the meadows was disputed, but now everyone
knows they belong to me. There is no room for discussion. Be so good as
to listen: my aunt's grandmother put these meadows, free from all costs,
into the hands of your father's grandfather's peasants for a certain time

while they were making bricks for my grandmother. These people used the meadows free of cost for about forty years, living there as they would on their own property. Later, however, when——

NATALIA. There's not a word of truth in that! My grandfather, and my great-grandfather, too, knew that their estate reached back to the swamp, so that the meadows belong to us. What further discussion can there be? I can't understand it. It is really most annoying.

LOMOV. I'll show you the papers, Natalia Stepanovna.

NATALIA. No, either you are joking, or trying to lead me into a discussion. That's not at all nice! We have owned this property for nearly three hundred years, and now all at once we hear that it doesn't belong to us. Ivan Vassiliyitch, you will pardon me, but I really can't believe my ears. So far as I am concerned, the meadows are worth very little. In all they don't contain more than five acres and they are worth only a few hundred roubles, say three hundred, but the injustice of the thing is what affects me. Say what you will, I can't bear injustice.

LOMOV. Only listen until I have finished, please! The peasants of your respected father's grandfather, as I have already had the honor to tell you, baked bricks for my grandmother. My aunt's grandmother wished to do them a favor——

NATALIA. Grandfather! Grandmother! Aunt! I know nothing about them. All I know is that the meadows belong to us, and that ends the matter.

LOMOV. No, they belong to me!

NATALIA. And if you keep on explaining it for two days, and put on five suits of evening clothes, the meadows are still ours, ours, ours! I don't want to take your property, but I refuse to give up what belongs to us!

LOMOV. Natalia Stepanovna, I don't need the meadows, I am only concerned with the principle. If you are agreeable, I beg of you, accept them as a gift from me!

NATALIA. But I can give them to you, because they belong to me! That is very peculiar, Ivan Vassiliyitch! Until now we have considered you as a good neighbor and a good friend; only last year we lent you our threshing machine so that we couldn't thresh until November, and now you treat us like thieves! You offer to give me my own land. Excuse me, but neighbors don't treat each other that way. In my opinion, it's very low trick—to speak frankly——

LOMOV. According to you I'm a usurper, then, am I? My dear lady, I have never appropriated other people's property, and I shall permit no one to accuse me of such a thing! (*He goes quickly to the bottle and drinks water*) The meadows are mine!

NATALIA. That's not the truth! They are mine!

LOMOV. Mine!

NATALIA. Eh? I'll prove it to you! This afternoon I'll send my reapers into the meadows.

LOMOV. W—h—a—t?

NATALIA. My reapers will be there to-day!

LOMOV. And I'll chase them off!

NATALIA. If you dare!

LOMOV. The meadows are mine, you understand? Mine!

NATALIA. Really, you needn't scream so! If you want to scream and snort and rage you may do it at home, but here please keep yourself within the limits of common decency.

LOMOV. My dear lady, if it weren't that I were suffering from palpitation of the heart and hammering of the arteries in my temples, I would deal with you very differently! (*In a loud voice*) The meadows belong to me!

NATALIA. Us!

LOMOV. Me!

(*Enter* TSCHUBUKOV, *right.*)

TSCHUB. What's going on here? What is he yelling about?

NATALIA. Papa, please tell this gentleman to whom the meadows belong, to us or to him?

TSCHUB (*To* LOMOV). My dear fellow, the meadows are ours.

LOMOV. But, merciful heavens, Stepan Stepanovitch, how do you make that out? You at least might be reasonable. My aunt's grandmother gave the use of the meadows free of cost to your grandfather's peasants; the peasants lived on the land for forty years and used it as their own, but later when——

TSCHUB. Permit me, my dear friend. You forget that your grandmother's peasants never paid, because there had been a lawsuit over the meadows, and everyone knows that the meadows belong to us. You haven't looked at the map.

LOMOV. I'll prove to you that they belong to me!

TSCHUB. Don't try to prove it, my dear fellow.

LOMOV. I will!

TSCHUB. My good fellow, what are you shrieking about? You can't prove anything by yelling, you know. I don't ask for anything that belongs to you, nor do I intend to give up anything of my own. Why should I? If it has gone so far, my dear man, that you really intend to claim the meadows, I'd rather give them to the peasants than you, and I certainly shall!

LOMOV. I can't believe it! By what right can you give away property that doesn't belong to you?

TSCHUB. Really, you must allow me to decide what I am to do with my own land! I'm not accustomed, young man, to have people address me in that tone of voice. I, young man, am twice your age, and I beg you to address me respectfully.

LOMOV. No! No! You think I'm a fool! You're making fun of me! You call my property yours and then expect me to stand quietly by and talk to you like a human being. That isn't the way a good neighbor behaves, Stepan Stepanovitch! You are no neighbor, you're no better than a land-grabber. That's what you are!

TSCHUB. Wh—at? What did he say?

NATALIA. Papa, send the reapers into the meadows this minute!

TSCHUB (*To* LOMOV) What was that you said, sir?

NATALIA. The meadows belong to us and I won't give them up! I won't give them up! I won't give them up!

LOMOV. We'll see about that! I'll prove in court that they belong to me.

TSCHUB. In court! You may sue in court, sir, if you like! Oh, I know you, you are only waiting to find an excuse to go to law! You're an intriguer, that's what you are! Your whole family were always looking for quarrels. The whole lot!

LOMOV. Kindly refrain from insulting my family. The entire race of Lomov has always been honorable! And never has one been brought to trial for embezzlement, as your dear uncle was!

TSCHUB. And the whole Lomov family were insane!

NATALIA. Every one of them!

TSCHUB. Your grandmother was a dipsomaniac,[1] and the younger aunt, Nastasia Michailovna, ran off with an architect.

LOMOV. And your mother limped. (*He puts his hand over his heart*) Oh, my side pains! My temples are bursting! Lord in Heaven! Water!

TSCHUB. And your dear father was a gambler—and a glutton!

NATALIA. And your aunt was a gossip like few others!

LOMOV. And you are an intriguer. Oh, my heart! And it's an open secret that you cheated at the elections—my eyes are blurred! Where is my hat?

NATALIA. Oh, how low! Liar! Disgusting thing!

LOMOV. Where's the hat—? My heart! Where shall I go? Where is the door—? Oh—it seems—as though I were dying! I can't—my legs won't hold me— (*Goes to the door*)

TSCHUB (*Following him*). May you never darken my door again!

NATALIA. Bring your suit to court! We'll see!

(LOMOV *staggers out, center.*)

---

[1]Alcoholic

TSCHUB (*Angrily*). The devil!

NATALIA. Such a good-for-nothing! And then they talk about being good neighbors!

TSCHUB. Loafer! Scarecrow! Monster!

NATALIA. A swindler like that takes over a piece of property that doesn't belong to him and then dares to argue about it!

TSCHUB. And to think that this fool dares to make a proposal of marriage!

NATALIA. What? A proposal of marriage?

TSCHUB. Why, yes! He came here to make you a proposal of marriage.

NATALIA. Why didn't you tell me that before?

TSCHUB. That's why he had on his evening clothes! The poor fool!

NATALIA. Proposal for me? Oh! (*Falls into an armchair and groans*) Bring him back! Bring him back!

TSCHUB. Bring whom back?

NATALIA. Faster, faster, I'm sinking! Bring him back! (*She becomes hysterical*)

TSCHUB. What is it? What's wrong with you? (*His hands to his head*) I'm cursed with bad luck! I'll shoot myself! I'll hang myself!

NATALIA. I'm dying! Bring him back!

TSCHUB. Bah! In a minute! Don't bawl! (*He rushes out, center*)

NATALIA (*Groaning*). What have they done to me? Bring him back! Bring him back!

TSCHUB (*Comes running in*). He's coming at once! The devil take him! Ugh! Talk to him yourself, I can't.

NATALIA (*Groaning*). Bring him back!

TSCHUB. He's coming, I tell you! "Oh, Lord! What a task it is to be the father of a grown daughter!" I'll cut my throat! I really will cut my throat! We've argued with the fellow, insulted him, and now we've thrown him out!— and you did it all, you!

NATALIA. No, you! You haven't any manners, you are brutal! If it weren't for you, he wouldn't have gone!

TSCHUB. Oh, yes, I'm to blame! If I shoot or hang myself, remember *you'll* be to blame. You forced me to it! You! (LOMOV *appears in the doorway*) There, talk to him yourself! (*He goes out*)

LOMOV. Terrible palpitation!—My leg is lamed! My side hurts me——

NATALIA. Pardon us, we were angry, Ivan Vassiliyitch. I remember now—the meadows really belong to you.

LOMOV. My heart is beating terribly! My meadows—my eyelids tremble—(*They sit down*) We were wrong. It was only the principle of the thing—the property isn't worth much to me, but the principle is worth a great deal.

NATALIA. Exactly, the principle! Let us talk about something else.

LOMOV. Because I have proofs that my aunt's grandmother had, with the peasants of your good father——

NATALIA. Enough, enough. (*Aside*) I don't know how to begin. (*To* LOMOV) Are you going hunting soon?

LOMOV. Yes, heath-cock shooting, respected Natalia Stepanovna. I expect to begin after the harvest. Oh, did you hear? My dog, Ugadi, you know him—limps!

NATALIA. What a shame! How did that happen?

LOMOV. I don't know. Perhaps it's a dislocation, or maybe he was bitten by some other dog. (*He sighs*) The best dog I ever had—to say nothing of his price! I paid Mironov a hundred and twenty-five roubles for him.

NATALIA. That was too much to pay, Ivan Vassilivitch.

LOMOV. In my opinion it was very cheap. A wonderful dog!

NATALIA. Papa paid eighty-five roubles for his Otkatai, and Otkatai is much better than your Ugadi.

LOMOV. Really? Otkatai is better than Ugadi? What an idea! (*He laughs*) Otkatai better than Ugadi!

NATALIA. Of course he is better. It is true Otkatai is still young; he isn't full-grown yet, but in the pack or on the leash with two or three, there is no better than he, even—

LOMOV. I really beg your pardon, Natalia Stepanovna, but you quite over-looked the fact that he has a short lower jaw, and a dog with a short lower jaw can't snap.

NATALIA. Short lower jaw? That's the first time I ever heard that!

LOMOV. I assure you, his lower jaw is shorter than the upper.

NATALIA. Have you measured it?

LOMOV. I have measured it. He is good at running, though.

NATALIA. In the first place, our Otkatai is purebred, a full-blooded son of Sapragavas and Stameskis, and as for your mongrel, nobody could ever figure out his pedigree; he's old and ugly, and as skinny as an old hag.

LOMOV. Old, certainly! I wouldn't take five of your Otkatais for him! Ugadi is a dog and Otkatai is—it is laughable to argue about it! Dogs like your Otkatai can be found by the dozens at any dog dealer's, a whole pound-full!

NATALIA. Ivan Vassiliyitch, you are very contrary to-day. First our meadows belong to you an then Ugadi is better than Otkatai. I don't like it when a person doesn't say what he really thinks. You know perfectly well that Otkatai is a hundred times better than your silly Ugadi. What makes you keep on saying he isn't?

LOMOV. I can see, Natalia Stepanovna, that you consider me either a blind-man or a fool. But at least you may as well admit that Otkatai has a short lower jaw!

NATALIA. It isn't so!

LOMOV. Yes, a short lower jaw!

NATALIA (*Loudly*). It's not so!

LOMOV. What makes you scream, my dear lady?

NATALIA. What makes you talk such nonsense? It's disgusting! It is high time that Ugadi was shot, and yet you compare him with Otkatai!

LOMOV. Pardon me, but I can't carry on this argument any longer. I have palpitation of the heart!

NATALIA. I have always noticed that the hunters who do the most talking know the least about hunting.

LOMOV. My dear lady, I beg of you to be still. My heart is bursting! (*He shouts*) Be still!

NATALIA. I won't be still until you admit that Otkatai is better!

(*Enter* TSCHUBUKOV)

TSCHUB. Well, has it begun again?

NATALIA. Papa, say frankly, on your honor, which dog is better: Otkatai or Ugadi?

LOMOV. Stepan Stepanovitch, I beg of you, just answer this: has your dog a short lower jaw or not? Yes or no?

TSCHUB. And what if he has? Is it of such importance? There is no better dog in the whole country.

LOMOV. My Ugadi is better. Tell the truth, now!

TSCHUB. Don't get so excited, my dear fellow! Permit me. Your Ugadi certainly has his good points. He is from a good breed, has a good stride, strong haunches, and so forth. But the dog, if you really want to know it, has two faults; he is old and he has a short lower jaw.

LOMOV. Pardon me, I have palpitation of the heart!—Let us keep to facts— just remember in Maruskins's meadows, my Ugadi kept ear to ear with the Count Rasvachai and your dog.

TSCHUB. He was behind, because the Count struck him with his whip.

LOMOV. Quite right. All the other dogs were on the fox's scent, but Otkatai found it necessary to bite a sheep.

TSCHUB. That isn't so!—I am sensitive about that and beg you to stop this argument. He struck him because everybody looks on a strange dog of good blood with envy. Even you, sir, aren't free from the sin. No sooner do you find a dog better than Ugadi than you begin to—this, that—his, mine—and so forth! I remember distinctly.

LOMOV. I remember something, too!

TSCHUB (*Mimicking him*). I remember something, too! What do you remember?

LOMOV. Palpitation! My leg is lame—I can't—

NATALIA. Palpitation! What kind of hunter are you? You ought to stay in the kitchen by the stove and wrestle with the potato peelings, and not go fox-hunting! Palpitation!

TSCHUB. And what kind of hunter are you? A man with your diseases ought to stay at home and not jolt around in the saddle. If you were a hunter—! But you only ride round in order to find out about other people's dogs, and make trouble for everyone. I am sensitive! Let's drop the subject. Besides, you're no hunter.

LOMOV. And are you a hunter? You only ride around to flatter the Count!—My heart! You intriguer! Swindler!

TSCHUB. And what of it? (*Shouting*) Be still!

LOMOV. Intriguer!

TSCHUB. Baby! Puppy! Walking drug-store!

LOMOV. Old rat! Jesuit! Oh, I know you!

TSCHUB. Be still! Or I'll shoot you—with my worst gun, like a partridge! Fool! Loafer!

LOMOV. Everyone knows that—oh, my heart!—that your poor late wife beat you. My leg—my temples—Heavens—I'm dying—I——

TSCHUB. And your housekeeper wears the trousers in your house!

LOMOV. Here—here—there—there—my heart has burst! My shoulder is torn apart. Where is my shoulder? I'm dying! (*He falls into a chair*) The doctor! (*Faints*)

TSCHUB. Baby! Half-baked clam! Fool!

NATALIA. Nice sort of hunter you are! You can't even sit on a horse. (*To* TSCHUB) Papa, what's the matter with him? (*She screams*) Ivan Vassiliyitch! He is dead!

LOMOV. I'm ill! I can't breathe! Air!

NATALIA. He is dead! (*She shakes* LOMOV *in the chair*) Ivan Vassiliyitch! What have we done! He is dead! (*She sinks into a chair*) The doctor—doctor! (*She goes into hysterics*)

TSCHUB. Ahh! What is it? What's the matter with you?

NATALIA (*Groaning*) He's dead!—Dead!

TSCHUB. Who is dead? Who? (*Looking at* LOMOV) Yes, he is dead! Good God! Water! The doctor! (*Holding the glass to* LOMOV'S *lips*) Drink! No, he won't drink! He's dead! What a terrible situation! Why didn't I shoot myself? Why have I never cut my throat? What am I waiting for now? Only give me a knife! Give me a pistol! (*Lomov moves*) He's coming to! Drink some water—there!

LOMOV. Sparks! Mists! Where am I?

TSCHUB. Get married! Quick, and then go to the devil! She's willing! (*He joins the hands of* LOMOV *and* NATALIA) She's agreed! Only leave me in peace!

LOMOV. Wh—what? (*Getting up*) Whom?

TSCHUB. She's willing! Well? Kiss each other and—the devil take you both!

NATALIA (*Groans*) He lives! Yes, yes, I'm willing!

TSCHUB. Kiss each other!

LOMOV. Eh? Whom? (NATALIA *and* LOMOV *kiss*) Very nice—! Pardon me, but what is this for? Oh, yes, I understand! My heart—sparks—I am happy, Natalia Stepanovna. (*He kisses her hand*) My leg is lame!

NATALIA. I'm happy, too!

TSCHUB. Ahh! A load off my shoulders! Ahh!

NATALIA. And now at least you'll admit that Ugadi is worse than Otkatai!

LOMOV. Better!

NATALIA. Worse!

TSCHUB. Now the domestic joys have begun.—Champagne!

LOMOV. Better!

NATALIA. Worse, worse, worse!

TSCHUB (*Trying to drown them out*). Champagne, champagne!

CURTAIN

[1888]

QUESTIONS

ANTON CHEKHOV, *A Marriage Proposal*

1. What situation does Chekov set out at the beginning of *A Marriage Proposal*?

2. How would you characterize Tschubukov? His daughter, Natalie? His neighbor, Lomov?

3. The title of *A Marriage Proposal* encourages audiences to anticipate romance. Is the title misleading? Why or why not?

4. Over what issues do Natalie and Lomov fight?

5. Comedy generally centers on young lovers, who encounter problems but ultimately find a solution that leads to a happy ending. What problems do the young lovers face here? Can we, in fact, characterize them as "young lovers"? Why or why not?

6. What is the conclusion of this play? Is it funny? Explain your opinion using evidence from the text.

7. Because *A Marriage Proposal* is a one-act play, it necessarily offers less room for rich character development and complex thematic subtexts. Most one-acts take place in a single location, focus on a limited number of characters, and depict a single, powerful incident. Like a short story or a poem, the material must be presented efficiently and, consequently, one-acts sometimes seem less subtle than longer plays. Where do you see the form of the one-act strengthening the play? Weakening it?

8. Designed to draw laughter from its audiences, the farce is a type of comedy featuring exaggerated characters in ridiculous situations. Often, farces rely on caricature, broad humor, sexual misunderstandings, and physical comedy to engage audiences. Is *A Marriage Proposal* a farce? Explain your position using evidence from the text.

9. Humor sometimes couches important social messages. What critiques of culture and society are lodged within *A Marriage Proposal*? Is Chekhov shedding light on the demise of land-owning aristocracy or the rise of middle classes? Is he asking audiences to look critically at the institution of marriage? Locate and explain moments in which you believe Chekhov is employing humor to advance a serious commentary on issues related to gender and/or class.

Charlotte Perkins Gilman
[1860–1935]

Born in Hartford, Connecticut to a branch of the famous New England Beecher family, CHARLOTTE PERKINS GILMAN *grew up in near poverty after her father abandoned the family. Her sense of independence may well have been fostered by her encounters with great-aunt Harriet Beecher Stowe, author of the abolitionist novel* Uncle Tom's Cabin; *and feminist/suffragist great-aunts Catherine Beecher and Isabella Beecher Hooker. Despite a childhood pledge to retain her independence by remaining single, Gilman married at twenty-three, had a child a year later, and immediately plunged into depression. The treatment prescribed by the highly respected nerve specialist S. Weir Mitchell was for her to avoid writing and intellectual activity of any kind, and this only served to deepen her depression. She divorced her husband and took her mother and daughter to California. There Gilman resumed writing and lecturing on women's rights, and eventually married a cousin, George Gilman, in 1900.*

The year 1894 found Gilman in San Francisco, where she helped to organize the California Women's Congresses of 1894–1895; she and social reformer Jane Addams cofounded the Women's Peace Party in 1895. Her activism on behalf of women's rights took her to cities and towns throughout the United States and England. She argued that women were not biologically inferior to men, but rather had been conditioned to behave subserviently. "Women are human beings as much as men, by nature; and as women, are even more sympathetic with human processes," she argued. "To develop human life in its true powers we need fully equal citizenship for women." Toward that end, Gilman advocated communal living in which women could leave household duties and childcare to trained domestic workers, and then participate fully in the public sphere.

In 1935, a year after her husband's death and with a diagnosis of breast cancer, Gilman committed suicide, explaining her choice in the most rational terms: "When one is assured of unavoidable and imminent death, it is the simplest of human rights to choose a quick and easy death in place of a slow and horrible one."

Gilman was a prolific writer, and published a highly acclaimed exploration of women's status in Women and Economics *(1898) and a thoughtful, witty feminist-utopian novel in* Herland *(1915). She also published the magazine* The Forerunner, *for which she was the sole contributor, from 1910 to 1916; and wrote several novels, a poetry collection, and over two hundred short stories. "The Yellow Wallpaper," published in 1892 in* New England Magazine, *after a rejection from the* Atlantic Monthly, *draws from her experience with the common* treatment of depression in women at the turn of the century. Carrie Chapman Catt, one of the most revered pioneers of the women's rights movement, called Charlotte Perkins Gilman, "the most original and challenging mind the movement produced." That sentiment was echoed by contemporary feminists in 1994, when Gilman was inducted into the National Women's Hall of Fame in Seneca Falls, New York.

The Yellow Wall-Paper

CHARLOTTE PERKINS GILMAN

friend?

IT IS VERY SELDOM that mere ordinary people like John and myself secure halls for the summer.

A colonial mansion, a hereditary estate, I would say a haunted house, and reach the height of romantic felicity—but that would be asking too much of fate!

Still I will proudly declare that there is something queer about it.

Else, why should it be let so cheaply? And why have stood so long untenanted?

John laughs at me, of course, but one expects that in marriage.

John is practical in the extreme. He has no patience with faith, an intense horror of superstition, and he scoffs openly at any talk of things not to be felt and seen and put down in figures.

John is a physician, and *perhaps*—(I would not say it to a living soul, of course, but this is dead paper and a great relief to my mind—) *perhaps* that is one reason I do not get well faster.

You see he does not believe I am sick!

And what can one do?

If a physician of high standing, and one's own husband, assures friends and relatives that there is really nothing the matter with one but temporary nervous depression—a slight hysterical tendency—what is one to do?

My brother is also a physician, and also of high standing, and he says the same thing.

So I take phosphates or phosphites—whichever it is, and tonics, and journeys, and air, and exercise, and am absolutely forbidden to "work" until I am well again.

Personally, I disagree with their ideas.

Personally, I believe that congenial work, with excitement and change, would do me good.

But what is one to do?

I did write for a while in spite of them; but it *does* exhaust me a good deal—having to be so sly about it, or else meet with heavy opposition.

First published in *New England Magazine*, August 1892.

I sometimes fancy that in my condition if I had less opposition and more society and stimulus—but John says the very worst thing I can do is to think about my condition, and I confess it always makes me feel bad.

So I will let it alone and talk about the house.

The most beautiful place! It is quite alone, standing well back from the road, quite three miles from the village. It makes me think of English places that you read about, for there are hedges and walls and gates that lock, and lots of separate little houses for the gardeners and people.

There is a *delicious* garden! I never saw such a garden—large and shady, full of box-bordered paths, and lined with long grape-covered arbors with seats under them.

There were greenhouses, too, but they are all broken now.

There was some legal trouble, I believe, something about the heirs and coheirs; anyhow, the place has been empty for years.

That spoils my ghostliness, I am afraid, but I don't care—there is something strange about the house—I can feel it.

I even said so to John one moonlight evening, but he said what I felt was a *draught*, and shut the window.

I get unreasonably angry with John sometimes. I'm sure I never used to be so sensitive. I think it is due to this nervous condition.

But John says if I feel so, I shall neglect proper self-control; so I take pains to control myself—before him, at least, and that makes me very tired.

I don't like our room a bit. I wanted one downstairs that opened on the piazza and had roses all over the window, and such pretty old-fashioned chintz hangings! but John would not hear of it.

He said there was only one window and not room for two beds, and no near room for him if he took another.

He is very careful and loving, and hardly lets me stir without special direction.

I have a schedule prescription for each hour in the day; he takes all care from me, and so I feel basely ungrateful not to value it more.

He said we came here solely on my account, that I was to have perfect rest and all the air I could get. "Your exercise depends on your strength, my dear," said he, "and your food somewhat on your appetite; but air you can absorb all the time." So we took the nursery at the top of the house.

It is a big, airy room, the whole floor nearly, with windows that look all ways, and air and sunshine galore. It was nursery first and then playroom and gymnasium, I should judge; for the windows are barred for little children, and there are rings and things in the walls.

The paint and paper look as if a boys' school had used it. It is stripped off—the paper—in great patches all around the head of my bed, about as far as I can reach, and in a great place on the other side of the room low down. I never saw a worse paper in my life.

One of those sprawling flamboyant patterns committing every artistic sin.

It is dull enough to confuse the eye in following, pronounced enough to constantly irritate and provoke study, and when you follow the lame uncertain curves for a little distance they suddenly commit suicide—plunge off at outrageous angles, destroy themselves in unheard of contradictions.

The color is repellant, almost revolting; a smouldering unclean yellow, strangely faded by the slow-turning sunlight.

It is a dull yet lurid orange in some places, a sickly sulphur tint in others.

No wonder the children hated it! I should hate it myself if I had to live in this room long.

There comes John, and I must put this away,—he hates to have me write a word.

We have been here two weeks, and I haven't felt like writing before, since that first day.

I am sitting by the window now, up in this atrocious nursery, and there is nothing to hinder my writing as much as I please, save lack of strength.

John is away all day, and even some nights when his cases are serious.

I am glad my case is not serious!

But these nervous troubles are dreadfully depressing.

John does not know how much I really suffer. He knows there is no *reason* to suffer, and that satisfies him.

Of course it is only nervousness. It does weigh on me so not to do my duty in any way!

I meant to be such a help to John, such a real rest and comfort, and here I am a comparative burden already!

Nobody would believe what an effort it is to do what little I am able,—to dress and entertain, and order things.

It is fortunate Mary is so good with the baby. Such a dear baby!

And yet I *cannot* be with him, it makes me so nervous.

I suppose John never was nervous in his life. He laughs at me so about this wall-paper!

At first he meant to repaper the room, but afterwards he said that I was letting it get the better of me, and that nothing was worse for a nervous patient than to give way to such fancies.

He said that after the wall-paper was changed it would be the heavy bedstead, and then the barred windows, and then that gate at the head of the stairs, and so on.

"You know the place is doing you good," he said, "and really, dear, I don't care to renovate the house just for a three months' rental."

"Then do let us go downstairs," I said, "there are such pretty rooms there."

Then he took me in his arms and called me a blessed little goose, and said he would go down cellar, if I wished, and have it whitewashed into the bargain.

But he is right enough about the beds and windows and things.

It is an airy and comfortable room as any one need wish, and, of course, I would not be so silly as to make him uncomfortable just for a whim.

I'm really getting quite fond of the big room, all but that horrid paper.

Out of one window I can see the garden, those mysterious deep-shaded arbors, the riotous old-fashioned flowers, and bushes and gnarly trees.

Out of another I get a lovely view of the bay and a little private wharf belonging to the estate. There is a beautiful shaded lane that runs down there from the house. I always fancy I see people walking in these numerous paths and arbors, but John has cautioned me not to give way to fancy in the least. He says that with my imaginative power and habit of story-making, a nervous weakness like mine is sure to lead to all manner of excited fancies, and that I ought to use my will and good sense to check the tendency. So I try.

I think sometimes that if I were only well enough to write a little it would relieve the press of ideas and rest me.

But I find I get pretty tired when I try.

It is so discouraging not to have any advice and companionship about my work. When I get really well, John says we will ask cousin Henry and Julia down for a long visit; but he says he would as soon put fireworks in my pillow-case as to let me have those stimulating people about now.

I wish I could get well faster.

But I must not think about that. This paper looks to me as if it *knew* what a vicious influence it had!

There is a recurrent spot where the pattern lolls like a broken neck and two bulbous eyes stare at you upside down.

I get positively angry with the impertinence of it and the everlastingness. Up and down and sideways they crawl, and those absurd, unblinking eyes are everywhere. There is one place where two breadths didn't match, and the eyes go all up and down the line, one a little higher than the other.

I never saw so much expression in an inanimate thing before, and we all know how much expression they have! I used to lie awake as a child and get more entertainment and terror out of blank walls and plain furniture than most children could find in a toy-store.

I remember what a kindly wink the knobs of our big, old bureau used to have, and there was one chair that always seemed like a strong friend.

I used to feel that if any of the other things looked too fierce I could always hop into that chair and be safe.

The furniture in this room is no worse than inharmonious, however, for we had to bring it all from downstairs. I suppose when this was used as a play-room they had to take the nursery things out, and no wonder! I never saw such ravages as the children have made here.

The wall-paper, as I said before, is torn off in spots, and it sticketh closer than a brother—they must have had perseverance as well as hatred.

Then the floor is scratched and gouged and splintered, the plaster itself is dug out here and there, and this great heavy bed which is all we found in the room, looks as if it had been through the wars.

But I don't mind it a bit—only the paper.

There comes John's sister. Such a dear girl as she is, and so careful of me! I must not let her find me writing.

She is a perfect and enthusiastic housekeeper, and hopes for no better profession. I verily believe she thinks it is the writing which made me sick!

But I can write when she is out, and see her a long way off from these windows.

There is one that commands the road, a lovely shaded winding road, and one that just looks off over the country. A lovely country, too, full of great elms and velvet meadows.

This wall-paper has a kind of subpattern in a different shade, a particularly irritating one, for you can only see it in certain lights, and not clearly then.

But in the places where it isn't faded and where the sun is just so—I can see a strange, provoking, formless sort of figure, that seems to skulk about behind that silly and conspicuous front design.

There's sister on the stairs!

Well, the Fourth of July is over! The people are all gone and I am tired out. John thought it might do me good to see a little company, so we just had mother and Nellie and the children down for a week.

Of course I didn't do a thing. Jennie sees to everything now.

But it tired me all the same.

John says if I don't pick up faster he shall send me to Weir Mitchell[1] in the fall.

But I don't want to go there at all. I had a friend who was in his hands once, and she says he is just like John and my brother, only more so!

Besides, it is such an undertaking to go so far.

---

[1]Dr. S. Weir Mitchell (1829–1914), physician famous for his "rest cures" for "hysterical" women. Mitchell treated Gilman for a time.

I don't feel as if it was worth while to turn my hand over for anything, and I'm getting dreadfully fretful and querulous.

I cry at nothing, and cry most of the time.

Of course I don't when John is here, or anybody else, but when I am alone.

And I am alone a good deal just now. John is kept in town very often by serious cases, and Jennie is good and lets me alone when I want her to.

So I walk a little in the garden or down that lovely lane, sit on the porch under the roses, and lie down up here a good deal.

I'm getting really fond of the room in spite of the wall-paper. Perhaps *because* of the wall-paper.

It dwells in my mind so!

I lie here on this great immovable bed—it is nailed down, I believe—and follow that pattern about by the hour. It is as good as gymnastics, I assure you. I start, we'll say, at the bottom, down in the corner over there where it has not been touched, and I determine for the thousandth time that I *will* follow that pointless pattern to some sort of a conclusion.

I know a little of the principle of design, and I know this thing was not arranged on any laws of radiation, or alternation, or repetition, or symmetry, or anything else that I ever heard of.

It is repeated, of course, by the breadths, but not otherwise.

Looked at in one way each breadth stands alone, the bloated curves and flourishes—a kind of "debased Romanesque" with *delirium tremens*—go waddling up and down in isolated columns of fatuity.

But, on the other hand, they connect diagonally, and the sprawling outlines run off in great slanting waves of optic horror, like a lot of wallowing seaweeds in full chase.

The whole thing goes horizontally, too, at least it seems so, and I exhaust myself in trying to distinguish the order of its going in that direction.

They have used a horizontal breadth for a frieze, and that adds wonderfully to the confusion.

There is one end of the room where it is almost intact, and there, when the crosslights fade and the low sun shines directly upon it, I can almost fancy radiation after all,—the interminable grotesques seem to form around a common centre and rush off in headlong plunges of equal distraction.

It makes me tired to follow it. I will take a nap I guess.

I don't know why I should write this.

I don't want to.

I don't feel able.

And I know John would think it absurd. But I *must* say what I feel and think in some way—it is such a relief!

But the effort is getting to be greater than the relief.

Half the time now I am awfully lazy, and lie down ever so much.

John says I mustn't lose my strength, and has me take cod liver oil and lots of tonics and things, to say nothing of ale and wine and rare meat.

Dear John! He loves me very dearly, and hates to have me sick. I tried to have a real earnest reasonable talk with him the other day, and tell him how I wish he would let me go and make a visit to Cousin Henry and Julia.

But he said I wasn't able to go, nor able to stand it after I got there; and I did not make out a very good case for myself, for I was crying before I had finished.

It is getting to be a great effort for me to think straight. Just this nervous weakness I suppose.

And dear John gathered me up in his arms, and just carried me upstairs and laid me on the bed, and sat by me and read to me till it tired my head.

He said I was his darling and his comfort and all he had, and that I must take care of myself for his sake, and keep well.

He says no one but myself can help me out of it, that I must use my will and self-control and not let any silly fancies run away with me.

There's one comfort, the baby is well and happy, and does not have to occupy this nursery with the horrid wall-paper.

If we had not used it, that blessed child would have! What a fortunate escape! Why, I wouldn't have a child of mine, an impressionable little thing, live in such a room for worlds.

I never thought of it before, but it is lucky that John kept me here after all, I can stand it so much easier than a baby, you see.

Of course I never mention it to them any more—I am too wise,—but I keep watch of it all the same.

There are things in that paper that nobody knows but me, or ever will.

Behind that outside pattern the dim shapes get clearer every day.

It is always the same shape, only very numerous.

And it is like a woman stooping down and creeping about behind that pattern. I don't like it a bit. I wonder—I begin to think—I wish John would take me away from here!

It is so hard to talk with John about my case, because he is so wise, and because he loves me so.

But I tried it last night.

It was moonlight. The moon shines in all around just as the sun does.

I hate to see it sometimes, it creeps so slowly, and always comes in by one window or another.

John was asleep and I hated to waken him, so I kept still and watched the moonlight on that undulating wall-paper till I felt creepy.

The faint figure behind seemed to shake the pattern, just as if she wanted to get out.

I got up softly and went to feel and see if the paper *did* move, and when I came back John was awake.

"What is it, little girl?" he said. "Don't go walking about like that—you'll get cold."

I thought it was a good time to talk, so I told him that I really was not gaining here, and that I wished he would take me away.

"Why, darling!" said he, "our lease will be up in three weeks, and I can't see how to leave before.

"The repairs are not done at home, and I cannot possibly leave town just now. Of course if you were in any danger, I could and would, but you really are better, dear, whether you can see it or not. I am a doctor, dear, and I know. You are gaining flesh and color, your appetite is better, I feel really much easier about you."

"I don't weigh a bit more," said I, "nor as much; and my appetite may be better in the evening when you are here, but it is worse in the morning when you are away!"

"Bless her little heart!" said he with a big hug, "she shall be as sick as she pleases! But now let's improve the shining hours by going to sleep, and talk about it in the morning!"

"And you won't go away?" I asked gloomily.

"Why, how can I, dear? It is only three weeks more and then we will take a nice little trip of a few days while Jennie is getting the house ready. Really dear you are better!"

"Better in body perhaps—" I began, and stopped short, for he sat up straight and looked at me with such a stern, reproachful look that I could not say another word.

"My darling," said he, "I beg of you, for my sake and for our child's sake, as well as for your own, that you will never for one instant let that idea enter your mind! There is nothing so dangerous, so fascinating, to a temperament like yours. It is a false and foolish fancy. Can you not trust me as a physician when I tell you so?"

So of course I said no more on that score, and we went to sleep before long. He thought I was asleep first, but I wasn't, and lay there for hours trying to decide whether that front pattern and the back pattern really did move together or separately.

On a pattern like this, by daylight, there is a lack of sequence, a defiance of law, that is a constant irritant to a normal mind.

The color is hideous enough, and unreliable enough, and infuriating enough, but the pattern is torturing.

You think you have mastered it, but just as you get well underway in following, it turns a back-somersault and there you are. It slaps you in the face, knocks you down, and tramples upon you. It is like a bad dream.

The outside pattern is a florid arabesque, reminding one of a fungus. If you can imagine a toadstool in joints, an interminable string of toadstools, budding and sprouting in endless convolutions—why, that is something like it.

That is, sometimes!

There is one marked peculiarity about this paper, a thing nobody seems to notice but myself, and that is that it changes as the light changes.

When the sun shoots in through the east window—I always watch for that first long, straight ray—it changes so quickly that I never can quite believe it.

That is why I watch it always.

By moonlight—the moon shines in all night when there is a moon—I wouldn't know it was the same paper.

At night in any kind of light, in twilight, candlelight, lamplight, and worst of all by moonlight, it becomes bars! The outside pattern I mean, and the woman behind it is as plain as can be.

I didn't realize for a long time what the thing was that showed behind, that dim sub-pattern, but now I am quite sure it is a woman.

By daylight she is subdued, quiet. I fancy it is the pattern that keeps her so still. It is so puzzling. It keeps me quiet by the hour.

I lie down ever so much now. John says it is good for me, and to sleep all I can.

Indeed he started the habit by making me lie down for an hour after each meal.

It is a very bad habit I am convinced, for you see I don't sleep.

And that cultivates deceit, for I don't tell them I'm awake—O no!

The fact is I am getting a little afraid of John.

He seems very queer sometimes, and even Jennie has an inexplicable look.

It strikes me occasionally, just as a scientific hypothesis,—that perhaps it is the paper!

I have watched John when he did not know I was looking, and come into the room suddenly on the most innocent excuses, and I've caught him several times *looking at the paper!* And Jennie too. I caught Jennie with her hand on it once.

She didn't know I was in the room, and when I asked her in a quiet, a very quiet voice, with the most restrained manner possible, what she was doing with the paper—she turned around as if she had been caught stealing, and looked quite angry—asked me why I should frighten her so!

Then she said that the paper stained everything it touched, that she had found yellow smooches on all my clothes and John's, and she wished we would be more careful!

Did not that sound innocent? But I know she was studying that pattern, and I am determined that nobody shall find it out but myself!

Life is very much more exciting now than it used to be. You see I have something more to expect, to look forward to, to watch. I really do eat better, and am more quiet than I was.

John is so pleased to see me improve! He laughed a little the other day, and said I seemed to be flourishing in spite of my wall-paper.

I turned it off with a laugh. I had no intention of telling him it was *because* of the wall-paper—he would make fun of me. He might even want to take me away.

I don't want to leave now until I have found it out. There is a week more, and I think that will be enough.

I'm feeling ever so much better! I don't sleep much at night, for it is so interesting to watch developments; but I sleep a good deal in the daytime.

In the daytime it is tiresome and perplexing.

There are always new shoots on the fungus, and new shades of yellow all over it. I cannot keep count of them, though I have tried conscientiously.

It is the strangest yellow, that wall-paper! It makes me think of all the yellow things I ever saw—not beautiful ones like buttercups, but old foul, bad yellow things.

But there is something else about that paper—the smell! I noticed it the moment we came into the room, but with so much air and sun it was not bad. Now we have had a week of fog and rain, and whether the windows are open or not, the smell is here.

It creeps all over the house.

I find it hovering in the dining-room, skulking in the parlor, hiding in the hall, lying in wait for me on the stairs.

It gets into my hair.

Even when I go to ride, if I turn my head suddenly and surprise it—there is that smell!

Such a peculiar odor, too! I have spent hours in trying to analyze it, to find what it smelled like.

It is not bad—at first, and very gentle, but quite the subtlest, most enduring odor I ever met.

In this damp weather it is awful, I wake up in the night and find it hanging over me.

It used to disturb me at first. I thought seriously of burning the house—to reach the smell.

But now I am used to it. The only thing I can think of that it is like is the *color* of the paper! A yellow smell.

There is a very funny mark on this wall, low down, near the mopboard. A streak that runs round the room. It goes behind every piece of furniture, except the bed, a long, straight, even *smooch*, as if it had been rubbed over and over.

I wonder how it was done and who did it, and what they did it for. Round and round and round—round and round and round—it makes me dizzy!

I really have discovered something at last.

Through watching so much at night, when it changes so, I have finally found out.

The front pattern *does* move—and no wonder! The woman behind shakes it!

Sometimes I think there are a great many women behind, and sometimes only one, and she crawls around fast, and her crawling shakes it all over.

Then in the very bright spots she keeps still, and in the very shady spots she just takes hold of the bars and shakes them hard.

And she is all the time trying to climb through. But nobody could climb through that pattern—it strangles so; I think that is why it has so many heads.

They get through, and then the pattern strangles them off and turns them upside down, and makes their eyes white!

If those heads were covered or taken off it would not be half so bad.

I think that woman gets out in the daytime!

And I'll tell you why—privately—I've seen her!

I can see her out of every one of my windows!

It is the same woman, I know, for she is always creeping, and most women do not creep by daylight.

I see her in that long shaded lane, creeping up and down. I see her in those dark grape arbors, creeping all around the garden.

I see her on that long road under the trees, creeping along, and when a carriage comes she hides under the blackberry vines.

I don't blame her a bit. It must be very humiliating to be caught creeping by daylight!

I always lock the door when I creep by daylight. I can't do it at night, for I know John would suspect something at once.

And John is so queer now, that I don't want to irritate him. I wish he would take another room! Besides, I don't want anybody to get that woman out at night but myself.

I often wonder if I could see her out of all the windows at once.

But, turn as fast as I can, I can only see out of one at one time.

And though I always see her, she *may* be able to creep faster than I can turn!

I have watched her sometimes away off in the open country, creeping as fast as a cloud shadow in a high wind.

If only that top pattern could be gotten off from the under one! I mean to try it, little by little.

I have found out another funny thing, but I shan't tell it this time! It does not do to trust people too much.

There are only two more days to get this paper off, and I believe John is beginning to notice. I don't like the look in his eyes.

And I heard him ask Jennie a lot of professional questions about me. She had a very good report to give.

She said I slept a good deal in the daytime.

John knows I don't sleep very well at night, for all I'm so quiet!

He asked me all sorts of questions, too, and pretended to be very loving and kind.

As if I couldn't see through him!

Still, I don't wonder he acts so, sleeping under this paper for three months.

It only interests me, but I feel sure John and Jennie are secretly affected by it.

Hurrah! This is the last day, but it is enough. John is to stay in town over night, and won't be out until this evening.

Jennie wanted to sleep with me—the sly thing! but I told her I should undoubtedly rest better for a night all alone.

That was clever, for really I wasn't alone a bit! As soon as it was moonlight and that poor thing began to crawl and shake the pattern, I got up and ran to help her.

I pulled and she shook, I shook and she pulled, and before morning we had peeled off yards of that paper.

A strip about as high as my head and half around the room.

And then when the sun came and that awful pattern began to laugh at me, I declared I would finish it to-day!

We go away to-morrow, and they are moving all my furniture down again to leave things as they were before.

Jennie looked at the wall in amazement, but I told her merrily that I did it out of pure spite at the vicious thing.

She laughed and said she wouldn't mind doing it herself, but I must not get tired.

How she betrayed herself that time!

But I am here, and no person touches this paper but me,—not *alive*!

She tried to get me out of the room—it was too patent! But I said it was so quiet and empty and clean now that I believed I would lie down again and sleep all I could; and not to wake me even for dinner—I would call when I woke.

So now she is gone, and the servants are gone, and the things are gone, and there is nothing left but that great bedstead nailed down, with the canvas mattress we found on it.

We shall sleep downstairs to-night, and take the boat home to-morrow.

I quite enjoy the room, now it is bare again.

How those children did tear about here!

This bedstead is fairly gnawed!

But I must get to work.

I have locked the door and thrown the key down into the front path.

I don't want to go out, and I don't want to have anybody come in, till John comes.

I want to astonish him.

I've got a rope up here that even Jennie did not find. If that woman does get out, and tries to get away, I can tie her!

But I forgot I could not reach far without anything to stand on!

This bed will *not* move!

I tried to lift and push it until I was lame, and then I got so angry I bit off a little piece at one corner—but it hurt my teeth.

Then I peeled off all the paper I could reach standing on the floor. It sticks horribly and the pattern just enjoys it! All those strangled heads and bulbous eyes and waddling fungus growths just shriek with derision!

I am getting angry enough to do something desperate. To jump out of the window would be admirable exercise, but the bars are too strong even to try.

Besides I wouldn't do it. Of course not. I know well enough that a step like that is improper and might be misconstrued.

I don't like to *look* out of the windows even—there are so many of those creeping women, and they creep so fast.

I wonder if they all come out of that wall-paper as I did?

But I am securely fastened now by my well-hidden rope—you don't get *me* out in the road there!

I suppose I shall have to get back behind the pattern when it comes night, and that is hard!

It is so pleasant to be out in this great room and creep around as I please!

I don't want to go outside. I won't, even if Jennie asks me to.

For outside you have to creep on the ground, and everything is green instead of yellow.

But here I can creep smoothly on the floor, and my shoulder just fits in that long smooch around the wall, so I cannot lose my way.

Why there's John at the door!

It is no use, young man, you can't open it!

How he does call and pound!

Now he's crying for an axe.

It would be a shame to break down that beautiful door!

"John dear!" said I in the gentlest voice, "the key is down by the front steps, under a plantain leaf!"

That silenced him for a few moments.

Then he said—very quietly indeed, "Open the door, my darling!"

"I can't," said I. "The key is down by the front door under a plantain leaf!"

And then I said it again, several times, very gently and slowly, and said it so often that he had to go and see, and he got it of course, and came in. He stopped short by the door.

"What is the matter?" he cried. "For God's sake, what are you doing!"

I kept on creeping just the same, but I looked at him over my shoulder.

"I've got out at last," said I, "in spite of you and Jane. And I've pulled off most of the paper, so you can't put me back!"

Now why should that man have fainted? But he did, and right across my path by the wall, so that I had to creep over him every time!

[1892]

QUESTIONS

CHARLOTTE PERKINS GILMAN, *The Yellow Wall-Paper*

1. At what point do you begin to suspect that the narrator is losing touch with objective reality? Trace her decline, and cite passages that indicate a progressive separation from the world around her.

2. What leads the narrator to determine that there is a woman behind the wallpaper? Why does she eventually refer to the woman as herself?

3. Of all the adult characters mentioned in this story, only the narrator remains nameless. Her husband refers to her as "my dear," "my darling," "little girl," and "she." Of what significance is the narrator's namelessness? How is the story affected by the fact that even the narrator herself does not offer her name?

4. The narrator is clearly invested her writing; just as clearly, her husband considers this occupation dangerous to her. Precisely what does writing mean to the narrator? To her husband? How does the notion of writing and creativity contribute to the theme of the story?

5. Early in the story, the narrator suggests that the house might be haunted; as the story progresses she obviously senses the presence of the woman behind the wallpaper. The story can be read as a supernatural tale or as the chronicle of a woman's descent into madness. How does the meaning of the story change, depending on which interpretation you accept?

6. In what ways is the narrator's situation comparable to the imprisonment of a convict? How do the descriptions of the room, the behavior of John and Jennie, and the narrator's language contribute to this impression?

7. The narrator's descriptions of the wallpaper are both vivid and disturbing. How do the images she conjures up reflect her state of mind? How do they reflect the oppression she feels as a result of her confinement?

8. In order to understand the importance of perspective in this story, consider how the narrator's actions must appear to her sister-in-law and husband. Compose a letter from Jennie to John describing the narrator's behavior. Just as the narrator's language reveals her condition, consider the language Jennie would use as a reflection of her attitude and position.

9. Research the treatment of women's nervous disorders at the turn of the last century, particularly those therapies promoted by Dr. S. Weir Mitchell, who treated Charlotte Perkins Gilman and whose treatment is feared by the narrator in the story. Using this information, write an essay analyzing the story as a feminist commentary on the oppression of women.

Jack London
[1876–1916]

JOHN GRIFFITH LONDON *was born in San Francisco to Flora Wellman, who did not reveal his father's name though he may have been William Chaney, a journalist and lawyer. The boy's nanny from infancy was an ex-slave, Virginia Prentiss. In 1876, Flora married John London and moved to Oakland, where Jack completed grade school. After school, London worked at hard labor jobs and then sailed the Pacific on a sealing ship; he returned to attend high school at nineteen. He became interested in socialism and ran for mayor, unsuccessfully, several times on the socialist ticket. He decided to become a writer and began to submit stories, jokes, and poems to various publications. The winter of 1897 spent in the Yukon gave London the material for his first stories, which began to be published in the* Overland Monthly *in 1899. He produced over fifty volumes of stories, novels, and political essays.* The Call of the Wild *(1903) is his most famous work, and his short stories are classics of their type.* The People of the Abyss *(1903) criticized capitalism and* John Barleycorn *(1913) showed the horrors of alcholism. In 1907 London sailed across the Pacific for two years in a small boat and then wrote books and stories about Polynesian and Melanesian cultures. London was among the most popular writers of his day though now is largely remembered as a children's writer. His novels were made into films, and* The Sea-Wolf *was the basis for an especially popular movie. London supported women's suffrage and created some of the most independent and strong female characters in American fiction. London's first marriage (1900) was to Bess Maddern, with whom he had two daughters, Joan and Bess. Using his relationship with his wife as an example, he co-wrote, with Anna Strunsky,* The Kempton-Wace Letters, *which opines that mates should be selected for good breeding, not love. He later married Charmian Kittredge, five years his senior, in 1905; she became the persona for many of his female characters. She wrote three books concerning their life* (The Log of the Snark, Our Hawaii, *and* The Book of Jack London). *London developed kidney disease of unknown origin and died of renal failure on November 22, 1916, on his ranch in California where he had lived most of his adult life. He brought to California elements of Japanese farming, such as terracing and careful animal management His influence spread around the world, and he is more widely read in countries outside of the United States than in his home country.*

—David L. G. Arnold, *University of Wisconsin, Stevens Point*

The Law of Life

JACK LONDON

OLD KOSKOOSH LISTENED GREEDILY. Though his sight had long since faded, his hearing was still acute, and the slightest sound penetrated to the glimmering intelligence which yet abode behind the withered forehead, but which no longer gazed forth upon the things of the world. Ah! that was Sit-cum-to-ha, shrilly anathematizing the dogs as she cuffed and beat them into the harnesses. Sit-cum-to-ha was his daughter's daughter, but she was too busy to waste a thought upon her broken grandfather, sitting alone there in the snow, forlorn and helpless. Camp must be broken. The long trail waited while the short day refused to linger. Life called her, and the duties of life, not death. And he was very close to death now.

The thought made the old man panicky for the moment, and he stretched forth a palsied hand which wandered tremblingly over the small heap of dry wood beside him. Reassured that it was indeed there, his hand returned to the shelter of his mangy furs, and he again fell to listening. The sulky crackling of half-frozen hides told him that the chief's moose-skin lodge had been struck, and even then was being rammed and jammed into portable compass. The chief was his son, stalwart and strong, head man of the tribesmen, and a mighty hunter. As the women toiled with the camp luggage, his voice rose, chiding them for their slowness. Old Koskoosh strained his ears. It was the last time he would hear that voice. There went Geehow's lodge! And Tusken's! Seven, eight, nine; only the Shaman's could be still standing. There! They were at work upon it now. He could hear the Shaman grunt as he piled it on the sled. A child whimpered, and a woman soothed it with soft, crooning gutturals. Little Koo-tee, the old man thought, a fretful child, and not over strong. It would die soon, perhaps, and they would burn a hole through the frozen tundra and pile rocks above to keep the wolverines away. Well, what did it matter? A few years at best, and as many an empty belly as a full one. And in the end, Death waited, ever-hungry and hungriest of them all.

What was that? Oh, the men lashing the sleds and drawing tight the thongs. He listened, who would listen no more. The whip-lashes snarled and bit among the dogs. Hear them whine! How they hated the work and the trail!

First published in *McClure's Magazine,* March 1901. Reprinted in *Children of the Frost* in 1902.

They were off! Sled after sled churned slowly away into the silence. They were gone. They had passed out of his life, and he faced the last bitter hour alone. No. The snow crunched beneath a moccasin; a man stood beside him; upon his head a hand rested gently. His son was good to do this thing. He remembered other old men whose sons had not waited after the tribe. But his son had. He wandered away into the past, till the young man's voice brought him back.

"Is it well with you?" he asked.

And the old man answered, "It is well."

"There be wood beside you," the younger man continued, "and the fire burns bright. The morning is gray, and the cold has broken. It will snow presently. Even now is it snowing."

"Ay, even now is it snowing."

"The tribesmen hurry. Their bales are heavy, and their bellies flat with lack of feasting. The trail is long and they travel fast. I go now. It is well?"

"It is well. I am as a last year's leaf, clinging lightly to the stem. The first breath that blows, and I fall. My voice is become like an old woman's. My eyes no longer show me the way of my feet, and my feet are heavy, and I am tired. It is well."

He bowed his head in content till the last noise of the complaining snow had died away, and he knew his son was beyond recall. Then his hand crept out in haste to the wood. It alone stood betwixt him and the eternity which yawned in upon him. At last the measure of his life was a handful of fagots. One by one they would go to feed the fire, and just so, step by step, death would creep upon him. When the last stick had surrendered up its heat, the frost would begin to gather strength. First his feet would yield, then his hands; and the numbness would travel, slowly, from the extremities to the body. His head would fall forward upon his knees, and he would rest. It was easy. All men must die.

He did not complain. It was the way of life, and it was just. He had been born close to the earth, close to the earth had he lived, and the law thereof was not new to him. It was the law of all flesh. Nature was not kindly to the flesh. She had no concern for that concrete thing called the individual. Her interest lay in the species, the race. This was the deepest abstraction old Koskoosh's barbaric mind was capable of, but he grasped it firmly. He saw it exemplified in all life. The rise of the sap, the bursting greenness of the willow bud, the fall of the yellow leaf—in this alone was told the whole history. But one task did nature set the individual. Did he not perform it, he died. Did he perform it, it was all the same, he died. Nature did not care; there were plenty who were obedient, and it was only the obedience in this matter, not the obedient, which lived and lived always. The tribe of Koskoosh was very old. The old men he had known when a boy, had known old men before them. Therefore it was true that the tribe lived, that it stood for the obedience of all its members, way down into the forgotten past, whose very resting places were unremembered. They did not count; they were episodes. They had passed away like clouds from a summer sky. He also was an episode, and would pass away. Nature did not care. To life she set one task, gave one law. To perpetuate was the task of life, its law was death. A maiden was a good creature to look upon, full-breasted and strong, with spring to her step and light in her eyes. But her task was yet before her. The light in her eyes brightened, her step quickened, she was now bold with the young men, now timid, and she gave them of her own unrest. And ever she grew fairer and yet fairer to look upon, till some hunter, able no longer to withhold himself, took her to his lodge to cook and toil for him and to become the mother of his children. And with the coming of her offspring her looks left her. Her limbs dragged and shuffled, her eyes dimmed and bleared, and only the little children found joy against the withered cheek of the old squaw by the fire. Her task was done. But a little while, on the first pinch of famine or the first long trail, and she would be left, even as he had been left, in the snow, with a little pile of wood. Such was the law.

He placed a stick carefully upon the fire and resumed his meditations. It was the same everywhere, with all things The mosquitos vanished with the first frost. The little tree-squirrel crawled away to die. When age settled upon the rabbit it became slow and heavy, and could no longer out-foot its enemies. Even the big bald-face grew clumsy and blind and quarrelsome, in the end to be dragged down by a handful of yelping huskies. He remembered how he had abandoned his own father on an upper reach of the Klondike one winter, the winter before the missionary came with his talk-books and his box of medicines. Many a time had Koskoosh smacked his lips over the recollection of that box, though now his mouth refused to moisten. The "painkiller" had been especially good. But the missionary was a bother after all, for he brought no meat into the camp, and he ate heartily, and the hunters grumbled. But he chilled his lungs on the divide by the Mayo, and the dogs afterwards nosed the stones away and fought over his bones.

Koskoosh placed another stick on the fire and harked back deeper into the past. There was the time of the Great Famine, when the old men crouched empty-bellied to the fire, and from their lips fell dim traditions of the ancient day when the Yukon ran wide open for three winters, and then lay frozen for three summers. He had lost his mother in that famine. In the summer the salmon run had failed, and the tribe looked forward to the winter and the coming of the caribou. Then the winter came, but with it there were no caribou. Never had the like been known, not even in the lives of the old men. But the caribou did not come, and it was the seventh year, and the rabbits had not replenished, and the dogs were naught but bundles of bones. And through the long darkness the children wailed and died, and the women, and the old men; and not one in ten of the tribe lived to meet the sun when it came back in the spring. That *was* a famine!

But he had seen times of plenty, too, when the meat spoiled on their hands, and the dogs were fat and worthless with over-eating—times when they let the game go unkilled, and the women were fertile, and the lodges were cluttered with sprawling men-children and women-children. Then it was the men became high-stomached, and revived ancient quarrels, and crossed the divides to the south to kill the Pellys, and to the west that they might sit by the dead fires of the Tananas. He remembered, when a boy, during a time of plenty, when he saw a moose pulled down by the wolves. Zing-ha lay with him in the snow and watched—Zing-ha, who later became the craftiest of hunters, and who, in the end, fell through an air-hole on the Yukon. They found him, a month afterward, just as he had crawled half-way out and frozen stiff to the ice.

But the moose. Zing-ha and he had gone out that day to play at hunting after the manner of their fathers. On the bed of the creek they struck the fresh track of a moose, and with it the tracks of many wolves. "An old one," Zing-ha, who was quicker at reading the sign, said—"an old one who cannot keep up with the herd. The wolves have cut him out from his brothers, and they will never leave him." And it was so. It was their way. By day and by night, never resting, snarling on his heels, snapping at his nose, they would stay by him to the end. How Zing-ha and he felt the blood-lust quicken! The finish would be a sight to see!

Eager-footed, they took the trail, and even he, Koskoosh, slow of sight and an unversed tracker, could have followed it blind, it was so wide. Hot were they on the heels of the chase, reading the grim tragedy, fresh-written, at every step. Now they came to where the moose had made a stand. Thrice the length of a grown man's body, in every direction, had the snow been stamped about and uptossed. In the midst were the deep impressions of the splay-hoofed game, and all about, everywhere, were the lighter footmarks of the wolves. Some, while their brothers harried the kill, had lain to one side and rested. The full-stretched impress of their bodies in the snow was as perfect as though made the moment before. One wolf had been caught in a wild lunge of the maddened victim and trampled to death. A few bones, well picked, bore witness.

Again, they ceased the uplift of their snowshoes at a second stand. Here the great animal had fought desperately. Twice had he been dragged down, as the snow attested, and twice had he shaken his assailants clear and gained footing once more. He had done his task long since, but none the less was life dear to him. Zing-ha said it was a strange thing, a moose once down to get free again; but this one certainly had. The Shaman would see signs and wonders in this when they told him.

And yet again, they came to where the moose had made to mount the bank and gain the timber. But his foes had laid on from behind, till he reared and fell back upon them, crushing two deep into the snow. It was plain the kill was at hand, for their brothers had left them untouched. Two more stands were hurried past, brief in time-length and very close together. The trail was red now, and the clean stride of the great beast had grown short and slovenly. Then they heard the first sounds of the battle—not the full-throated chorus of the chase, but the short, snappy bark which spoke of close quarters and teeth to flesh. Crawling up the wind, Zing-ha bellied it through the snow, and with him crept he, Koskoosh, who was to be chief of the tribesmen in the years to come. Together they shoved aside the under branches of a young spruce and peered forth. It was the end they saw.

The picture, like all of youth's impressions, was still strong with him, and his dim eyes watched the end played out as vividly as in that far-off time. Koskoosh marveled at this, for in the days which followed, when he was a leader of men and a head of councilors, he had done great deeds and made his name a curse in the mouths of the Pellys, to say naught of the strange white man he had killed, knife to knife, in open fight.

For long he pondered on the days of his youth, till the fire died down and the frost bit deeper. He replenished it with two sticks this time, and gauged his grip on life by what remained. If Sit-cum-to-ha had only remembered her grandfather, and gathered a larger armful, his hours would have been longer. It would have been easy. But she was ever a careless child, and honored not her ancestors from the time the Beaver, son of the son of Zing-ha, first cast eyes upon her. Well, what mattered it? Had he not done likewise in his own quick youth? For a while he listened to the silence. Perhaps the heart of his son might soften, and he would come back with the dogs to take his old father on with the tribe to where the caribou ran thick and the fat hung heavy upon them.

He strained his ears, his restless brain for the moment stilled. Not a stir, nothing. He alone took breath in the midst of the great silence. It was very lonely, Hark! What was that? A chill passed over his body. The familiar, long-drawn howl broke the void, and it was close at hand. Then on his darkened eyes was projected the vision of the moose—the old bull moose—the torn flanks and bloody sides, the riddled mane, and the great branching horns, down low and tossing to the last. He saw the flashing forms of gray, the gleaming eyes, the lolling tongues, the slavered fangs. And he saw the inexorable circle close in till it became a dark point in the midst of the stamped snow.

A cold muzzle thrust against his cheek, and at its touch his soul leaped back to the present. His hand shot into the fire and dragged out a burning fagot. Overcome for the nonce by his hereditary fear of man, the brute retreated, raising a prolonged call to his brothers; and greedily they answered, till a ring of crouching, jaw-slobbered gray was stretched round about. The old man listened to the drawing in of this circle. He waved his brand wildly, and sniffs turned to snarls; but the panting brutes refused to scatter. Now one wormed his chest forward, dragging his haunches after, now a second, now a third; but never a one drew back. Why should he cling to life? he asked, and dropped the blazing stick into the snow. It sizzled and he went out. The circle grunted uneasily, but held its own. Again he saw the last stand of the old bull moose, and Koskoosh dropped his head warily upon his knees. What did it matter after all? Was it not the law of life?

[1901]

QUESTIONS

JACK LONDON, *The Law of Life*

1. Write a brief journal entry about your experience of reading "The Law of Life." What kinds of feelings does this story evoke? Does the subject matter of the story bring to mind other texts, experiences, or associations?

2. In what sense can we describe this story as an example of literary Naturalism?

3. Of what significance is the setting of this story?

4. Describe this tribe's treatment of elders and its practices for the disposition of the dead. How do these differ from what you're used to, and how does this affect your understanding of the story?

5. A fair amount of time is spent on Koskoosh's memory of the moose. What happens in this anecdote, and what does Koskoosh learn by contemplating it?

6. What, finally, is the "law of life"?

7. For a larger research and writing project: compare and contrast London's "The Law of Life" with one of the following texts by American writer Stephen Crane: "A Man Adrift On A Slim Spar"; "A Man Said to the Universe"; "In the Desert"; "The Open Boat"; "The Blue Hotel." What is the vision of nature, humanity, and survival that emerges from each text? What literary schools or techniques inform the text at hand? How do London and Crane pursue similar philosophical themes in their respective works?

Susan Glaspell

[1876–1948]

Heralded mainly for her playwriting, SUSAN GLASPELL *was an adept editor, as well as a prolific author of children's stories, short stories, novels, and a memoir. As the co-founder of the Provincetown Players, she is one of the most important figures in early twentieth-century theater. Born in 1876, Glaspell grew up in the small, Midwestern town of Davenport, Iowa. Following college and a brief stint in journalism, she began writing full-time and was immediately successful in this endeavor, publishing short stories in* Ladies' Home Journal *and other popular magazines. In 1909, she published her first novel, a bestselling romance titled* The Glory of the Conquered.*

Glaspell and her husband, George Cram (Jig) Cook, were deeply involved in the cultural and artistic avant-garde centered in New York's Greenwich Village, a world that Glaspell critiqued in a series of short dramas. Around this time she also helped found the Provincetown Players, a small group of artists (including Edna St. Vincent Millay and Eugene O'Neill) committed to the communal production of experimental drama. This company worked to reject Broadway's popular commercial theater, but it nonetheless pleased audiences well enough to survive for eight years and to serve as the genesis of a national "little theater" movement. Glaspell not only wrote many plays for the company, but also directed and ably performed in a number of its productions.

Trifles, a one-act play depicting the investigation of a small-town murder, is Glaspell's most famous and most studied work. She wrote the play in only ten days, basing it on a murder investigation and trial she had reported on for the Des Moines Daily News *in 1901. The play opened at the Provincetown Players' Wharf Theater on August 8, 1916, with Glaspell taking the role of Mrs. Hale. A year after the American premiere of* Trifles, *she rewrote the play as a short story titled, "A Jury of Her Peers" (1917). Both works—by demonstrating how two women solve a murder case simply by looking at the domestic "trifles" men overlook—illustrate ways of viewing things with a critical eye. They also present the influences of patriarchy on how the world is perceived.*

Glaspell and Cook moved to Greece in 1922, where they lived until his death two years later. In 1931, Glaspell became the second woman ever to win a Pulitzer Prize for her three-act play Alison's House *(1930), which was inspired by the life of the poet Emily Dickinson. It was the last play she completed. However, she published seven novels between 1928 and 1945. Most of these novels were set in the American Midwest, where Glaspell was born, and explored the tension for individuals between traditional regional values and modern ways of living.*

Toward the end of her life, Glaspell synthesized two important aspects of her identity—her Midwestern roots and her passion for American theater—when she became director of the Midwest Play Bureau of the Federal Theater Project (1936–1938). She died of viral pneumonia in 1948.

A Jury of Her Peers

SUSAN GLASPELL

WHEN MARTHA HALE opened the storm-door and got the north wind, she ran back for her big woollen scarf. As she hurriedly wound that round her head her eye made a scandalized sweep of her kitchen. It was no ordinary thing that called her away—it was probably farther from ordinary than anything that had ever happened in Dickson County. But her kitchen was in no shape for leaving: bread ready for mixing, half the flour sifted and half unsifted.

She hated to see things half done; but she had been at that when they stopped to get Mr. Hale, and the sheriff came in to say his wife wished Mrs. Hale would come too—adding, with a grin, that he guessed she was getting scarey and wanted another woman along. So she had dropped everything right where it was.

"Martha!" now came her husband's impatient voice. "Don't keep folks waiting out here in the cold."

She joined the three men and the one woman waiting for her in the sheriff's car.

After she had the robes tucked in she took another look at the woman beside her. She had met Mrs. Peters the year before, at the county fair, and the thing she remembered about her was that she didn't seem like a sheriff's wife. She was small and thin and didn't have a strong voice. Mrs. Gorman, sheriff's wife before Gorman went out and Peters came in, had a voice that seemed to be backing up the law with every word. But if Mrs. Peters didn't look like a sheriff's wife, Peters made it up in looking like a sheriff—a heavy man with a big voice, who was particularly genial with the law-abiding, as if to make it plain that he knew the difference between criminals and non-criminals. And right there it came into Mrs. Hale's mind that this man who was so lively with all of them was going to the Wrights' now as a sheriff.

"The country's not very pleasant this time of year," Mrs. Peters at last ventured.

Mrs. Hale scarcely finished her reply, for they had gone up a little hill and could see the Wright place, and seeing it did not make her feel like talking. It looked very lonely this cold March morning. It had always been a lonesome-looking place. It was down in a hollow, and the poplar trees around it were lonely-looking trees. The men were looking at it and talking about what had happened. The county attorney was bending to one side, scrutinizing the place as they drew up to it.

"I'm glad you came with me," Mrs. Peters said nervously, as the two women were about to follow the men in through the kitchen door.

Even after she had her foot on the doorstep, Martha Hale had a moment of feeling she could not cross this threshold. And the reason it seemed she couldn't cross it now was because she hadn't crossed it before. Time and time again it had been in her mind, "I ought to go over and see Minnie Foster"— she still thought of her as Minnie Foster, though for twenty years she had been Mrs. Wright. And then there was always something to do and Minnie Foster would go from her mind. But now she could come.

The men went over to the stove. The women stood close together by the door. Young Henderson, the county attorney, turned around and said, "Come up to the fire, ladies."

Mrs. Peters took a step forward, then stopped. "I'm not—cold," she said.

And so the two women stood by the door, at first not even so much as looking around the kitchen.

The men talked about what a good thing it was the sheriff had sent his deputy out that morning to make a fire for them, and then Sheriff Peters stepped back from the stove, unbuttoned his outer coat, and leaned his hands on the kitchen table in a way that seemed to mark the beginning of official business. "Now, Mr. Hale," he said in a sort of semi-official voice, "before we move things about, you tell Mr. Henderson just what it was you saw when you came here yesterday morning."

The county attorney was looking around the kitchen.

"By the way," he asked, "has anything been moved?" He turned to the sheriff. "Are things just as you left them yesterday?"

Peters looked from cupboard to sink; to a small worn rocker a little to one side of the kitchen table.

"It's just the same."

"Well, Mr. Hale," said the county attorney, "tell just what happened when you came here yesterday morning."

. Mrs. Hale, still leaning against the door, had that sinking feeling of the mother whose child is about to speak a piece. Lewis often wandered along and got things mixed up in a story. She hoped he would tell this straight and plain, and not say unnecessary things that would make it harder for Minnie Foster. He didn't begin at once, and she noticed that he looked queer, as if thinking of what he had seen here yesterday.

"Yes, Mr. Hale?" the county attorney reminded.

"Harry and I had started to town with a load of wood," Mrs. Hale's husband began.

Harry was Mrs. Hale's oldest boy. He wasn't with them now, for the wood never got to town yesterday and he was taking it this morning, so he hadn't been home when the sheriff stopped to say he wanted Mr. Hale to come over to the Wright place and tell the county attorney his story there, where he could point it all out. With all Mrs. Hale's other emotions came the fear Harry wasn't dressed warm enough—they hadn't any of them realized how that north wind did bite.

"We come along this road," Hale was going on, "and as we got in sight of the house I says to Harry, 'I'm goin' to see if I can't get John Wright to take a telephone.' You see," he explained to Henderson, "unless *I* can get somebody to go in with me they won't come out this branch road except for a price I can't pay. I'd spoke to Wright about it before; but he put me off, saying folks talked too much anyway, and all he asked was peace and quiet—guess you know about how much he talked himself. But I thought maybe if I went to the house and talked about it before his wife, and said all the women-folks liked the telephones, and that in this lonesome stretch of road it would be a good thing— well, I said to Harry that that was what I was going to say—though I said at the same time that I didn't know as what his wife wanted made much difference to John—"

Now, there he was!—saying things he didn't need to say. Mrs. Hale tried to catch her husband's eye, but fortunately the county attorney interrupted with:

"Let's talk about that a little later, Mr. Hale. I do want to talk about that, but I'm anxious now to know just what happened when you got here."

When he began this time, it was deliberately, as if he knew it were important.

"I didn't see or hear anything. I knocked at the door. And still it was all quiet inside. I knew they must be up—it was past eight o'clock. So I knocked again, louder, and I thought I heard somebody say, 'Come in.' I wasn't sure—I'm not sure yet. But I opened the door—this door," jerking a hand toward the door by which the two women stood, "and there, in that rocker"—pointing to it—"sat Mrs. Wright."

Everyone in the kitchen looked at the rocker. It came into Mrs. Hale's mind that this chair didn't look in the least like Minnie Foster—the Minnie Foster of twenty years before. It was a dingy red, with wooden rungs up the back, and the middle rung gone; the chair sagged to one side.

"How did she—look?" the county attorney was inquiring.

"Well," said Hale, "she looked—queer."

"How do you mean—queer?"

He took out note-book and pencil. Mrs. Hale did not like the sight of that pencil. She kept her eye on her husband, as if to keep him from saying unnecessary things that would go into the book and make trouble.

Hale spoke guardedly: "Well, as if she didn't know what she was going to do next. And kind of—done up."

"How did she seem to feel about your coming?"

"Why, I don't think she minded—one way or other. She didn't pay much attention. I said, 'Ho'do, Mrs. Wright. It's cold, ain't it?' And she said, 'Is it?'—And went on pleatin' of her apron.

"Well, I was surprised. She didn't ask me to come up to the stove, but just set there, not even lookin' at me. And so I said, 'I want to see John.'

"And then she—laughed. I guess you would call it a laugh.

"I thought of Harry and the team outside, so I said, a little sharp, 'Can I see John?' 'No,' says she kind of dull like. 'Ain't he home?' says I. Then she looked at me. 'Yes,' says she, 'he's home.' 'Then why can't I see him?' I asked her, out of patience with her now. 'Cause he's dead,' says she just as quiet and dull—and fell to pleatin' her apron. 'Dead?' says I, like you do when you can't take in what you've heard.

"She just nodded her head, not getting a bit excited, but rockin' back and forth.

"Why—where is he?" says I, not knowing *what* to say.

"She just pointed upstairs—like this"—pointing to the room above.

"I got up, with the idea of going up there myself. By this time I—didn't know what to do. I walked from there to here, then I says 'Why, what did he die of?'

"'He died of a rope round his neck,' says she; and just went on pleatin' at her apron."

Hale stopped speaking, staring at the rocker. Nobody spoke; it was as if all were seeing the woman who had sat there the morning before.

"And what did you do then?" the attorney asked.

"I went out and called Harry. I thought I might—need help. I got Harry in, and we went upstairs." His voice fell almost to a whisper. "There he was—lying over the—

"I think I'd rather have you go into that upstairs," the county attorney interrupted, "where you can point it all out. Just go on now with the rest of the story."

"Well, my first thought was to get that rope off. It looked—"

He stopped; he did not say how it looked.

"But Harry, he went up to him and he said, 'No, he's dead all right, and we'd better not touch anythin'.' So we went downstairs.

"She was still sitting that same way. 'Has anybody been notified?' I asked. 'No,' says she, unconcerned.

"'Who did this, Mrs. Wright?' said Harry. He said it business-like, and she stopped pleatin' at her apron. 'I don't know,' she says. 'You don't *know*?' says Harry. 'Weren't you sleepin' in the bed with him?' 'Yes,' says she, 'but I was on the inside.' 'Somebody slipped a rope round his neck and strangled him, and you didn't wake up?' says Harry. 'I didn't wake up,' she said after him.

"We may have looked as if we didn't see how that could be, for after a minute she said, 'I sleep sound.'

"Harry was going to ask her more questions, but I said maybe that weren't our business; maybe we ought to let her tell her story first to the coroner or the sheriff. So Harry went as fast as he could over to High Road—the Rivers' place, where there's a telephone."

"And what did she do when she knew you had gone for the coroner?"

"She moved from that chair to this one over here, and just sat there with her hands held together and looking down. I got a feeling that I ought to make some conversation, so I said I had come in to see if John wanted to put in a telephone; and at that she started to laugh, and then she stopped and looked at me—scared."

At sound of a moving pencil the man who was telling the story looked up.

"I dunno—maybe it wasn't scared; I wouldn't like to say it was. Soon Harry got back, and then Dr. Lloyd came, and you, Mr. Peters, and so I guess that's all I know that you don't."

He said this with relief, moved as if relaxing. The county attorney walked to the stair door.

"I guess we'll go upstairs first—then out to the barn and around there."

He paused and looked around the kitchen.

"You're convinced there was nothing important here?" he asked. "Nothing that would—point to any motive?"

The sheriff too looked all around. "Nothing here but kitchen things," he said, with a little laugh for the insignificance of kitchen things.

The county attorney was looking at the cupboard. He opened the upper part and looked in. After a moment he drew his hand away sticky.

"Here's a nice mess," he said resentfully.

The two women had drawn nearer, and now the sheriff's wife spoke.

"Oh—her fruit," she said, looking to Mrs. Hale for understanding. "She worried about that when it turned so cold last night. She said the fire would go out and her jars might burst."

Mrs. Peters' husband broke into a laugh.

"Well, can you beat the women! Held for murder, and worrying about her preserves!"

The young attorney set his lips.

"I guess before we're through with her she may have something more serious than preserves to worry about."

"Oh, well," said Mrs. Hale's husband, with good-natured superiority, "women are used to worrying over trifles."

The two women moved a little closer together. Neither of them spoke. The county attorney seemed to remember his manners—and think of his future.

"And yet," said he, with the gallantry of a young politician, "for all their worries, what would we do without the ladies?"

The women did not speak. He went to the sink to wash his hands, turned to wipe them on the roller towel, pulled it for a cleaner place.

"Dirty towels! Not much of a housekeeper, would you say, ladies?" He kicked his foot against some dirty pans under the sink.

"There's a great deal of work to be done on a farm," said Mrs. Hale stiffly.

"To be sure. And yet"—with a little bow to her—"I know there are some Dickson County farm-houses that do not have such roller towels."

"Those towels get dirty awful quick. Men's hands aren't always as clean as they might be."

"Ah, loyal to your sex, I see," he laughed. He gave her a keen look. "But you and Mrs. Wright were neighbors. I suppose you were friends too."

Martha Hale shook her head.

"I've seen little enough of her of late years. I've not been in this house—it's more than a year."

"And why was that? You didn't like her?"

"I liked her well enough," she replied with spirit. "Farmers' wives have their hands full, Mr. Henderson. And then—" She looked around the kitchen.

"Yes?" he encouraged.

"It never seemed a very cheerful place," said she, more to herself than to him.

"No," he agreed; "I don't think anyone would call it cheerful. I shouldn't say she had the home-making instinct."

"Well, I don't know as Wright had either," she muttered.

"You mean they didn't get on very well?"

"No; I don't mean anything," she answered, with decision. "But I don't think a place would be any the cheerfuler for John Wright's bein' in it."

"I'd like to talk to you about that a little later, Mrs. Hale." He moved towards the stair door, followed by the two men.

"I suppose anything Mrs. Peters does'll be all right?" the sheriff inquired. "She was to take in some clothes for her, you know—and a few little things. We left in such a hurry yesterday."

The county attorney looked at the two women they were leaving alone among the kitchen things.

"Yes—Mrs. Peters," he said, his glance resting on the woman who was not Mrs. Peters, the big farmer woman who stood behind the sheriff's wife. "Of course Mrs. Peters is one of us," he added in a manner of entrusting responsibility. "And keep your eye out, Mrs. Peters, for anything that might be of use. No telling; you women might come upon a clue to the motive—and that's the thing we need."

Mr. Hale rubbed his face in the fashion of a slow man getting ready for a pleasantry. "But would the women know a clue if they did come upon it?" he said. Having delivered himself of this, he followed the others through the stair door.

The women stood motionless, listening to the footsteps, first upon the stairs, then in the room above them.

Then, as if releasing herself from something too strange, Mrs. Hale began to arrange the dirty pans under the sink, which the county attorney's disdainful push of the foot had upset.

"I'd hate to have men coming into my kitchen, snoopin' round and criticizing."

"Of course it's no more than their duty," said the sheriff's wife, in her timid manner.

"Duty's all right, but I guess that deputy sheriff that come out to make the fire might have got a little of this on." She gave the roller towel a pull. "Wish I'd thought of that sooner! Seems mean to talk about her for not having things slicked up, when she had to come away in such a hurry."

She looked around the kitchen. Certainly it was not "slicked up." Her eye was held by a bucket of sugar on a low shelf. The cover was off the wooden bucket, and beside it was a paper bag—half full.

Mrs. Hale moved towards it.

"She was putting this in there," she said to herself—slowly.

She thought of the flour in her kitchen at home half sifted, half not sifted. She had been interrupted, and had left things half done. What had interrupted Minnie Foster? Why had that work been left half done? She made a move as if to finish it—unfinished things always bothered her, and then she saw that Mrs. Peters was watching her, and she didn't want Mrs. Peters to get that feeling she had of work begun and then—for some reason—not finished.

"It's a shame about her fruit," she said, going to the cupboard. "I wonder if it's all gone.

"Here's one that's all right," she said at last. She held it towards the light. "This is cherries, too." She looked again. "I declare I believe that's the only one.

"She'll feel awful bad, after all her hard work in the hot weather. I remember the afternoon I put up my cherries last summer."

She put the bottle on the table, and was about to sit down in the rocker. But something kept her from sitting in that chair. She stood looking at it, seeing the woman who had sat there "pleatin' at her apron."

The thin voice of the sheriff's wife broke in upon her: "I must be getting those things from the front room closet." She opened the door into the other room, started in, stepped back. "You coming with me, Mrs. Hale?" she asked nervously.

"You—you could help me get them."

They were soon back. "My!" said Mrs. Peters, dropping the things on the table and hurrying to the stove.

Mrs. Hale stood examining the clothes the woman who was being detained in town had said she wanted.

"Wright was close!" she exclaimed, holding up a shabby black skirt that bore the marks of much making over. "I think maybe that's why she kept so much to herself. I s'pose she felt she couldn't do her part; and then, you don't enjoy things when you feel shabby. She used to wear pretty clothes and be lively—when she was Minnie Foster, one of the town girls, singing in the choir. But that—oh, that was twenty years ago."

With a carefulness in which there was something tender, she folded the shabby clothes and piled them at one corner of the table. She looked up at Mrs. Peters, and there was something in the other woman's look that irritated her.

"She don't care," she said to herself. "Much difference it makes to her whether Minnie Foster had pretty clothes when she was a girl."

Then she looked again, and she wasn't so sure; in fact, she hadn't at any time been sure about Mrs. Peters. She had that shrinking manner, and yet her eyes looked as if they could see a long way into things.

"This all you was to take in?" asked Mrs. Hale.

"No," said the sheriff's wife; "she said she wanted an apron. Funny thing to want," she ventured in her nervous way, "for there's not much to get you dirty in jail, goodness knows. But I suppose just to make her feel more natural. She said they were in the bottom drawer of this cupboard. Yes—here they are. And then her little shawl that always hung on the stair door."

She took the small grey shawl from behind the door leading upstairs.

Suddenly Mrs. Hale took a quick step towards the other woman.

"Mrs. Peters!"

"Yes, Mrs. Hale?"

"Do you think she—did it?"

Mrs. Peters looked frightened. "Oh, I don't know," she said, in a voice that seemed to shrink from the subject.

"Well, I don't think she did," affirmed Mrs. Hale. "Asking for an apron, and her little shawl. Worryin' about her fruit."

"Mr. Peters says—" Footsteps were heard in the room above; she stopped, looked up, then went on in a lowered voice: "Mr. Peters says—it looks bad for her. Mr. Henderson is awful sarcastic in a speech, and he's going to make fun of her saying she didn't wake up."

For a moment Mrs. Hale had no answer. Then, "Well, I guess John Wright didn't wake up—when they was slippin' that rope under his neck," she muttered.

"No, it's *strange*," breathed Mrs. Peters. "They think it was such a—funny way to kill a man."

"That's just what Mr. Hale said," said Mrs. Hale, in a resolutely natural voice. "There was a gun in the house. He says that's what he can't understand."

"Mr. Henderson said, coming out, that what was needed for the case was a motive. Something to show anger—or sudden feeling."

"Well, I don't see any signs of anger around here," said Mrs. Hale. "I don't—" She stopped. Her eye was caught by a dishtowel in the middle of the kitchen table. Slowly she moved towards the table. One half of it was wiped clean, the other half untidy. Her eyes made a slow, almost unwilling turn to the bucket of sugar and the half-empty bag beside it. Things begun—and not finished.

She stepped back. "Wonder how they're finding things upstairs? I hope she had it in better shape up there. Seems kind of sneaking, locking her up in town and coming out here to get her own house to turn against her!"

"But, Mrs. Hale," said the sheriff's wife, "the law is the law."

"I s'pose it is," answered Mrs. Hale shortly.

She turned to the stove, saying something about that fire not being much to brag of.

"The law is the law—and a bad stove is a bad stove. How'd you like to cook on this?" with the poker pointing to the broken lining. She opened the oven door. The thought of Minnie Foster trying to bake in that oven—and the thought of her never going over to see Minnie Foster—

She was startled by hearing Mrs. Peters say, "A person gets discouraged—and loses heart."

The sheriff's wife had looked from the stove to the sink—the pail of water which had been carried in from outside. The two women stood there silent, above them the footsteps of the men who were looking for evidence against the woman who had worked in that kitchen. That look of seeing into things, of seeing through a thing to something else, was in the eyes of the sheriff's wife now. When Mrs. Hale next spoke to her, it was gently.

"Better loosen up your things, Mrs. Peters. We'll not feel them when we go out."

Mrs. Peters went to the back of the room to hang up the fur tippet she was wearing. "Why, she was piecing a quilt," she exclaimed, and held up a large sewing basket piled high with quilt pieces.

Mrs. Hale spread some of the blocks on the table.

"It's log-cabin pattern," she said, putting several of them together. "Pretty, isn't it?"

They were so engaged with the quilt that they did not hear the footsteps on the stairs. As the stair door opened Mrs. Hale was saying, "Do you suppose she was going to quilt it, or just knot it?"

The sheriff threw up his hands.

"They wonder whether she was going to quilt it, or just knot it!"

There was a laugh for the ways of women, a warming of hands over the stove, and then the county attorney said briskly, "Well, let's go right out to the barn and get that cleared up."

"I don't see as there's anything so strange," Mrs. Hale said resentfully, after the outside door had closed on the three men— "our taking up our time with little things while we're waiting for them to get the evidence. I don't see as it's anything to laugh about."

"Of course they've got awful important things on their minds," said the sheriff's wife apologetically.

They returned to an inspection of the blocks for the quilt. Mrs. Hale was looking at the fine, even sewing, preoccupied with thoughts of the woman who had done that sewing, when she heard the sheriff's wife say, in a startled tone, "Why, look at this one."

"The sewing," said Mrs. Peters, in a troubled way. "All the rest of them have been so nice and even—but—this one. Why, it looks as if she didn't know what she was about!"

Their eyes met—something flashed to life, passed between them; then, as if with an effort, they seemed to pull away from each other. A moment Mrs. Hale sat there, her fingers upon those stitches so unlike the rest of the sewing. Then she had pulled a knot and drawn the threads.

"Oh, what are you doing, Mrs. Hale?" asked the sheriff's wife.

"Just pulling out a stitch or two that's not sewed very good," said Mrs. Hale mildly.

"I don't think we ought to touch things," Mrs. Peters said.

"I'll just finish up this end," answered Mrs. Hale.

She threaded a needle and started to replace bad sewing with good. Then in that thin, timid voice, she heard: "Mrs. Hale!"

"Yes, Mrs. Peters?"

"What do you suppose she was so—nervous about?"

"Oh, *I* don't know," said Mrs. Hale, as if dismissing a thing not important enough to spend much time on. "I don't know as she was—nervous. I sew awful queer sometimes when I'm just tired."

"Well, I must get these clothes wrapped. They may be through sooner than we think. I wonder where I could find a piece of paper—and string."

"In that cupboard, maybe," suggested Mrs. Hale.

One piece of the crazy sewing remained unripped. Mrs. Peters' back turned, Martha Hale scrutinized that piece, compared it with the dainty, accurate stitches of the other blocks. The difference was startling. Holding this block it was hard to remain quiet, as if the distracted thoughts of the woman who had perhaps turned to it to try and quiet herself were communicating themselves to her.

"Here's a bird-cage," Mrs. Peters said. "Did she have a bird, Mrs. Hale?"

"Why, I don't know whether she did or not." She turned to took at the cage Mrs. Peters was holding up. "I've not been here in so long." She sighed. "There was a man round last year selling canaries cheap—but I don't know as she took one. Maybe she did. She used to sing real pretty herself."

"Seems kind of funny to think of a bird here. But she must have had one—or why would she have a cage? I wonder what happened to it."

"I suppose maybe the cat got it," suggested Mrs. Hale, resuming her sewing.

"No; she didn't have a cat. She's got that feeling some people have about cats—being afraid of them. When they brought her to our house yesterday, my cat got in the room, and she was real upset and asked me to take it out."

"My sister Bessie was like that," laughed Mrs. Hale.

The sheriff's wife did not reply. The silence made Mrs. Hale turn. Mrs. Peters was examining the bird-cage.

"Look at this door," she said slowly. "It's broke. One hinge has been pulled apart."

Mrs. Hale came nearer.

"Looks as if someone must have been—rough with it."

Again their eyes met—startled, questioning, apprehensive. For a moment neither spoke nor stirred. Then Mrs. Hale, turning away, said brusquely, "If they're going to find any evidence, I wish they'd be about it. I don't like this place."

"But I'm awful glad you came with me, Mrs. Hale." Mrs. Peters put the bird-cage on the table and sat down. "It would be lonesome for me—sitting here alone."

"Yes, it would, wouldn't it?" agreed Mrs. Hale. She had picked up the sewing, but now it dropped to her lap, and she murmured: "But I tell you what I do wish, Mrs. Peters. I wish I had come over sometimes when she was here. I wish—I had."

"But of course you were awful busy, Mrs. Hale. Your house—and your children."

"I could've come. I stayed away because it weren't cheerful—and that's why I ought to have come. I"—she looked around—"I've never liked this place. Maybe because it's down in a hollow and you don't see the road. I don't know what it is, but it's a lonesome place, and always was. I wish I had come over to see Minnie Foster sometimes. I can see now—"

"Well, you mustn't reproach yourself. Somehow we just don't see how it is with other folks till—something comes up."

"Not having children makes less work," mused Mrs. Hale, "but it makes a quiet house. And Wright out to work all day—and no company when he did come in. Did you know John Wright, Mrs. Peters?"

"Not to know him. I've seen him in town. They say he was a good man."

"Yes—good," conceded John Wright's neighbor grimly. "He didn't drink, and kept his word as well as most, I guess, and paid his debts. But he was a hard man, Mrs. Peters. Just to pass the time of day with him—" she shivered. "Like a raw wind that gets to the bone." Her eye fell upon the cage on the table before her, and she added, "I should think she would've wanted a bird!"

Suddenly she leaned forward, looking intently at the cage. "But what do you s'pose went wrong with it?"

"I don't know," returned Mrs. Peters; "unless it got sick and died."

But after she said this she reached over and swung the broken door. Both women watched it.

"You didn't know—her?" Mrs. Hale asked.

"Not till they brought her yesterday," said the sheriff's wife.

"She—come to think of it, she was kind of like a bird herself. Real sweet and pretty, but kind of timid and—fluttery. How—she—did—change."

Finally, as if struck with a happy thought and relieved to get back to everyday things: "Tell you what, Mrs. Peters, why don't you take the quilt in with you? It might take up her mind."

"Why, I think that's a real nice idea, Mrs. Hale. There couldn't possibly be any objection to that, could there? Now, just what will I take? I wonder if her patches are in here?" They turned to the sewing basket.

"Here's some red," said Mrs. Hale, bringing out a roll of cloth. Underneath this was a box. "Here, maybe her scissors are in here—and her things." She held it up. "What a pretty box! I'll warrant that was something she had a long time ago—when she was a girl."

She held it in her hand a moment; then, with a little sigh, opened it.

Instantly her hand went to her nose. "Why!"

Mrs. Peters drew nearer—then turned away.

"There's something wrapped up in this piece of silk," faltered Mrs. Hale.

"This isn't her scissors," said Mrs. Peters, in a shrinking voice.

Mrs. Hale raised the piece of silk. "Oh, Mrs. Peters!" she cried. "It's—"

Mrs. Peters bent closer.

"It's the bird," she whispered.

"But, Mrs. Peters!" cried Mrs. Hale. "Look at it! Its neck—look at its neck! It's all—other side *to*."

The sheriff's wife again bent closer.

"Somebody wrung its neck," said she, in a voice that was slow and deep.

The eyes of the two women met—this time clung together in a look of dawning comprehension, of growing horror. Mrs. Peters looked from the dead bird to the broken door of the cage. Again their eyes met. And just then there was a sound at the outside door.

Mrs. Hale slipped the box under the quilt pieces in the basket. The county attorney and sheriff came in.

"Well, ladies," said the attorney, as one turning from serious things to little pleasantries, "have you decided whether she was going to quilt it or knot it?"

"We think," said the sheriff's wife hastily, "that she was going to knot it."

"Well, that's very interesting, I'm sure." He caught sight of the cage. "Has the bird flown?"

"We think the cat got it," said Mrs. Hale in a prosaic voice.

He was walking up and down, as if thinking something out.

"Is there a cat?" he asked absently.

Mrs. Hale shot a look up at the sheriff's wife.

"Well, not *now*," said Mrs. Peters. "They're superstitious, you know; they leave."

The county attorney did not heed her. "No sign at all of anyone having come in from the outside," he said to Peters, continuing an interrupted conversation. "Their own rope. Now let's go upstairs again and go over it, piece by piece. It would have to have been someone who knew just the—"

The stair door closed behind them and their voices were lost.

The two women sat motionless, not looking at each other, but as if peering into something and at the same time holding back. When they spoke now it was as if they were afraid of what they were saying, but could not help saying it.

"She liked the bird," said Martha Hale. "She was going to bury it in that pretty box."

"When I was a girl," said Mrs. Peters, under her breath, "my kitten—there was a boy took a hatchet, and before my eyes—before I could get there—" She covered her face an instant. "If they hadn't held me back I would have"—she caught herself, and finished weakly—"hurt him."

Then they sat without speaking or moving.

"I wonder how it would seem," Mrs. Hale began, as if feeling her way over strange ground—"never to have had any children around." Her eyes made a sweep of the kitchen. "No, Wright wouldn't like the bird—a thing that sang. She used to sing. He killed that too."

Mrs. Peters moved. "Of course we don't know who killed the bird."

"I knew John Wright," was the answer.

"It was an awful thing was done in this house that night, Mrs. Hale," said the sheriff's wife. "Killing a man while he slept—slipping a thing round his neck that choked the life out of him."

Mrs. Hale's hand went to the bird-cage. "His neck. Choked the life out of him."

"We don't *know* who killed him," whispered Mrs. Peters wildly. "We don't *know*."

Mrs. Hale had not moved. "If there had been years and years of nothing, then a bird to sing to you, it would be awful—still, after the bird was still."

"I know what stillness is," whispered Mrs. Peters. "When we homesteaded in Dakota, and my first baby died—after he was two years old—and me with no other then—"

Mrs. Hale stirred. "How soon do you suppose they'll be through looking for the evidence?"

"I know what stillness is," repeated Mrs. Peters. Then she too pulled back. "The law has got to punish crime, Mrs. Hale."

"I wish you'd seen Minnie Foster when she wore a white dress with blue ribbons, and stood up there in the choir and sang."

The picture of that girl, the thought that she had lived neighbor to her for twenty years, and had let her die for lack of life, was suddenly more than the woman could bear.

"Oh, I *wish* I'd come over here once in a while!" she cried. "That was a crime! That was a crime! Who's going to punish *that*?"

"We mustn't—take on," said Mrs. Peters, with a frightened look towards the stairs.

"I might 'a' *known* she needed help! I tell you, it's *queer*, Mrs. Peters. We live close together, and we live far apart. We all go through the same things— it's all just a different kind of the same thing! If it weren't—why do you and I *know*—what we know this minute?"

Seeing the jar of fruit on the table, she reached for it. "If I was you I wouldn't *tell* her her fruit was gone! Tell her it *ain't*. Tell her it's all right—all of it. Here—take this in to prove it to her! She—she may never know whether it was broke or not."

Mrs. Peters took the bottle of fruit as if glad to take it—as if touching a familiar thing, having something to do, could keep her from something else. She looked about for something to wrap the fruit in, took a petticoat from the pile of clothes she had brought from the front room, nervously started winding that round the bottle.

"My!" she began, in a high voice, "it's a good thing the men couldn't hear us! Getting all stirred up over a little thing like a—dead canary. As if that could have anything to do with—with—My, wouldn't they *laugh?*"

There were footsteps on the stairs.

"Maybe they would," muttered Mrs. Hale—"maybe they wouldn't."

"No, Peters," said the county attorney, "it's all perfectly clear, except the reason for doing it. But you know juries when it comes to women. If there was some definite thing—something to *show*. Something to make a story about. A thing that would connect up with this clumsy way of doing it."

Mrs. Hale looked at Mrs. Peters. Mrs. Peters was looking at her. Quickly they looked away from one another. The outer door opened and Mr. Hale came in.

"I've nailed back that board we ripped off," he said.

"Much obliged, Mr. Hale," said the sheriff. "We'll be getting along now."

"I'm going to stay here awhile by myself," the county attorney suddenly announced. "You can send Frank out for me, can't you?" he asked the sheriff. "I want to go over everything. I'm not satisfied we can't do better."

Again, for one brief moment, the women's eyes met.

The sheriff came up to the table.

"Did you want to see what Mrs. Peters was going to take in?"

The county attorney picked up the apron. He laughed.

"Oh, I guess they're not very dangerous things the ladies have picked out."

Mrs. Hale's hand was on the sewing basket in which the box was concealed. She felt that she ought to take her hand off the basket. She did not seem able to. She picked up one of the quilt blocks she had piled on to cover the box. She had a fear that if he took up the basket she would snatch it from him.

But he did not take it. With another laugh he turned away, saying, "No, Mrs. Peters doesn't need supervising. For that matter, a sheriff's wife is married to the law. Ever think of it that way, Mrs. Peters?"

Mrs. Peters had turned her face away. "Not—just that way," she said.

"Married to the law!" chuckled Mrs. Peters' husband. He moved towards the door into the front room, and said to the county attorney, "I just want you to come here a minute, George. We ought to take a look at these windows."

"Oh—windows!" scoffed the county attorney.

"We'll be leaving in a second, Mr. Hale," Mr. Peters told the farmer, as he followed the county attorney into the other room.

"Can't be leavin' too soon to suit me," muttered Hale, and went out.

Again, for one final moment, the two women were alone in that kitchen.

Martha Hale sprang up, her hands tight together, looking at that other woman, with whom it rested. At first she could not see her eyes, for the sheriff's wife had not turned back since she turned away at that suggestion of being married to the law. Slowly, unwillingly, Mrs. Peters turned her head until her eyes met the eyes of the other woman. There was a moment when they held each other in a steady, burning look in which there was no evasion nor flinching. Then Martha Hale's eyes pointed the way to the basket in which was hidden the thing that would convict the third woman—that woman who was not there, and yet who had been there with them through that hour.

For a moment Mrs. Peters did not move. And then she did it. Threw back the quilt pieces, got the box, tried to put it in her hand-bag. It was too big. Desperately she opened it, started to take the bird out. But there she broke— she could not touch the bird. She stood there helpless, foolish.

There was a sound at the door. Martha Hale snatched the box from the sheriff's wife and got it in the pocket of her big coat just as the sheriff and the county attorney came back into the kitchen.

"Well, Henry," said the county attorney, facetiously, "at least we found out that she was not going to quilt it. She was going to—what is it you call it, ladies?"

Mrs. Hale's hand was against the pocket of her coat.

"We call it—knot it," was her answer.

[1917]

SUSAN GLASPELL, *A Jury of Her Peers*

1. What is the significance of the title of this story? How does your perception of the title change as you read the story?

2. Martha Hale is bothered about leaving her kitchen in disarray; she then bristles at the men's comments about Minnie Wright's kitchen. What does a clean, orderly kitchen mean to Mrs. Hale? Why does she attach more significance than the men do to the state of Mrs. Wright's kitchen?

3. Twice Mrs. Peters recalls incidents in her own life: her kitten's death and her baby's death. What is the significance of these recollections? What role do they play in her ultimate decision to protect Mrs. Wright?

4. Throughout this story Glaspell compares the reactions of men and women to ordinary household items. How do these reactions contribute to the theme of the story?

5. Neither John nor Minnie Wright appears in this story, and yet each character comes through quite clearly as the story progresses. How does Glaspell develop the characters of John and Minnie?

6. Much of the women's attention centers on the quilt that Mrs. Wright has been working on. How does the image of a quilt, particularly the materials and methods involved in its construction, contribute to the theme of the story?

7. Analyze the conversation between Mrs. Peters and Mrs. Hale after they discover the bird. Which specific lines indicate their sense of duty to the law? Which lines suggest their solidarity with Mrs. Wright? How do the references to their own lives contribute to their conclusions about Mrs. Wright?

8. In addition to guilt and innocence, this story also explores concepts of community and isolation, personal and public responsibility, loyalty and betrayal. Analyze the story as a commentary on the complexity of human relations with regard to these concepts, focusing on relationships between husbands and wives, men and women, friends, and citizens of a community.

9. Susan Glaspell also wrote the play *Trifles*, a leaner, dramatic version of this story. Read that play, noting what is omitted from the story form and what appears more immediate because of the dramatic form. Write an essay analyzing the differences between the play and the story. Which version do you consider more compelling? Why?

D. H. Lawrence
[1885-1930]

D. H. LAWRENCE *was born David Herbert in a coal town in the dusty industrial area of England. Eastwood, Nottinghamshire, was on its way downhill as a source of coal, but Lawrence's father managed to work the mines until his retirement. Lawrence's mother was particularly attached to this fourth child, for by this time her husband had become one of the hard-drinking, hard-working miners who supported their families financially but not necessarily emotionally. Lawrence became his mother's favorite and, because of illness, did not find his way into the mines. Instead, he became an outstanding student at the local Board school, was enrolled at Nottingham High School, and then became a teacher at Nottingham University College. His first novel,* The White Peacock *(1911), was published shortly after the death of his mother. In 1912 he began an affair with Frieda Weekley, the German wife of a fellow professor. Meanwhile, his next novel,* Sons and Lovers *(1913), which is an autobiographical account of his relationship with his possessive mother and with the various young women who passed through his life, was quickly followed by the novel* The Rainbow *(1915). Its successor,* Women in Love *(1920), caused a scandal for its intimate account of two women's lives. The novels are now critically acclaimed, but were considered outrageous at the time of their publication.*

Lawrence and Frieda traveled the world, but returned to Europe in 1925 when he fell seriously ill. He finished Aaron's Rod *(1922),* Kangaroo *(1923), and* The Plumed Serpent *(1926) as his illness progressed. These novels portray his understanding of the lives of those Europeans who wander through other countries looking for meaning in their own lives. In* Serpent, *a white woman of a certain age wanders among the various cults of Mexico, experiencing life in a world to which she can never belong. The novel is fascinating in that a male author attempts to portray not only the inner life of a woman but that of an older woman, and one who leads a totally different life from his. The novel does not totally succeed, but it certainly tantalizes. Two years before his death, he published the novel that he thought was his best,* Lady Chatterley's Lover *(1928), a work that shocked and scandalized some British readers and most American readers when it appeared. In it, a noblewoman has a love affair with her gardener, an affair that Lawrence attempts to portray with sympathy, but in his efforts to write realistic love scenes, he offends those with delicate sensibilities and amuses those of more raucous temperament. Laughter destroys any intended romance for the modern reader of the novel. Still it was a wild and rebellious text at its time and is still interesting for the same reason as* The Plumed Serpent: *A male attempts to enter the consciousness of a female protagonist, with some surprising effects. Lawrence was also a prolific poet, publishing seven volumes containing hundreds of poems in his lifetime.*

The Rocking-Horse Winner

D. H. LAWRENCE

THERE WAS A WOMAN WHO was beautiful, who started with all the advantages, yet she had no luck. She married for love, and the love turned to dust. She had bonny children, yet she felt they had been thrust upon her, and she could not love them. They looked at her coldly, as if they were finding fault with her. And hurriedly she felt she must cover up some fault in herself. Yet what it was that she must cover up she never knew. Nevertheless, when her children were present, she always felt the center of her heart go hard. This troubled her, and in her manner she was all the more gentle and anxious for her children, as if she loved them very much. Only she herself knew that at the center of her heart was a hard little place that could not feel love, no, not for anybody. Everybody else said of her: "She is such a good mother. She adores her children." Only she herself, and her children themselves, knew it was not so. They read it in each other's eyes.

There were a boy and two little girls. They lived in a pleasant house, with a garden, and they had discreet servants, and felt themselves superior to anyone in the neighborhood.

Although they lived in style, they felt always an anxiety in the house. There was never enough money. The mother had a small income, and the father had a small income, but not nearly enough for the social position which they had to keep up. The father went in to town to some office. But though he had good prospects, these prospects never materialized. There was always the grinding sense of the shortage of money, though the style was always kept up.

At last the mother said: "I will see if *I* can't make something." But she did not know where to begin. She racked her brains, and tried this thing and the other, but could not find anything successful. The failure made deep lines come into her face. Her children were growing up, they would have to go to school. There must be more money, there must be more money. The father, who was always very handsome and expensive in his tastes, seemed as if he never *would* be able to do anything worth doing. And the mother, who had a great belief in herself, did not succeed any better, and her tastes were just as expensive.

And so the house came to be haunted by the unspoken phrase: *There must be more money! There must be more money!* The children could hear it all the time, though nobody said it aloud. They heard it at Christmas, when the expensive and splendid toys filled the nursery. Behind the shining modern rocking-horse, behind the smart doll's house, a voice would start whispering. "There *must* be more money! There *must* be more money!" And the children would stop playing, to listen for a moment. They would look into each other's eyes, to see if they had all heard. And each one saw in the eyes of the other two that they too had heard. "There *must* be more money! There *must* be more money!"

It came whispering from the springs of the still-swaying rocking-horse, and even the horse, bending his wooden, champing head, heard it. The big doll, sitting so pink and smirking in her new pram, could hear it quite plainly, and seemed to be smirking all the more self-consciously because of it. The foolish puppy, too, that took the place of the teddy-bear, he was looking so extraordinarily foolish for no other reason but that he heard the secret whisper all over the house: "There *must* be more money!"

Yet nobody ever said it aloud. The whisper was everywhere, and therefore no one spoke it. Just as no one ever says: "We are breathing!" in spite of the fact that breath is coming and going all the time.

"Mother," said the boy Paul one day, "why don't we keep a car of our own? Why do we always use uncle's, or else a taxi?"

"Because we're the poor members of the family," said the mother.

"But why *are* we, mother?"

"Well—I suppose," she said slowly and bitterly, "it's because your father has no luck."

The boy was silent for some time.

"Is luck money, mother?" he asked rather timidly.

"No, Paul. Not quite. It's what causes you to have money."

"Oh!" said Paul vaguely. "I thought when Uncle Oscar said *filthy lucker*, it meant money."

"*Filthy lucre* does mean money," said the mother. "But it's lucre, not luck."

"Oh!" said the boy. "Then what *is* luck, mother?"

"It's what causes you to have money. If you're lucky you have money. That's why it's better to be born lucky than rich. If you're rich, you may lose your money. But if you're lucky, you will always get more money."

"Oh! Will you? And is father not lucky?"

"Very unlucky, I should say," she said bitterly.

The boy watched her with unsure eyes.

"Why?" he asked.

"I don't know. Nobody ever knows why one person is lucky and another unlucky."

"Don't they? Nobody at all? Does *nobody* know?"

"Perhaps God. But He never tells."

"He ought to, then. And aren't you lucky either, mother?"

"I can't be, if I married an unlucky husband."

"But by yourself, aren't you?"

"I used to think I was, before I married. Now I think I am very unlucky indeed."

"Why?"

"Well—never mind! Perhaps I'm not really," she said.

The child looked at her, to see if she meant it. But he saw, by the lines of her mouth, that she was only trying to hide something from him.

"Well, anyhow," he said stoutly, "I'm a lucky person."

"Why?" said his mother, with a sudden laugh.

He stared at her. He didn't even know why he had said it.

"God told me," he asserted, brazening it out.

"I hope He did, dear!" she said, again with a laugh, but rather bitter.

"He did, mother!"

"Excellent!" said the mother, using one of her husband's exclamations.

The boy saw she did not believe him; or, rather, that she paid no attention to his assertion. This angered him somewhat, and made him want to compel her attention.

He went off by himself, vaguely, in a childish way, seeking for the clue to "luck." Absorbed, taking no heed of other people, he went about with a sort of stealth, seeking inwardly for luck. He wanted luck, he wanted it, he wanted it. When the two girls were playing dolls in the nursery, he would sit on his big rocking-horse, charging madly into space, with a frenzy that made the little girls peer at him uneasily. Wildly the horse careered, the waving dark hair of the boy tossed, his eyes had a strange glare in them. The little girls dared not speak to him.

When he had ridden to the end of his mad little journey, he climbed down and stood in front of his rocking-horse, staring fixedly into its lowered face. Its red mouth was slightly open, its big eye was wide and glassy-bright.

"Now!" he would silently command the snorting steed. "Now, take me to where there is luck! Now take me!"

And he would slash the horse on the neck with the little whip he had asked Uncle Oscar for. He *knew* the horse could take him to where there was luck, if only he forced it. So he would mount again, and start on his furious ride, hoping at last to get there. He knew he could get there.

"You'll break your horse, Paul!" said the nurse.

"He's always riding like that! I wish he'd leave off!" said his elder sister Joan.

But he only glared down on them in silence. Nurse gave him up. She could make nothing of him. Anyhow he was growing beyond her.

One day his mother and his Uncle Oscar came in when he was on one of his furious rides. He did not speak to them.

"Hallo, you young jockey! Riding a winner?" said his uncle.

"Aren't you growing too big for a rocking-horse? You're not a very little boy any longer, you know," said his mother.

But Paul only gave a blue glare from his big, rather close-set eyes. He would speak to nobody when he was in full tilt. His mother watched him with an anxious expression on her face.

At last he suddenly stopped forcing his horse into the mechanical gallop, and slid down.

"Well, I got there!" he announced fiercely, his blue eyes still flaring, and his sturdy long legs straddling apart.

"Where did you get to?" asked his mother.

"Where I wanted to go," he flared back at her.

"That's right, son!" said Uncle Oscar. "Don't you stop till you get there. What's the horse's name?"

"He doesn't have a name," said the boy.

"Gets on without all right?" asked the uncle.

"Well, he has different names. He was called Sansovino last week."

"Sansovino, eh? Won the Ascot. How did you know his name?"

"He always talks about horse-races with Bassett," said Joan.

The uncle was delighted to find that his small nephew was posted with all the racing news. Bassett, the young gardener, who had been wounded in the left foot in the war and had got his present job through Oscar Cresswell, whose batman he had been, was a perfect blade of the "turf." He lived in the racing events, and the small boy lived with him.

Oscar Cresswell got it all from Bassett.

"Master Paul comes and asks me, so I can't do more than tell him, sir," said Bassett, his face terribly serious, as if he were speaking of religious matters.

"And does he ever put anything on a horse he fancies?"

"Well—I don't want to give him away—he's a young sport, a fine sport, sir. Would you mind asking him himself? He sort of takes a pleasure in it, and perhaps he'd feel I was giving him away, sir, if you don't mind."

Bassett was serious as a church.

The uncle went back to his nephew and took him off for a ride in the car.

"Say, Paul, old man, do you ever put anything on a horse?" the uncle asked.

The boy watched the handsome man closely.

"Why, do you think I oughtn't to?" he parried.

"Not a bit of it. I thought perhaps you might give me a tip for the Lincoln."

The car sped on into the country, going down to Uncle Oscar's place in Hampshire.

"Honor bright?" said the nephew.

"Honor bright, son!" said the uncle.

"Well, then, Daffodil."

"Daffodil! I doubt it, sonny. What about Mirza?"

"I only know the winner," said the boy. "That's Daffodil."

"Daffodil, eh?"

There was a pause. Daffodil was an obscure horse comparatively.

"Uncle!"

"Yes, son?"

"You won't let it go any further, will you? I promised Bassett."

"Bassett be damned, old man! What's he got to do with it?"

"We're partners. We've been partners from the first. Uncle, he lent me my first five shillings, which I lost. I promised him, honor bright, it was only between me and him; only you gave me that ten-shilling note I started winning with, so I thought you were lucky. You won't let it go any further, will you?"

The boy gazed at his uncle from those big, hot, blue eyes, set rather close together. The uncle stirred and laughed uneasily.

"Right you are, son! I'll keep your tip private. Daffodil, eh? How much are you putting on him?"

"All except twenty pounds," said the boy. "I keep that in reserve."

The uncle thought it a good joke.

"You keep twenty pounds in reserve, do you, you young romancer? What are you betting, then?"

"I'm betting three hundred," said the boy gravely. "But it's between you and me, Uncle Oscar! Honor bright?"

The uncle burst into a roar of laughter.

"It's between you and me all right, you young Nat Gould," he said, laughing. "But where's your three hundred?"

"Bassett keeps it for me. We're partners."

"You are, are you! And what is Bassett putting on Daffodil?"

"He won't go quite as high as I do, I expect. Perhaps he'll go a hundred and fifty."

"What, pennies?" laughed the uncle.

"Pounds," said the child, with a surprised look at his uncle. "Bassett keeps a bigger reserve than I do."

Between wonder and amusement Uncle Oscar was silent. He pursued the matter no further, but he determined to take his nephew with him to the Lincoln races.

"Now, son," he said, "I'm putting twenty on Mirza, and I'll put five for you on any horse you fancy. What's your pick?"

"Daffodil, uncle."

"No, not the fiver on Daffodil!"

"I should if it was my own fiver," said the child.

"Good! Good! Right you are! A fiver for me and a fiver for you on Daffodil."

The child had never been to a race-meeting before, and his eyes were blue fire. He pursed his mouth tight, and watched. A Frenchman just in front had put his money on Lancelot. Wild with excitement, he flayed his arms up and down, yelling, "*Lancelot! Lancelot!*" in his French accent.

Daffodil came in first, Lancelot second, Mirza third. The child, flushed and with eyes blazing, was curiously serene. His uncle brought him four five-pound notes, four to one.

"What am I to do with these?" he cried, waving them before the boy's eyes.

"I suppose we'll talk to Bassett," said the boy. "I expect I have fifteen hundred now; and twenty in reserve; and this twenty."

His uncle studied him for some moments.

"Look here, son!" he said. "You're not serious about Bassett and that fifteen hundred, are you?"

"Yes, I am. But it's between you and me, uncle. Honor bright!"

"Honor bright all right, son! But I must talk to Bassett."

"If you'd like to be a partner, uncle, with Bassett and me, we could all be partners. Only, you'd have to promise, honor bright, uncle, not to let it go beyond us three. Bassett and I are lucky, and you must be lucky, because it was your ten shillings I started winning with. . . ."

Uncle Oscar took both Bassett and Paul into Richmond Park for an afternoon, and there they talked.

"It's like this, you see, sir," Bassett said. "Master Paul would get me talking about racing events, spinning yarns, you know, sir. And he was always keen on knowing if I'd made or if I'd lost. It's about a year since, now, that I put five shillings on Blush of Dawn for him—and we lost. Then the luck turned, and with ten shillings he had from you, that we put on Singhalese. And since that time, it's been pretty steady, all things considering. What do you say, Master Paul?"

"We're all right when we're sure," said Paul. "It's when we're not quite sure that we go down."

"Oh, but we're careful then," said Bassett.

"But when are you *sure*?" smiled Uncle Oscar.

"It's Master Paul, sir," said Bassett, in a secret, religious voice. "It's as if he had it from heaven. Like Daffodil, now, for the Lincoln. That was as sure as eggs."

"Did you put anything on Daffodil?" asked Oscar Cresswell.

"Yes, sir. I made my bit."

"And my nephew?"

Bassett was obstinately silent, looking at Paul.

"I made twelve hundred, didn't I, Bassett? I told uncle I was putting three hundred on Daffodil."

"That's right," said Bassett, nodding.

"But where's the money?" asked the uncle.

"I keep it safe locked up, sir. Master Paul he can have it any minute he likes to ask for it."

"What, fifteen hundred pounds?"

"And twenty! And *forty*, that is, with the twenty he made on the course."

"It's amazing!" said the uncle.

"If Master Paul offers you to be partners, sir, I would, if I were you; if you'll excuse me," said Bassett.

Oscar Cresswell thought about it.

"I'll see the money," he said.

They drove home again, and sure enough, Bassett came round to the garden-house with fifteen hundred pounds in notes. The twenty pounds reserve was left with Joe Glee, in the Turf Commission deposit.

"You see, it's all right, uncle, when I'm *sure!* Then we go strong, for all we're worth. Don't we, Bassett!"

"We do that, Master Paul."

"And when are you sure?" said the uncle, laughing.

"Oh, well, sometimes I'm *absolutely* sure, like about Daffodil," said the boy; "and sometimes I have an idea; and sometimes I haven't even an idea, have I, Bassett? Then we're careful, because we mostly go down."

"You do, do you! And when you're sure, like about Daffodil, what makes you sure, sonny?"

"Oh, well, I don't know," said the boy uneasily. "I'm sure, you know, uncle; that's all."

"It's as if he had it from heaven, sir," Bassett reiterated.

"I should say so!" said the uncle.

But he became a partner. And when the Leger was coming on, Paul was "sure" about Lively Spark, which was a quite inconsiderable horse. The boy insisted on putting a thousand on the horse, Bassett went for five hundred, and Oscar Cresswell two hundred. Lively Spark came in first, and the betting had been ten to one against him. Paul had made ten thousand.

"You see," he said, "I was absolutely sure of him."

Even Oscar Cresswell had cleared two thousand.

"Look here, son," he said, "this sort of thing makes me nervous."

"It needn't, uncle! Perhaps I shan't be sure again for a long time."

"But what are you going to do with your money?" asked the uncle.

"Of course," said the boy, "I started it for mother. She said she had no luck, because father is unlucky, so I thought if *I* was lucky, it might stop whispering."

"What might stop whispering?"

"Our house. I *hate* our house for whispering."

"What does it whisper?"

"Why—why"—the boy fidgeted—"why, I don't know. But it's always short of money, you know, uncle."

"I know it, son, I know it."

"You know people send mother writs, don't you, uncle?"

"I'm afraid I do," said the uncle.

"And then the house whispers, like people laughing at you behind your back. It's awful, that is! I thought if I was lucky . . ."

"You might stop it," added the uncle.

The boy watched him with big blue eyes, that had an uncanny cold fire in them, and he said never a word.

"Well, then!" said the uncle. "What are we doing?"

"I shouldn't like mother to know I was lucky," said the boy.

"Why not, son?"

"She'd stop me."

"I don't think she would."

"Oh!"—and the boy writhed in an odd way—"I *don't* want her to know, uncle."

"All right, son! We'll manage it without her knowing."

They managed it very easily. Paul, at the other's suggestion, handed over five thousand pounds to his uncle, who deposited it with the family lawyer, who was then to inform Paul's mother that a relative had put five thousand pounds into his hands, which sum was to be paid out a thousand pounds at a time, on the mother's birthday, for the next five years.

"So she'll have a birthday present of a thousand pounds for five successive years," said Uncle Oscar. "I hope it won't make it all the harder for her later."

Paul's mother had her birthday in November. The house had been "whispering" worse than ever lately, and, even in spite of his luck, Paul could not bear up against it. He was very anxious to see the effect of the birthday letter, telling his mother about the thousand pounds.

When there were no visitors, Paul now took his meals with his parents, as he was beyond the nursery control. His mother went into town nearly every day. She had discovered that she had an odd knack of sketching furs and dress materials, so she worked secretly in the studio of a friend who was the chief "artist" for the leading drapers. She drew the figures of ladies in furs and ladies in silk and sequins for the newspaper advertisements. This young woman artist earned several thousand pounds a year, but Paul's mother only made several hundreds, and she was again dissatisfied. She so wanted to be first in something, and she did not succeed, even in making sketches for drapery advertisements.

She was down to breakfast on the morning of her birthday. Paul watched her face as she read the letters. He knew the lawyer's letter. As his mother read it, her face hardened and became more expressionless. Then a cold, determined look came on her mouth. She hid the letter under the pile of others, and said not sword about it.

"Didn't you have anything nice in the post for your birthday, mother?" said Paul.

"Quite moderately nice," she said, her voice cold and absent.

She went away to town without saying more.

But in the afternoon Uncle Oscar appeared. He said Paul's mother had had a long interview with the lawyer, asking if the whole five thousand could not be advanced at once, as she was in debt.

"What do you think, uncle?" said the boy.

"I leave it to you, son."

"Oh, let her have it, then! We can get some more with the other," said the boy.

"A bird in the hand is worth two in the bush, laddie!" said Uncle Oscar.

"But I'm sure to *know* for the Grand National; or the Lincolnshire; or else the Derby. I'm sure to know for *one* of them," said Paul.

So Uncle Oscar signed the agreement, and Paul's mother touched the whole five thousand. Then something very curious happened. The voices in the house suddenly went mad, like a chorus of frogs on a spring evening. There were certain new furnishings, and Paul had a tutor. He was *really* going to Eton, his father's school, in the following autumn. There were flowers in the winter, and a blossoming of the luxury Paul's mother had been used to. And yet the voices in the house, behind the sprays of mimosa and almond blossom, and from under the piles of iridescent cushions, simply trilled and screamed in a sort of ecstasy: "There *must* be more money! Oh-h-h; there *must* be more money. Oh, now, now-w! Now-w-w—there *must* be more money—more than ever! More than ever!"

It frightened Paul terribly. He studied away at his Latin and Greek with his tutors. But his intense hours were spent with Bassett. The Grand National had gone by: he had not "known," and had lost a hundred pounds. Summer was at hand. He was in agony for the Lincoln. But even for the Lincoln he didn't "know," and he lost fifty pounds. He became wild-eyed and strange, as if something were going to explode in him.

"Let it alone, son! Don't you bother about it!" urged Uncle Oscar. But it was as if the boy couldn't really hear what his uncle was saying.

"I've got to know for the Derby! I've got to know for the Derby!" the child reiterated, his big blue eyes blazing with a sort of madness.

His mother noticed how overwrought he was.

"You'd better go to the seaside. Wouldn't you like to go now to the seaside, instead of waiting? I think you'd better," she said, looking down at him anxiously, her heart curiously heavy because of him.

But the child lifted his uncanny blue eyes.

"I couldn't possibly go before the Derby, mother!" he said. "I couldn't possibly!"

"Why not?" she said, her voice becoming heavy when she was opposed. "Why not? You can still go from the seaside to see the Derby with your Uncle Oscar, if that's what you wish. No need for you to wait here. Besides, I think you care too much about these races. It's a bad sign. My family has been a gambling family, and you won't know till you grow up how much damage it has done. But it has done damage. I shall have to send Bassett away, and ask Uncle Oscar not to talk racing to you, unless you promise to be reasonable about it; go away to the seaside and forget it. You're all nerves!"

"I'll do what you like, mother, so long as you don't send me away till after the Derby," the boy said.

"Send you away from where? Just from this house?"

"Yes," he said, gazing at her.

"Why, you curious child, what makes you care about this house so much suddenly? I never knew you loved it."

He gazed at her without speaking. He had a secret within a secret, something he had not divulged, even to Bassett or to his Uncle Oscar.

But his mother, after standing undecided and a little bit sullen for some moments, said:

"Very well, then! Don't go to the seaside till after the Derby, if you don't wish it. But promise me you won't let your nerves go to pieces. Promise you won't think so much about horse-racing and *events*, as you call them!"

"Oh, no," said the boy casually. "I won't think much about them, mother. You needn't worry. I wouldn't worry, mother, if I were you."

"If you were me and I were you," said his mother, "I wonder what we *should* do!"

"But you know you needn't worry, mother, don't you?" the boy repeated.

"I should be awfully glad to know it," she said wearily.

"Oh, well, you *can*, you know. I mean, you *ought* to know you needn't worry," he insisted.

"Ought I? Then I'll see about it," she said.

Paul's secret of secrets was his wooden horse, that which had no name. Since he was emancipated from a nurse and a nursery-governess, he had had his rocking-horse removed to his own bedroom at the top of the house.

"Surely, you're too big for a rocking-horse!" his mother had remonstrated.

"Well, you see, mother, till I can have a *real* horse, I like to have *some* sort of animal about," had been his quaint answer.

"Do you feel he keeps you company?" she laughed.

"Oh, yes! He's very good, he always keeps me company, when I'm there," said Paul.

So the horse, rather shabby, stood in an arrested prance in the boy's bedroom.

The Derby was drawing near, and the boy grew more and more tense. He hardly heard what was spoken to him, he was very frail, and his eyes were really uncanny. His mother had sudden strange seizures of uneasiness about him. Sometimes, for half-an-hour, she would feel a sudden anxiety about him that was almost anguish. She wanted to rush to him at once, and know he was safe.

Two nights before the Derby, she was at a big party in town, when one of her rushes of anxiety about her boy, her first-born, gripped her heart till she could hardly speak. She fought with the feeling, might and main, for she believed in common-sense. But it was too strong. She had to leave the dance and go downstairs to telephone to the country. The children's nursery-governess was terribly surprised and startled at being rung up in the night.

"Are the children all right, Miss Wilmot?"

"Oh, yes, they are quite all right."

"Master Paul? Is he all right?"

"He went to bed as right as a trivet. Shall I run up and look at him?"

"No," said Paul's mother reluctantly. "No! Don't trouble. It's all right. Don't sit up. We shall be home fairly soon." She did not want her son's privacy intruded upon.

"Very good," said the governess.

It was about one-o'clock when Paul's mother and father drove up to their house. All was still. Paul's mother went to her room and slipped off her white fur cloak. She had told her maid not to wait up for her. She heard her husband downstairs, mixing a whisky-and-soda.

And then, because of the strange anxiety at her heart, she stole upstairs to her son's room. Noiselessly she went along the upper corridor. Was there a faint noise! What was it?

She stood, with arrested muscles, outside his door, listening. There was a strange, heavy, and yet not loud noise. Her heart stood still. It was a soundless noise, yet rushing and powerful. Something huge, in violent, hushed motion.

What was it? What in God's name was it? She ought to know. She felt that she knew the noise. She knew what it was.

Yet she could not place it. She couldn't say what it was. And on and on it went, like a madness.

Softly, frozen with anxiety and fear, she turned the door-handle.

The room was dark. Yet in the space near the window, she heard and saw something plunging to and fro. She gazed in fear and amazement.

Then suddenly she switched on the light, and saw her son, in his green pajamas, madly surging on the rocking-horse. The blaze of light suddenly lit him up, as he urged the wooden horse, and lit her up, as she stood, blonde, in her dress of pale green and crystal, in the doorway.

"Paul!" she cried. "Whatever are you doing?"

"It's Malabar!" he screamed, in a powerful, strange voice. "It's Malabar!"

His eyes blazed at her for one strange and senseless second, as he ceased urging his wooden horse. Then he fell with a crash to the ground, and she, all her tormented motherhood flooding upon her, rushed to gather him up.

But he was unconscious, and unconscious he remained, with some brain-fever. He talked and tossed, and his mother sat stonily by his side.

"Malabar! It's Malabar! Bassett, Bassett I *know*! It's Malabar!"

So the child cried, trying to get up and urge the rocking-horse that gave him his inspiration.

"What does he mean by Malabar?" asked the heart-frozen mother.

"I don't know," said the father stonily.

"What does he mean by Malabar?" she asked her brother Oscar.

"It's one of the horses running for the Derby," was the answer.

And, in spite of himself, Oscar Cresswell spoke to Bassett, and himself put a thousand on Malabar: at fourteen to one.

The third day of the illness was critical: they were waiting for a change. The boy, with his rather long, curly hair, was tossing ceaselessly on the pillow. He neither slept nor regained consciousness, and his eyes were like blue stones. His mother sat, feeling her heart had gone, turned actually into a stone.

In the evening, Oscar Cresswell did not come, but Bassett sent a message saying could he come up for one moment, just one moment? Paul's mother was very angry at the intrusion, but on second thought she agreed. The boy was the same. Perhaps Bassett might bring him to consciousness.

The gardener, a shortish fellow with a little brown moustache, and sharp little brown eyes, tiptoed into the room, touched his imaginary cap to Paul's mother, and stole to the bedside, staring with glittering, smallish eyes, at the tossing, dying child.

"Master Paul!" he whispered. "Master Paul! Malabar came in first all right, a clean win. I did as you told me. You've made over seventy thousand pounds, you have; you've got over eighty thousand. Malabar came in all right, Master Paul."

"Malabar! Malabar! Did I say Malabar, mother? Did I say Malabar? Do you think I'm lucky, mother? I knew Malabar, didn't I? Over eighty thousand pounds! I call that lucky, don't you, mother? Over eighty thousand pounds! I knew, didn't I know I knew? Malabar came in all right. If I ride my horse till I'm sure, then I tell you, Bassett, you can go as high as you like. Did you go for all you were worth, Bassett?"

"I went a thousand on it, Master Paul."

"I never told you, mother, that if I can ride my horse, and *get there*, then I'm absolutely sure—oh, absolutely! Mother, did I ever tell you? I *am* lucky!"

"No, you never did," said the mother.

But the boy died in the night.

And even as he lay dead, his mother heard her brother's voice saying to her: "My God, Hester, you're eighty-odd thousand to the good, and a poor devil of son to the bad. But, poor devil, poor devil, he's best gone out of a life where he rides his rocking-horse to find a winner."

[1933]

QUESTIONS

D. H. LAWRENCE, *The Rocking-Horse Winner*

1. What makes the mother in the family so unhappy? What does she want in life that she does not have? Is it money?

2. What kind of temperament does Paul have as a child? What does he want to do for his mother? Why does he want so much to please her?

3. What part does the uncle have in the tragedy? What part does the father have? Why is the mother unaware of her son's sacrifice for her?

4. What does money represent in this story? Does the money make a difference in the family? Does money ever make a difference?

5. What effect does magic have on the people who use it? Why is magic always liable to change the user? Why do characters in fantasy stories always have to be very careful with their magical abilities?

6. What is it about a horse race that differs from other kinds of gambling? What noble nature of the horse seems to rub off on those who get near it? What deception is there in horse racing?

7. Read some of the dialogue in this story aloud. What kinds of interactions takes place among the characters? Do the people in the story actually talk to one another? What is missing?

8. What sort of child is Paul? Why do his goodness and innocence work against him? What actions does he take that lead to his death?

9. Early on Paul confuses luck and lucre. Why is money referred to as filthy? Is the meaning literal as well as symbolic? Why does the money eventually kill Paul?

10. Write about a fantasy story that contains magic that you find fascinating. How does the magic in the story work? Is it the same as the magic in this story? What are the rules for the magician? What does magic symbolize?

11. Mothers often control children's views of themselves, not necessarily intentionally. What effect does the mother in the story have on her son? Lawrence's own mother was both unhappy in her marriage and very attached to her son. How does the emotion in the story reflect that double bind for a child?

William Faulkner

[1897–1962]

Born in New Albany, Mississippi, WILLIAM CUTHBERT FALKNER *(The writer added the "u" to his name as a young man) moved with his family to Oxford, Mississippi in 1902, where his father worked as a livery stable owner, a hardware store owner, and finally as a business manager at the University of Mississippi. Although the presence of the university in this otherwise small, nondescript southern town likely influenced Faulkner's decision to become a writer, it is more probable that he looked to his paternal grandfather, William Clark Falkner (1825–1889), as a source of inspiration. A writer and a figure out of antebellum mythology, the Old Colonel, as the family referred to him, lead a life of almost cartoonish violence and bravado, stories of which filled the young Faulkner with wonder. With some modifications, this larger-than-life figure made his way into Faulkner's fiction as Colonel John Sartoris, a recurrent character in Faulkner's fiction.*

Faulkner's relationships with both his parents also enhanced and complicated his literary aspirations. While his mother was devoted to reading and culture, his father was immersed in the masculine world of horses, whisky, and physical violence. These parental influences are evident in a body of fiction that is both dizzyingly intellectual and insistently physical. Though he demonstrated early precociousness at school, he was drifting away by the eighth grade, and he never managed to take a degree at the local university. In 1918 he volunteered for and was rejected by the Army Air Corps because of his diminutive size. Not to be cheated out of the opportunity to relive the martial grandeur of his grandfather, he traveled to Toronto and enlisted in the RAF in July 1918, only to have World War I end before he could complete his training. He returned to Oxford in December of that year sporting an RAF captain's uniform, a phony limp, and a story about being shot down over enemy lines in France. Though no one in Oxford much believed him, he carried an obsession with World War I that stayed with him from his first novel, Soldier's Pay *(1926), through the late work* A Fable *(1954), both of which focus on the hollowness and hypocrisy that sometimes overshadow the heroics of war.*

Faulkner's literary career can be considered in terms of three phases. Throughout the early 1920s, Faulkner wrote a series of unsuccessful works—a collection of poetry titled the The Marble Faun *(1924) and the early novels* Soldier's Pay, Mosquitoes *(1927), and* Flags in the Dust *(published in 1929 as* Sartoris*). This period is also marked by transience and uncertainty, as Faulkner moved to New York, New Orleans, and back to Oxford. He studied briefly at the University of Mississippi, served for a time as the university's postmaster, and* *worked at odd jobs about the town of Oxford. Despite its flaws,* Flags in the Dust *represents Faulkner's first attempt to use the history of his family and his region as a source for his art. The novel therefore heralds the second, mature phase of his career. Faulkner gained critical acclaim with* The Sound and the Fury *(1929), the story of a disintegrating Southern family told through the modernist techniques of stream-of-consciousness narration and multiple, fragmented points of view. In 1930, the noteworthy Faulkner then became somewhat notorious with the publication of* Sanctuary, *a lurid potboiler about bootlegging, prostitution, and rape. In the same year, Faulkner completed yet another important novel,* As I Lay Dying. *Here again presented through the distracted comments of several narrators (including a purported lunatic, a traumatized young boy, and a delusional religious zealot), this harrowing tale treats a poor rural family who struggle to carry their dead mother to a cemetery many miles away. In this story, the language of the rural South becomes a kind of mythological poetry. This burst of creative activity launched the major period of Faulkner's career, eleven or twelve years that saw the publication of* Light in August *(1932),* Absalom, Absalom! *(1935),* The Unvanquished *(1938),* The Wild Palms *(1939), and* Go Down, Moses *(1942). During this time Faulkner also wrote short stories and worked in Hollywood as a screenwriter, an occupation he loathed. His near destitution would only begin to abate in 1948, when he was paid $50,000 by MGM for the film rights to his 1948 novel* Intruder in the Dust *and when, in 1949, he received the Nobel Prize for Literature. The third and final phase of Faulkner's career is characterized by a mellowing of his artistic vision, as is evident in his final novel,* The Rievers *(1962). In his later years, Faulkner assumed the role of "elder man of letters." He traveled to Japan as a kind of literary ambassador, served as a writer-in-residence at the University of Virginia, and addressed cadets at West Point, where his son-in-law had gone to school. He also weighed in on the racial controversies of the time, but his comments seemed to anger equally those on all sides of the debate. As he aged, Faulkner's health suffered from his heavy drinking and from several falls sustained while riding horses. It is suspected that one of these falls landed him in the hospital on July 5, 1962, where he died of a heart attack the next day.*

Critical reception of Faulkner's work ranged from prudish dismissal to adulation, but today he is widely regarded as the best American writer of the twentieth century. During the eighties and nineties many critics began to question this status, given the apparent racism and misogyny that color Faulkner's canon. This debate is ongoing, but what remains unimpeachable, besides the explosive beauty of his experiments with language and style, and with the form of the novel itself, is his quiet confidence in the perseverance of the human soul.

—David L. G. Arnold, *University of Wisconsin, Stevens Point*

A Rose for Emily

WILLIAM FAULKNER

I

WHEN MISS EMILY GRIERSON DIED, our whole town went to her funeral: the men through a sort of respectful affection for a fallen monument, the women mostly out of curiosity to see the inside of her house, which no one save an old manservant—a combined gardener and cook—had seen in at least ten years.

It was a big, squarish frame house that had once been white, decorated with cupolas and spires and scrolled balconies in the heavily lightsome style of the seventies, set on what had once been our most select street. But garages and cotton gins had encroached and obliterated even the august names of that neighborhood; only Miss Emily's house was left, lifting its stubborn and coquettish decay above the cotton wagons and the gasoline pumps—an eyesore among eyesores. And now Miss Emily had gone to join the representatives of those august names where they lay in the cedar-bemused cemetery among the ranked and anonymous graves of Union and Confederate soldiers who fell at the battle of Jefferson.

Alive, Miss Emily had been a tradition, a duty, and a care; a sort of hereditary obligation upon the town, dating from that day in 1894 when Colonel Sartoris, the mayor—he who fathered the edict that no Negro woman should appear on the streets without an apron—remitted her taxes, the dispensation dating from the death of her father on into perpetuity. Not that Miss Emily would have accepted charity. Colonel Sartoris invented an involved tale to the effect that Miss Emily's father had loaned money to the town, which the town, as a matter of business, preferred this way of repaying. Only a man of Colonel Sartoris' generation and thought could have invented it, and only a woman could have believed it.

When the next generation, with its more modern ideas, became mayors and aldermen, this arrangement created some little dissatisfaction. On the first of the year they mailed her a tax notice. February came, and there was no

Reprinted from *The Collected Short Stories of William Faulkner*, by permission of Lee Caplin.

reply. They wrote her a formal letter, asking her to call at the sheriff's office at her convenience. A week later the mayor wrote her himself, offering to call or to send his car for her, and received in reply a note on paper of an archaic shape, in a thin, flowing calligraphy in faded ink, to the effect that she no longer went out at all. The tax notice was also enclosed, without comment.

They called a special meeting of the Board of Aldermen. A deputation waited upon her, knocked at the door through which no visitor had passed since she ceased giving china-painting lessons eight or ten years earlier. They were admitted by the old Negro into a dim hall from which a staircase mounted into still more shadow. It smelled of dust and disuse—a close, dank smell. The Negro led them into the parlor. It was furnished in heavy, leather-covered furniture. When the Negro opened the blinds of one window, a faint dust rose sluggishly about their thighs, spinning with slow motes in the single sun-ray. On a tarnished gilt easel before the fireplace stood a crayon portrait of Miss Emily's father.

They rose when she entered—a small, fat woman in black, with a thin gold chain descending to her waist and vanishing into her belt, leaning on an ebony cane with a tarnished gold head. Her skeleton was small and spare; perhaps that was why what would have been merely plumpness in another was obesity in her. She looked bloated, like a body long submerged in motionless water, and of that pallid hue. Her eyes, lost in the fatty ridges of her face, looked like two small pieces of coal pressed into a lump of dough as they moved from one face to another while the visitors stated their errand.

She did not ask them to sit. She just stood in the door and listened quietly until the spokesman came to a stumbling halt. Then they could hear the invisible watch ticking at the end of the gold chain.

Her voice was dry and cold. "I have no taxes in Jefferson. Colonel Sartoris explained it to me. Perhaps one of you can gain access to the city records and satisfy yourselves."

"But we have. We are the city authorities, Miss Emily. Didn't you get a notice from the sheriff, signed by him?"

"I received a paper, yes," Miss Emily said. "Perhaps he considers himself the sheriff. . . . I have no taxes in Jefferson."

"But there is nothing on the books to show that, you see. We must go by the—"

"See Colonel Sartoris. I have no taxes in Jefferson."

"But, Miss Emily—"

"See Colonel Sartoris." (Colonel Sartoris had been dead almost ten years.) "I have no taxes in Jefferson. Tobe!" The Negro appeared. "Show these gentlemen out."

II

So she vanquished them, horse and foot, just as she had vanquished their fathers thirty years before about the smell. That was two years after her father's death and a short time after her sweetheart—the one we believed would marry her—had deserted her. After her father's death she went out very little; after her sweetheart went away, people hardly saw her at all. A few of the ladies had the temerity to call, but were not received, and the only sign of life about the place was the Negro man—a young man then—going in and out with a market basket.

"Just as if a man—any man—could keep a kitchen properly," the ladies said, so they were not surprised when the smell developed. It was another link between the gross, teeming world and the high and mighty Griersons.

A neighbor, a woman, complained to the mayor, Judge Stevens, eighty years old.

"But what will you have me do about it, madam?" he said.

"Why, send her word to stop it," the woman said. "Isn't there a law?"

"I'm sure that won't be necessary," Judge Stevens said. "It's probably just a snake or a rat that nigger of hers killed in the yard. I'll speak to him about it."

The next day he received two more complaints, one from a man who came in diffident deprecation. "We really must do something about it, Judge. I'd be the last one in the world to bother Miss Emily, but we've got to do something." That night the Board of Aldermen met—three graybeards and one younger man, a member of the rising generation.

"It's simple enough," he said. "Send her word to have her place cleaned up. Give her a certain time to do it in, and if she don't . . ."

"Dammit, sir," Judge Stevens said, "will you accuse a lady to her face of smelling bad?"

So the next night, after midnight, four men crossed Miss Emily's lawn and slunk about the house like burglars, sniffing along the base of the brickwork and at the cellar openings while one of them performed a regular sowing motion with his hand out of a sack slung from his shoulder. They broke open the cellar door and sprinkled lime there, and in all the outbuildings. As they recrossed the lawn, a window that had been dark was lighted and Miss Emily sat in it, the light behind her, and her upright torso motionless as that of an idol. They crept quietly across the lawn and into the shadow of the locusts that lined the street. After a week or two the smell went away.

That was when people had begun to feel sorry for her. People in our town remembering how old lady Wyatt, her great-aunt, had gone completely crazy at last, believed that the Griersons held themselves a little too high for what they really were. None of the young men were quite good enough for Miss Emily and such. We had long thought of them as a tableau: Miss Emily a slender figure in white in the background, her father a spraddled silhouette in the foreground, his back to her and clutching a horsewhip, the two of them framed by the backflung front door. So when she got to be thirty and was still single, we were not pleased exactly, but vindicated; even with insanity in the family she wouldn't have turned down all of her chances if they had really materialized.

When her father died, it got about that the house was all that was left to her; and in a way, people were glad. At last they could pity Miss Emily. Being left alone, and a pauper, she had become humanized. Now she too would know the old thrill and the old despair of a penny more or less.

The day after his death all the ladies prepared to call at the house and offer condolence and aid, as is our custom. Miss Emily met them at the door, dressed as usual and with no trace of grief on her face. She told them that her father was not dead. She did that for three days, with the ministers calling on her, and the doctors trying to persuade her to let them dispose of the body. Just as they were about to resort to law and force, she broke down, and they buried her father quickly.

We did not say she was crazy then. We believed she had to do that. We remembered all the young men her father had driven away, and we knew that with nothing left, she would have to cling to that which had robbed her, as people will.

III

She was sick for a long time. When we saw her again, her hair was cut short, making her look like a girl, with a vague resemblance to those angels in colored church windows—sort of tragic and serene.

The town had just let the contracts for paving the sidewalks, and in the summer after her father's death they began to work. The construction company came with niggers and mules and machinery, and a foreman named Homer Barron, a Yankee—a big, dark, ready man, with a big voice and eyes lighter than his face. The little boys would follow in groups to hear him cuss the niggers, and the niggers singing in time to the rise and fall of picks. Pretty soon he knew everybody in town. Whenever you heard a lot of laughing anywhere about the square, Homer Barron would be in the center of the group. Presently we began to see him and Miss Emily on Sunday afternoons driving in the yellow-wheeled buggy and the matched team of bays from the livery stable.

At first we were glad that Miss Emily would have an interest, because the ladies all said, "Of course a Grierson would not think seriously of a Northerner, a day laborer." But there were still others, older people, who said that even grief could not cause a real lady to forget *noblesse oblige*—without calling it *noblesse oblige*. They just said, "Poor Emily. Her kinsfolk should come to her." She had some kin in Alabama; but years ago her father had fallen out with them over the estate of old lady Wyatt, the crazy woman, and there was no communication between the two families. They had not even been represented at the funeral.

And as soon as the old people said, "Poor Emily," the whispering began. "Do you suppose it's really so?" they said to one another. "Of course it is. What else could . . ." This behind their hands; rustling of craned silk and satin behind jalousies closed upon the sun of Sunday afternoon as the thin, swift clop-clop-clop of the matched team passed: "Poor Emily."

She carried her head high enough—even when we believed that she was fallen. It was as if she demanded more than ever the recognition of her dignity as the last Grierson; as if it had wanted that touch of earthliness to reaffirm her imperviousness. Like when she bought the rat poison, the arsenic. That was over a year after they had begun to say "Poor Emily," and while the two female cousins were visiting her.

"I want some poison," she said to the druggist. She was over thirty then, still a slight woman, though thinner than usual, with cold, haughty black eyes in a face the flesh of which was strained across the temples and about the eye-sockets as you imagine a lighthouse-keeper's face ought to look. "I want some poison," she said.

"Yes, Miss Emily. What kind? For rats and such? I'd recom—"

"I want the best you have. I don't care what kind."

The druggist named several. "They'll kill anything up to an elephant. But what you want is—"

"Arsenic," Miss Emily said. "Is that a good one?"

"Is . . . arsenic? Yes ma'am. But what you want—"

"I want arsenic."

The druggist looked down at her. She looked back at him, erect, her face like a strained flag. "Why, of course," the druggist said. "If that's what you want. But the law requires you to tell what you are going to use it for."

Miss Emily just stared at him, her head tilted back in order to look him eye for eye, until he looked away and went and got the arsenic and wrapped it up. The Negro delivery boy brought her the package; the druggist didn't come back. When she opened the package at home there was written on the box, under the skull and bones: "For rats."

IV

So the next day we all said, "She will kill herself"; and we said it would be the best thing. When she had first begun to be seen with Homer Barron, we had said, "She will marry him." Then we said, "She will persuade him yet," because Homer himself had remarked—he liked men, and it was known that he drank with the younger men in the Elk's Club—that he was not a marrying man. Later we said, "Poor Emily," behind the jalousies as they passed on Sunday afternoon in the glittering buggy, Miss Emily with her head high and Homer Barron with his hat cocked and a cigar in his teeth, reins and whip in a yellow glove.

Then some of the ladies began to say that it was a disgrace to the town and a bad example to the young people. The men did not want to interfere, but at last the ladies forced the Baptist minister—Miss Emily's people were Episcopal—to call upon her. He would never divulge what happened during that interview, but he refused to go back again. The next Sunday they again drove about the streets and the following day the minister's wife wrote to Miss Emily's relations in Alabama.

So she had blood-kin under her roof again and we sat back to watch developments. At first nothing happened. Then we were sure that they had to be married. We learned that Miss Emily had been to the jeweler's and ordered a man's toilet set in silver, with the letters H.B. on each piece. Two days later we learned that she had bought a complete outfit of men's clothing, including a nightshirt, and we said "They are married." We were really glad. We were glad because the two female cousins were even more Grierson than Miss Emily had ever been.

So we were surprised when Homer Barron—the streets had been finished some time since—was gone. We were a little disappointed that there was not a public blowing-off, but we believed that he had gone on to prepare for Miss Emily's coming, or to give a chance to get rid of the cousins. (By that time it was a cabal, and we were all Miss Emily's allies to help circumvent the cousins.) Sure enough, after another week they departed. And, as we had expected all along, within three days Homer Barron was back in town. A neighbor saw the Negro man admit him at the kitchen door at dusk one evening.

And that was the last we saw of Homer Barron. And of Miss Emily for some time. The Negro man went in and out with the market basket, but the front door remained closed. Now and then we would see her at a window for a moment, as the men did that night when they sprinkled the lime, but for almost six months she did not appear on the streets. Then we knew that this was to be expected too; as if that quality of her father which had thwarted her woman's life so many times had been too virulent and too furious to die.

When we next saw Miss Emily, she had grown fat and her hair was turning gray. During the next few years it grew grayer and grayer until it attained an even pepper-and-salt iron-gray, when it ceased turning. Up to the day of her death at seventy-four it was still that vigorous iron-gray, like the hair of an active man.

From that time on her front door remained closed, save for a period of six or seven years, when she was about forty, during which she gave lessons in china-painting. She fitted up a studio in one of the downstairs rooms, where the daughters and granddaughters of Colonel Sartoris' contemporaries were sent to her with the same regularity and in the same spirit that they were sent on Sundays with a twenty-five cent piece for the collection plate. Meanwhile her taxes had been remitted.

Then the newer generation became the backbone and the spirit of the town, and the painting pupils grew up and fell away and did not send their children to her with boxes of color and tedious brushes and pictures cut from the ladies' magazines. The front door closed upon the last one and remained closed for good. When the town got free postal delivery Miss Emily alone refused to let them fasten the metal numbers above her door and attach a mailbox to it. She would not listen to them.

Daily, monthly, yearly we watched the Negro grow grayer and more stooped, going in and out with the market basket. Each December we sent her a tax notice, which would be returned by the post office a week later, unclaimed. Now and then we would see her in one of the downstairs windows—she had evidently shut up the top floor of the house—like the carven torso of an idol in a niche, looking or not looking at us, we could never tell which. Thus she passed from generation to generation—dear, inescapable, impervious, tranquil, and perverse.

And so she died. Fell ill in the house filled with dust and shadows, with only a doddering Negro man to wait on her. We did not even know she was sick; we had long since given up trying to get any information from the Negro. He talked to no one, probably not even to her, for his voice had grown harsh and rusty, as if from disuse.

She died in one of the downstairs rooms, in a heavy walnut bed with a curtain, her gray head propped on a pillow yellow and moldy with age and lack of sunlight.

V

The Negro met the first of the ladies at the front door and let them in, with their hushed, sibilant voices and their quick, curious glances, and then he disappeared. He walked right through the house and out the back and was not seen again.

The two female cousins came at once. They held the funeral on the second day, with the town coming to look at Miss Emily beneath a mass of bought flowers, with the crayon face of her father musing profoundly above the bier and the ladies sibilant and macabre; and the very old men—some in their brushed Confederate uniforms—on the porch and the lawn, talking of Miss Emily as if she had been a contemporary of theirs, believing that they had danced with her and courted her perhaps, confusing time with its mathematical progression, as the old do, to whom all the past is not a diminishing road, but, instead, a huge meadow which no winter ever quite touches, divided from them now by the narrow bottleneck of the most recent decade of years.

Already we knew that there was one room in the region above the stairs which no one had seen in forty years, and which would have to be forced. They waited until Miss Emily was decently in the ground before they opened it.

The violence of breaking down the door seemed to fill this room with pervading dust. A thin, acrid pall as of the tomb seemed to lie everywhere upon this room decked and furnished as for a bridal: upon the valance curtains of faded rose color, upon the rose-shaded lights, upon the dressing table, upon the delicate array of crystal and the man's toilet things backed with tarnished silver, silver so tarnished that the monogram was obscured. Among them lay a collar and tie, as if they had just been removed, which, lifted, left upon the surface a pale crescent in the dust. Upon a chair hung the suit, carefully folded; beneath it the two mute shoes and the discarded socks.

The man himself lay in the bed.

For a long while we just stood there, looking down at the profound and fleshless grin. The body had aparently once lain in the attitude of an embrace, but now the long sleep that outlasts love, that conquers even the grimace of love, had cuckolded him. What was left of him, rotted beneath what was left of the nightshirt, had become inextricable from the bed in which he lay; and upon him and upon the pillow beside him lay that even coating of the patient and biding dust.

Then we noticed that in the second pillow was the indentation of a head. One of us lifted something from it, and leaning forward, that faint and invisible dust dry and acrid in the nostrils, we saw a long strand of iron-gray hair.

[1930]

QUESTIONS

WILLIAM FAULKNER, *A Rose for Emily*

1. Describe your experience of reading "A Rose for Emily." What portions of the story do you find intriguing, surprising, or unsettling?

2. How does Faulkner use the tactic of suspense and surprise to captivate the reader?

3. Who narrates this story? Why is this figure's perspective important in the understanding we gain of Emily Grierson?

4. Describe Emily's relationship with her father. How is this important in our attempt to understand Emily's character?

5. How does the narrator describe Emily's house and neighborhood? How is this description important in our attempt to understand Emily's character?

6. Describe Homer Barron. How does his character and the relationship he develops with Emily help us understand Emily's character?

7. In what sense does the notion that Emily has been sleeping beside a corpse suggest a critique of the South on Faulkner's part?

8. Research and compose an interpretive essay about Faulkner's participation in the literary Gothic. What are the basic conventions of Gothic literature? What are some of its cultural, philosophical, and even political implications? How does Faulkner interpret Gothic traditions in "A Rose for Emily"?

Shirley Jackson
[1919–1965]

At once a doting mother who wrote humorous accounts of her family life and a self-described witch who penned incisive studies of psychologic aberration and unsettling tales of the supernatural, SHIRLEY JACKSON *explored the unstable boundary between domesticity and horror. Considered one of the finest American fiction writers of the 1950s and 1960s, Jackson is now best known for the widely anthologized short story "The Lottery" (1948).*

Jackson was born in 1919 in San Francisco, the first child of an affluent and conservative family. During childhood and adolescence and well into adulthood, this unruly and overweight daughter struggled against her mother Geraldine's firmly held standards of propriety and femininity. As she resisted the conventions of class and gender, Jackson developed her gift of seeing beneath the decorous surface of middle-class life into its vicious core. In the sunny and seemingly placid northern California suburb of Burlingame, where she attended high school and began writing poetry and short stories, Jackson discerned her neighbors' intolerance and cruelty—traits that later characterized the suburbanites of her fiction.

In 1933 Jackson's family moved to Rochester, New York. After attending the University of Rochester from 1934 to 1936, Jackson withdrew from school and spent a year at home, writing a thousand words a day. In 1937 she entered Syracuse University, where she edited the campus humor magazine, won second prize in a poetry contest, and founded the literary magazine Spectre. She married the magazine's managing editor, Stanley Edgar Hyman, immediately after her graduation in 1940. The couple moved to New York City, where Jackson held a variety of unsatisfying jobs while continuing to write. In 1941 her experience selling books at Macy's formed the basis for "My Life with R. H. Macy," published in the New Republic. This success was followed by the birth of her first child and the publication of many stories in the New Yorker. Her reputation as a writer of short fiction grew, and in 1944 "Come Dance with Me in Ireland" was the first of her four stories chosen for Best American Short Stories.

Jackson's family continued to grow, and her body of writing continued to expand after she moved to North Bennington, Vermont. She had three more children and published short stories, novels, family chronicles, a one-act play, a children's book, and a nonfictional account of witchcraft in Salem. Her works were made into plays, films, and television shows. "The Lottery" appeared as a short play, a television drama, a radio show, an opera, and a ballet. The family chronicles Life Among the Savages (1953) and Raising Demons (1957) were best-sellers, and Jackson's popular success was matched by critical acclaim for her short fiction and novels alike. These latter include The Road Through the Wall (1948), *a look at the dark side of suburban life inspired by Jackson's years in Burlingame;* Hangsaman *(1951) and* The Bird's Nest *(1954), two penetrating depictions of mental illness; and* The Sundial *(1958), a Gothic fantasy about the end of the world. Jackson's last two novels,* The Haunting of Hill House *(1959) and* We Have Always Lived in the Castle *(1962), are her best. At once chilling and tender, these haunted-house stories transcend their genre, portraying the often-strained relationship between mother and daughter with consummate sympathy and skill. Three years after* We Have Always Lived in the Castle *appeared on the bestseller list and was named one of the year's best novels by* Time *magazine, Shirley Jackson died of heart failure on August 8, 1965.*

—Jamil Musstafa, *Lewis University*

The Lottery

SHIRLEY JACKSON

THE MORNING OF JUNE 27TH was clear and sunny, with the fresh warmth of a full-summer day; the flowers were blossoming profusely and the grass was richly green. The people of the village began to gather in the square, between the post office and the bank, around ten o'clock; in some towns there were so many people that the lottery took two days and had to be started on June 26th, but in this village, where there were only about three hundred people, the whole lottery took less than two hours, so it could begin at ten o'clock in the morning and still be through in time to allow the villagers to get home for noon dinner.

The children assembled first, of course. School was recently over for the summer, and the feeling of liberty sat uneasily on most of them; they tended to gather together quietly for a while before they broke into boisterous play, and their talk was still of the classroom and the teacher, of books and reprimands. Bobby Martin had already stuffed his pockets full of stones, and the other boys soon followed his example, selecting the smoothest and roundest stones; Bobby and Harry Jones and Dickie Delacroix—the villagers pronounced this name "Dellacroy"—eventually made a great pile of stones in one corner of the square and guarded it against the raids of the other boys. The girls stood aside, talking among themselves, looking over their shoulders at the boys, and the very small children rolled in the dust or clung to the hands of their older brothers or sisters.

Soon the men began to gather, surveying their own children, speaking of planting and rain, tractors and taxes. They stood together, away from the pile of stones in the corner, and their jokes were quiet and they smiled rather than laughed. The women, wearing faded house dresses and sweaters, came shortly after their menfolk. They greeted one another and exchanged bits of gossip as they went to join their husbands. Soon the women, standing by their husbands, began to call to their children, and the children came reluctantly, having to be called four or five times. Bobby Martin ducked under his mother's grasping hand and ran, laughing, back to the pile of stones. His father spoke up sharply, and Bobby came quickly and took his place between his father and his oldest brother.

The lottery was conducted—as were the square dances, the teenage club, the Halloween program—by Mr. Summers, who had time and energy to devote to civic activities. He was a round-faced, jovial man and he ran the coal business, and people were sorry for him, because he had no children and his wife was a scold. When he arrived in the square, carrying the black wooden box, there was a murmur of conversation among the villagers, and he waved and called, "Little late today, folks." The postmaster, Mr. Graves, followed him, carrying a three-legged stool, and the stool was put in the center of the square and Mr. Summers set the black box down on it. The villagers kept their distance, leaving a space between themselves and the stool, and when Mr. Summers said, "Some of you fellows want to give me a hand?" there was a hesitation before two men, Mr. Martin and his oldest son, Baxter, came forward to hold the box steady on the stool while Mr. Summers stirred up the papers inside it.

The original paraphernalia for the lottery had been lost long ago, and the black box now resting on the stool had been put into use even before Old Man Warner, the oldest man in town, was born. Mr. Summers spoke frequently to the villagers about making a new box, but no one liked to upset even as much tradition as was represented by the black box. There was a story that the present box had been made with some pieces of the box that had preceded it, the one that had been constructed when the first people settled down to make a village here. Every year, after the lottery, Mr. Summers began talking again about a new box, but every year the subject was allowed to fade off without anything's being done. The black box grew shabbier each year; by now it was no longer completely black but splintered badly along one side to show the original wood color, and in some places faded or stained.

Mr. Martin and his oldest son, Baxter, held the black box securely on the stool until Mr. Summers had stirred the papers thoroughly with his hand. Because so much of the ritual had been forgotten or discarded, Mr. Summers had been successful in having slips of paper substituted for the chips of wood that had been used for generations. Chips of wood, Mr. Summers had argued, had been all very well when the village was tiny, but now that the population was more than three hundred and likely to keep on growing, it was necessary to use something that would fit more easily into the black box. The night before the lottery, Mr. Summers and Mr. Graves made up the slips of paper and put them in the box, and it was then taken to the safe of Mr. Summers' coal company and locked up until Mr. Summers was ready to take it to the square next morning. The rest of the year, the box was put away, sometimes one place, sometimes another; it had spent one year in Mr. Graves's barn and another year underfoot in the post office, and sometimes it was set on a shelf in the Martin grocery and left there.

There was a great deal of fussing to be done before Mr. Summers declared the lottery open. There were the lists to make up—of heads of families, heads of households in each family, members of each household in each family. There was the proper swearing-in of Mr. Summers by the postmaster, as the official of the lottery; at one time, some people remembered, there had been a recital of some sort, performed by the official of the lottery, a perfunctory, tuneless chant that had been rattled off duly each year; some people believed that the official of the lottery used to stand just so when he said or sang it, others believed that he was supposed to walk among the people, but years and years ago this part of the ritual had been allowed to lapse. There had been, also, a ritual salute, which the official of the lottery had had to use in addressing each person who came up to draw from the box, but this also had changed with time, until now it was felt necessary only for the official to speak to each person approaching. Mr. Summers was very good at all this; in his clean white shirt and blue jeans, with one hand resting carelessly on the black box, he seemed very proper and important as he talked interminably to Mr. Graves and the Martins.

Just as Mr. Summers finally left off talking and turned to the assembled villagers, Mrs. Hutchinson came hurriedly along the path to the square, her sweater thrown over her shoulders, and slid into place in the back of the crowd. "Clean forgot what day it was," she said to Mrs. Delacroix, who stood next to her, and they both laughed softly. "Thought my old man was out back stacking wood," Mrs. Hutchinson went on, "and then I looked out the window and the kids were gone, and then I remembered it was the twentyseventh and came a-running." She dried her hands on her apron, and Mrs. Delacroix said, "You're in time, though. They're still talking away up there."

Mrs. Hutchinson craned her neck to see through the crowd and found her husband and children standing near the front. She tapped Mrs. Delacroix on the arm as a farewell and began to make her way through the crowd. The people separated good-humoredly to let her through; two or three people said, in voices just loud enough to be heard across the crowd, "Here comes your Missus, Hutchinson," and "Bill, she made it after all." Mrs. Hutchinson reached her husband, and Mr. Summers, who had been waiting, said cheerfully, "Thought we were going to have to get on without you, Tessie." Mrs. Hutchinson said, grinning, "Wouldn't have me leave m'dishes in the sink, now, would you, Joe?" and soft laughter ran through the crowd as the people stirred back into position after Mrs. Hutchinson's arrival.

"Well, now," Mr. Summers said soberly, "guess we better get started, get this over with, so's we can go back to work. Anybody ain't here?"

"Dunbar," several people said. "Dunbar, Dunbar."

Mr. Summers consulted his list. "Clyde Dunbar," he said. "That's right. He's broke his leg, hasn't he? Who's drawing for him?"

"Me, I guess," a woman said, and Mr. Summers turned to look at her. "Wife draws for her husband," Mr. Summers said. "Don't you have a grown boy to do it for you, Janey?" Although Mr. Summers and everyone else in the village knew the answer perfectly well, it was the business of the official of the lottery to ask such questions formally. Mr. Summers waited with an expression of polite interest while Mrs. Dunbar answered.

"Horace's not but sixteen yet," Mrs. Dunbar said regretfully. "Guess I gotta fill in for the old man this year."

"Right," Mr. Summers said. He made a note on the list he was holding. Then he asked, "Watson boy drawing this year?"

A tall boy in the crowd raised his hand. "Here," he said. "I'm drawing for m'mother and me." He blinked his eyes nervously and ducked his head as several voices in the crowd said things like "Good fellow, Jack," and "Glad to see your mother's got a man to do it."

"Well," Mr. Summers said, "guess that's everyone. Old Man Warner make it?"

"Here," a voice said, and Mr. Summers nodded.

A sudden hush fell on the crowd as Mr. Summers cleared his throat and looked at the list. "All ready?" he called. "Now, I'll read the names—heads of families first—and the men come up and take a paper out of the box. Keep the paper folded in your hand without looking at it until everyone has had a turn. Everything clear?"

The people had done it so many times that they only half listened to the directions; most of them were quiet, wetting their lips, not looking around. Then Mr. Summers raised one hand high and said, "Adams." A man disengaged himself from the crowd and came forward. "Hi, Steve," Mr. Summers said, and Mr. Adams said, "Hi, Joe." They grinned at one another humorlessly and nervously. Then Mr. Adams reached into the black box and took out a folded paper. He held it firmly by one corner as he turned and went hastily back to his place in the crowd, where he stood a little apart from his family, not looking down at his hand.

"Allen," Mr. Summers said. "Anderson . . . Bentham."

"Seems like there's no time at all between lotteries any more," Mrs. Delacroix said to Mrs. Graves in the back row. "Seems like we got through with the last one only last week."

"Time sure goes fast," Mrs. Graves said.

"Clark . . . Delacroix."

"There goes my old man," Mrs. Delacroix said. She held her breath while her husband went forward.

"Dunbar," Mr. Summers said, and Mrs. Dunbar went steadily to the box while one of the women said, "Go on, Janey," and another said, "There she goes."

"We're next," Mrs. Graves said. She watched while Mr. Graves came around from the side of the box, greeted Mr. Summers gravely, and selected a slip of paper from the box. By now, all through the crowd there were men holding the small folded papers in their large hands, turning them over and over nervously. Mrs. Dunbar and her two sons stood together, Mrs. Dunbar holding the slip of paper.

"Harburt . . . Hutchinson."

"Get up there, Bill," Mrs. Hutchinson said, and the people near her laughed.

"Jones."

"They do say," Mr. Adams said to Old Man Warner, who stood next to him, "that over in the north village they're talking of giving up the lottery."

Old Man Warner snorted. "Pack of crazy fools," he said. "Listening to the young folks, nothing's good enough for *them*. Next thing you know, they'll be wanting to go back to living in caves, nobody work any more, live *that* way for a while. Used to be a saying about 'Lottery in June, corn be heavy soon.' First thing you know, we'd all be eating stewed chickweed and acorns. There's *always* been a lottery," he added petulantly. "Bad enough to see young Joe Summers up there joking with everybody."

"Some places have already quit lotteries," Mrs. Adams said.

"Nothing but trouble in *that*," Old Man Warner said stoutly. "Pack of young fools."

"Martin." And Bobby Martin watched his father go forward. "Overdyke . . . Percy."

"I wish they'd hurry," Mrs. Dunbar said to her older son. "I wish they'd hurry."

"They're almost through," her son said.

"You get ready to run tell Dad," Mrs. Dunbar said.

Mr. Summers called his own name and then stepped forward precisely and selected a slip from the box. Then he called, "Warner."

"Seventy-seventh year I been in the lottery," Old Man Warner said as he went through the crowd. "Seventy-seventh time."

"Watson." The tall boy came awkwardly through the crowd. Someone said, "Don't be nervous, Jack," and Mr. Summers said, "Take your time, son."

"Zanini."

After that, there was a long pause, a breathless pause, until Mr. Summers, holding his slip of paper in the air, said, "All right, fellows." For a minute, no one moved, and then all the slips of paper were opened. Suddenly, all the women began to speak at once, saying, "Who is it?" "Who's got it?" "Is it the Dunbars?" "Is it the Watsons?" Then the voices began to say, "It's Hutchinson. It's Bill," "Bill Hutchinson's got it."

"Go tell your father," Mrs. Dunbar said to her older son.

People began to look around to see the Hutchinsons. Bill Hutchinson was standing quiet, staring down at the paper in his hand. Suddenly, Tessie Hutchinson shouted to Mr. Summers, "You didn't give him time enough to take any paper he wanted. I saw you. It wasn't fair."

"Be a good sport, Tessie," Mrs. Delacroix called, and Mrs. Graves said, "All of us took the same chance."

"Shut up, Tessie," Bill Hutchinson said.

"Well, everyone," Mr. Summers said, "that was done pretty fast, and now we've got to be hurrying a little more to get done in time." He consulted his next list. "Bill," he said, "you draw for the Hutchinson family. You got any other households in the Hutchinsons?"

"There's Don and Eva," Mrs. Hutchinson yelled. "Make them take their chance!"

"Daughters draw with their husbands' families, Tessie," Mr. Summers said gently. "You know that as well as anyone else."

"It wasn't *fair*," Tessie said.

"I guess not, Joe," Bill Hutchinson said regretfully. "My daughter draws with her husband's family, that's only fair. And I've got no other family except the kids."

"Then, as far as drawing for families is concerned, it's you." Mr. Summers said in explanation, "and as far as drawing for households is concerned, that's you, too. Right?"

"Right," Bill Hutchinson said.

"How many kids, Bill?" Mr. Summers asked formally.

"Three," Bill Hutchinson said. "There's Bill, Jr., and Nancy, and little Dave. And Tessie and me."

"All right, then," Mr. Summers said. "Harry, you got their tickets back?"

Mr. Graves nodded and held up the slips of paper. "Put them in the box, then," Mr. Summers directed. "Take Bill's and put it in."

"I think we ought to start over," Mrs. Hutchinson said, as quietly as she could. "I tell you it wasn't *fair*. You didn't give him time enough to choose. *Every*body saw that."

Mr. Graves had selected the five slips and put them in the box, and he dropped all the papers but those onto the ground, where the breeze caught them and lifted them off.

"Listen, everybody," Mrs. Hutchinson was saying to the people around her.

"Ready, Bill?" Mr. Summers asked, and Bill Hutchinson, with one quick glance around at his wife and children, nodded.

"Remember," Mr. Summers said, "take the slips and keep them folded until each person has taken one. Harry, you help little Dave." Mr. Graves took the hand of the little boy, who came willingly with him up to the box. "Take a paper out of the box, Davy," Mr. Summers said. Davy put his hand into the box and laughed. "Take just *one* paper," Mr. Summers said. "Harry, you hold it for him." Mr. Graves took the child's hand and removed the folded paper from the tight fist and held it while little Dave stood next to him and looked up at him wonderingly.

"Nancy next," Mr. Summers said. Nancy was twelve, and her school friends breathed heavily as she went forward, switching her skirt, and took a slip daintily from the box. "Bill, Jr.," Mr. Summers said, and Billy, his face red and his feet over-large, nearly knocked the box over as he got a paper out. "Tessie," Mr. Summers said. She hesitated for a minute, looking around defiantly, and then set her lips and went up to the box. She snatched a paper out and held it behind her.

"Bill," Mr. Summers said, and Bill Hutchinson reached into the box and felt around, bringing his hand out at last with the slip of paper in it.

The crowd was quiet. A girl whispered, "I hope it's not Nancy," and the sound of the whisper reached the edges of the crowd.

"It's not the way it used to be," Old Man Warner said clearly. "People ain't the way they used to be."

"All right," Mr. Summers said. "Open the papers. Harry, you open little Dave's."

Mr. Graves opened the slip of paper and there was a general sigh through the crowd as he held it up and everyone could see that it was blank. Nancy and Bill, Jr., opened theirs at the same time, and both beamed and laughed, turning around to the crowd and holding their slips of paper above their heads.

"Tessie," Mr. Summers said. There was a pause, and then Mr. Summers looked at Bill Hutchinson, and Bill unfolded his paper and showed it. It was blank.

"It's Tessie," Mr. Summers said, and his voice was hushed. "Show us her paper, Bill."

Bill Hutchinson went over to his wife and forced the slip of paper out of her hand. It had a black spot on it, the black spot Mr. Summers had made the night before with the heavy pencil in the coal-company office. Bill Hutchinson held it up, and there was a stir in the crowd.

"All right, folks," Mr. Summers said. "Let's finish quickly."

Although the villagers had forgotten the ritual and lost the original black box, they still remembered to use stones. The pile of stones the boys had made earlier was ready; there were stones on the ground with the blowing scraps of paper that had come out of the box. Mrs. Delacroix selected a stone so large she had to pick it up with both hands and turned, to Mrs. Dunbar. "Come on," she said. "Hurry up."

Mrs. Dunbar had small stones in both hands, and she said, gasping for breath, "I can't run at all. You'll have to go ahead and I'll catch up with you."

The children had stones already, and someone gave little Davy Hutchinson a few pebbles.

Tessie Hutchinson was in the center of a cleared space by now, and she held her hands out desperately as the villagers moved in on her. "It isn't fair," she said. A stone hit her on the side of the head.

Old Man Warner was saying, "Come on, come on, everyone." Steve Adams was in the front of the crowd of villagers, with Mrs. Graves beside him.

"It isn't fair, it isn't right," Mrs. Hutchinson screamed, and then they were upon her.

[1949]

QUESTIONS

SHIRLEY JACKSON, *The Lottery*

1. Where is the village located? How does the story's setting influence our response to its ending?

2. At what point do we suspect that the lottery is not what it appears to be? What is the significance of Old Man Warner's saying, "Lottery in June, corn be heavy soon"? What was the lottery's original function, and what is its current function?

3. How do characters' names reflect their personalities and roles?

4. How does irony function in the story?

5. What does the black box symbolize? What other symbols are important to the story?

6. What does the story suggest about tradition and change? about gender roles? about community?

7. Write an essay focused on Tessie Hutchinson as the story's protagonist. Identify her antagonist(s), and consider why she is late to the lottery.

8. Jackson tells the story from an omniscient point of view. Write an essay analyzing how this point of view contributes to the story's plot, especially its ending. Speculate about how the story might differ if it were told from another perspective.

Ray Bradbury

RAY DOUGLAS BRADBURY (1920–) *was born in Waukegan, Illinois, where he grew up and where he began his writing career. The Douglas in his name is for the great actor Douglas Fairbanks, but Bradbury created stories that others were to act rather than acting himself. He did become host of his own television show, a production that gave him an opportunity to talk about his early life in Illinois and its influence on his writing. Bradbury is a storywriter and novelist, a playwright, a screenwriter, and a poet. In order to evoke memories of his childhood and to create stories from those memories, he drew a map of his home town and marked off spots where interesting adventures happened in his childhood. These adventures became the materials for his later writing, and he continues to use this idea as he writes. Waukegan becomes "Greentown," Illinois, where adventures both good and frightening occur in Bradbury's fiction.*

In 1934, the Bradbury family moved to Los Angeles, California, where Bradbury later met many famous actors and writers, such as the great comedian, George Burns, who became the first to pay Bradbury for writing. The pay was for a joke written for Burns' comedy show, The Burns and Allan Show. *In 1947 Bradbury published his first collection of short stories,* Dark Carnival. *The Martian Chronicles in 1950 made Bradbury famous; in the novel he imagined humans colonizing Mars and gave readers a taste of Martians who were human in mind and spirit, rather than the "green men" of magazine science fiction. In 1953* Fahrenheit 451 *struck a darker note as it imagined a world where books were burned and ideas suppressed. This novel evoked the issues of the repression of writers and actors during an era when communists where suspected behind every door.*

Bradbury's stories evoke many kinds of fears and hopes that people the human imagination. In "There Will Come Soft Rains," he deals with the fear of nuclear war and its effects on humanity; in Something Wicked This Way Comes, *he deals with the fear of aging and of death. Bradbury's ideas are never simplistic or moralistic but always pushing the edges of human concerns and of human consciousness. He continues to write though he is well into his eighties. Bradbury has won the O. Henry Memorial Award, the Benjamin Franklin Award (1954), the Aviation-Space Writer's Association Award for Best Space Article in an American Magazine (1967), the World Fantasy Award for Lifetime Achievement. His work was included in the Best American Short Stories collections for 1946, 1948 and 1952. Bradbury's most unusual honor came when an Apollo astronaut named Dandelion Crater on the moon after Bradbury's novel,* Dandelion Wine.

There Will Come Soft Rains

RAY BRADBURY

In THE LIVING room the voice-clock sang, *Tick-tock, seven o'clock, time to get up, time to get up, seven o'clock!* as if it were afraid that nobody would. The morning house lay empty. The clock ticked on, repeating and repeating its sounds into the emptiness. *Seven-nine, breakfast time, seven-nine!*

In the kitchen the breakfast stove gave a hissing sigh and ejected from its warm interior eight pieces of perfectly browned toast, eight eggs sunnyside up, sixteen slices of bacon, two coffees, and two cool glasses of milk.

"Today is August 4, 2026," said a second voice from the kitchen ceiling, "in the city of Allendale, California." It repeated the date three times for memory's sake. "Today is Mr. Featherstone's birthday. Today is the anniversary of Tilita's marriage. Insurance is payable, as are the water, gas, and light bills."

Somewhere in the walls, relays clicked, memory tapes glided under electric eyes.

Eight-one, tick-tock, eight-one o'clock, off to school, off to work, run, run, eight-one! But no doors slammed, no carpets took the soft tread of rubber heels. It was raining outside. The weather box on the front door sang quietly: "Rain, rain, go away; rubbers, raincoats for today . . ." And the rain tapped on the empty house, echoing.

Outside, the garage chimed and lifted its door to reveal the waiting car. After a long wait the door swung down again.

At eight-thirty the eggs were shriveled and the toast was like stone. An aluminum wedge scraped them into the sink, where hot water whirled them down a metal throat which digested and flushed them away to the distant sea. The dirty dishes were dropped into a hot washer and emerged twinkling dry.

Nine-fifteen, sang the clock, *time to clean.*

Out of warrens in the wall, tiny robot mice darted. The rooms were acrawl with the small cleaning animals, all rubber and metal. They thudded against chairs, whirling their mustached runners, kneading the rug nap, sucking gently at hidden dust. Then, like mysterious invaders, they popped into their burrows. Their pink electric eyes faded. The house was clean.

Ten o'clock. The sun came out from behind the rain. The house stood alone in a city of rubble and ashes. This was the one house left standing. At night the ruined city gave off a radioactive glow which could be seen for miles.

Ten-fifteen. The garden sprinklers whirled up in golden founts, filling the soft morning air with scatterings of brightness. The water pelted windowpanes, running down the charred west side where the house had been burned evenly free of its white paint. The entire west face of the house was black, save for five places. Here the silhouette in paint of a man mowing a lawn. Here, as in a photograph, a woman bent to pick flowers. Still farther over, their images burned on wood in one titanic instant, a small boy, hands flung into the air; higher up, the image of a thrown ball, and opposite him a girl, hands raised to catch a ball which never came down.

The five spots of paint—the man, the woman, the children, the ball—remained. The rest was a thin charcoaled layer.

The gentle sprinkler rain filled the garden with falling light.

Until this day, how well the house had kept its peace. How carefully it had inquired, "Who goes there? What's the password?" and, getting no answer from lonely foxes and whining cats, it had shut up its windows and drawn shades in an old-maidenly preoccupation with self-protection which bordered on a mechanical paranoia.

It quivered at each sound, the house did. If a sparrow brushed a window, the shade shapped up. The bird, startled, flew off! No, not even a bird must touch the house!

The house was an altar with ten thousand attendants, big, small, servicing, attending, in choirs. But the gods had gone away, and the ritual of the religion continued senselessly, uselessly.

Twelve noon.

A dog whined, shivering, on the front porch.

The front door recognized the dog voice and opened. The dog, once huge and fleshy, but now gone to bone and covered with sores, moved in and through the house, tracking mud. Behind it whirred angry mice, angry at having to pick up mud, angry at inconvenience.

For not a leaf fragment blew under the door but what the wall panels flipped open and the copper scrap rats flashed swiftly out. The offending dust, hair, or paper, seized in miniature steel jaws, was raced back to the burrows. There, down tubes which fed into the cellar, it was dropped into the sighing vent of an incinerator which sat like evil Baal in a dark corner.

The dog ran upstairs, hysterically yelping to each door, at last realizing, as the house realized, that only silence was here.

It sniffed the air and scratched the kitchen door. Behind the door, the stove was making pancakes which filled the house with a rich baked odor and the scent of maple syrup.

The dog frothed at the mouth, lying at the door, sniffing, its eyes turned to fire. It ran wildly in circles, biting at its tail, spun in a frenzy, and died. It lay in the parlor for an hour.

Two o'clock, sang a voice.

Delicately sensing decay at last, the regiments of mice hummed out as softly as blown gray leaves in an electrical wind.

Two-fifteen.

The dog was gone.

In the cellar, the incinerator glowed suddenly and a whirl of sparks leaped up the chimney.

Two thirty-five.

Bridge tables sprouted from patio walls. Playing cards fluttered onto pads in a shower of pips. Martinis manifested on an oaken bench with egg-salad sandwiches. Music played.

But the tables were silent and the cards untouched.

At four o'clock the tables folded like great butterflies back through the paneled walls.

Four-thirty.

The nursery walls glowed.

Animals took shape: yellow giraffes, blue lions, pink antelopes, lilac panthers cavorting in crystal substance. The walls were glass. They looked out upon color and fantasy. Hidden films clocked through well-oiled sprockets, and the walls lived. The nursery floor was woven to resemble a crisp, cereal meadow. Over this ran aluminum roaches and iron crickets, and in the hot still air butterflies of delicate red tissue wavered among the sharp aroma of animal spoors! There was the sound like a great matted yellow hive of bees within a dark bellows, the lazy bumble of a purring lion. And there was the patter of okapi feet and the murmur of a fresh jungle rain, like other hoofs, falling upon the summer-starched grass. Now the walls dissolved into distances of parched weed, mile on mile, and warm endless sky. The animals drew away into thorn brakes and water holes.

It was the children's hour.

Five o'clock. The bath filled with clear hot water.

Six, seven, eight o'clock. The dinner dishes manipulated like magic tricks, and in the study a *click.* In the metal stand opposite the hearth where a fire now blazed up warmly, a cigar popped out, half an inch of soft gray ash on it, smoking, waiting.

Nine o'clock. The beds warmed their hidden circuits, for nights were cool here.

Nine-five. A voice spoke from the study ceiling:

"Mrs. McClellan, which poem would you like this evening?"

The house was silent.

The voice said at last, "Since you express no preference, I shall select a poem at random." Quiet music rose to back the voice. "Sara Teasdale. As I recall, your favorite. . . .

"There will come soft rains and the smell of the ground,
And swallows circling with their shimmering sound;

And frogs in the pools singing at night,
And wild plum trees in tremulous white;

Robins will wear their feathery fire,
Whistling their whims on a low fence-wire;

And not one will know of the war, not one
Will care at last when it is done.

Not one would mind, neither bird nor tree,
If mankind perished utterly;

And Spring herself, when she woke at dawn
Would scarcely know that we were gone."

The fire burned on the stone hearth and the cigar fell away into a mound of quiet ash on its tray. The empty chairs faced each other between the silent walls, and the music played.

At ten o'clock the house began to die.

The wind blew. A falling tree bough crashed through the kitchen window. Cleaning solvent, bottled, shattered over the stove. The room was ablaze in an instant!

"Fire!" screamed a voice. The house lights flashed, water pumps shot water from the ceilings. But the solvent spread on the linoleum, licking, eating, under the kitchen door, while the voices took it up in chorus: "Fire, fire, fire!"

The house tried to save itself. Doors sprang tightly shut, but the windows were broken by the heat and the wind blew and sucked upon the fire.

The house gave ground as the fire in ten billion angry sparks moved with flaming ease from room to room and then up the stairs. While scurrying water rats squeaked from the walls, pistoled their water, and ran for more. And the wall sprays let down showers of mechanical rain.

But too late. Somewhere, sighing, a pump shrugged to a stop. The quenching rain ceased. The reserve water supply which had filled baths and washed dishes for many quiet days was gone.

The fire crackled up the stairs. It fed upon Picassos and Matisses in the upper halls, like delicacies, baking off the oily flesh, tenderly crisping the canvases into black shavings.

Now the fire lay in beds, stood in windows, changed the colors of drapes! And then, reinforcements.

From attic trapdoors, blind robot faces peered down with faucet mouths gushing green chemical.

The fire backed off, as even an elephant must at the sight of a dead snake. Now there were twenty snakes whipping over the floor, killing the fire with a clear cold venom of green froth.

But the fire was clever. It had sent flames outside the house, up through the attic to the pumps there. An explosion! The attic brain which directed the pumps was shattered into bronze shrapnel on the beams.

The fire rushed back into every closet and felt of the clothes hung there.

The house shuddered, oak bone on bone, its bared skeleton cringing from the heat, its wire, its nerves revealed as if a surgeon had torn the skin off to let the red veins and capillaries quiver in the scalded air. Help, help! Fire! Run, run! Heat snapped mirrors like the brittle winter ice. And the voices wailed Fire, fire, run, run, like a tragic nursery rhyme, a dozen voices, high, low, like children dying in a forest, alone, alone. And the voices fading as the wires popped their sheathings like hot chestnuts. One, two, three, four, five voices died.

In the nursery the jungle burned. Blue lions roared, purple giraffes bounded off. The panthers ran in circles, changing color, and ten million animals, running before the fire, vanished off toward a distant steaming river. . . .

Ten more voices died. In the last instant under the fire avalanche, other choruses, oblivious, could be heard announcing the time, playing music, cutting the lawn by remote-control mower, or setting an umbrella frantically out and in the slamming and opening front door, a thousand things happening, like a clock shop when each clock strikes the hour insanely before or after the other, a scene of maniac confusion, yet unity; singing, screaming, a few last cleaning mice darting bravely out to carry the horrid ashes away! And one voice, with sublime disregard for the situation, read poetry aloud in the fiery study, until all the film spools burned, until all the wires withered and the circuits cracked.

The fire burst the house and let it slam flat down, puffing out skirts of spark and smoke.

In the kitchen, an instant before the rain of fire and timber, the stove could be seen making breakfasts at a psychopathic rate, ten dozen eggs, six loaves of toast, twenty dozen bacon strips, which, eaten by fire, started the stove working again, hysterically hissing!

The crash. The attic smashing into kitchen and parlor. The parlor into cellar, cellar into sub-cellar. Deep freeze, armchair, film tapes, circuits, beds, and all like skeletons thrown in a cluttered mound deep under.

Smoke and silence. A great quantity of smoke.

Dawn showed faintly in the east. Among the ruins, one wall stood alone. Within the wall, a last voice said, over and over again and again, even as the sun rose to shine upon the heaped rubble and steam:

"Today is August 5, 2026, today is August 5, 2026, today is . . ."

QUESTIONS

RAY BRADBURY, *There Will Come Soft Rains*

1. This story takes place in 2026. It was written in 1950. At that time everyone was trying to build bomb shelters to protect themselves from nuclear war. How was this house built to withstand even nuclear explosions?

2. What has happened to the family, despite the super house? How does the dog put a final end to the picture of the family and its life?

3. Why is the fire at the end of the story so disturbing? What does the fire say about our efforts to protect ourselves?

4. Has the fear of war changed over the last fifty or so years? What kinds of fears are indicated by the way that the house is built?

5. What do we learn about the lives of the family who lived in the house? Were they rich? Were they saved by being able to build such a house? Why not?

6. Are humans as important to the earth as they think? What would happen to the earth if humans disappeared? Would it be better or worse?

7. The story is built around time. How does the use of time in the narrative suggest the passing of life? What does it say about the scheduled lives of the house's inhabitants?

8. What kinds of paintings does the fire eat as it moves through the house? What does the fact that the family owned Picassos and read poetry say about them?

9. Why is the poem so ironic? Why does it provide the name for the story?

10. How many species become extinct each day on earth? How do humans contribute to these extinctions? Write about the footprint of the human race in some specific way: a species that has disappeared, a forest that has been cut down, etc.

11. Read about the Cold War of the fifties and sixties. What kinds of dark fears affected people's thoughts in those days? How are those thoughts alike and different from current terrorist fears?

12. Find out more about Sara Teasdale. Who was she? Find more poems by her, and write about her perspective as a poet.

Flannery O'Connor
[1925–1964]

Born an only child in Savannah, Georgia, FLANNERY O'CONNOR *moved with her parents to a farm near Milledgeville, Georgia, at age twelve. Her father died of lupus, a disease of the immune system, when O'Connor was fifteen; O'Connor herself succumbed to the disease at age thirty-nine. An intellectual in a rural environment, she quickly began to see the world as sometimes annoying, but often amusing. O'Connor graduated from Georgia State College of Women in 1945, where she was a cartoonist for the student newspaper. Many of her stories draw characters in cartoonish ways, a whimsical, and sometimes slightly cruel, way of seeing humanity. O'Connor went on to the University of Iowa, where she received her Masters of Fine Arts in 1947. It was at the University of Iowa where she published her first short story, "The Geranium," in* Accent *(1946). She went on to an artist's residency at Yaddo in Saratoga Springs, New York, where she developed the professional friendships that were to sustain her throughout her artistic life. Though she returned to the family farm permanently due to her health, she continued to correspond with her artistic colleagues. Her correspondence was collected and published in 1979 as* Letters of Flannery O'Connor: The Habit of Being.*

O'Connor wrote constantly throughout her short life, producing two novels and numerous short stories that have amused readers for the last forty years. Her novels,* Wise Blood *(1952) and* The Violent Bear It Away *(1960), present a world where grotesque characters search for meaning, almost without awareness of their own searches. Critics found the novels somewhat perplexing and gave mixed reviews, but the critical reaction to O'Connor's short stories, collected in* A Good Man Is Hard to Find *(1955) and* Everything That Rises Must Converge *(1965), has been consistent and positive throughout the years. There are two important things to know about O'Connor, without which none of her work can be adequately understood: she was a devout Catholic and a southerner. The stories portray the southern qualities much more obviously than they do the Catholicism, but the human search for grace and forgiveness is an important theme throughout her writing. O'Connor depicted the rural south in comic strokes that sometimes bordered on cruel, such as in her description of the idiot blue-eyed cooing daughter of the old farm woman in "A Good Man Is Hard to Find," and the young Bible salesman in "Good Country People" with hair like brown gravy rolling down his head. In a later story, "Revelation," a young college-educated woman hits a pious farm woman with a large human psychology book* *for mouthing meaningless platitudes. The scene is one of O'Connor's best, but it also demonstrates why some readers find her offensive. Her characters may seem to be on the road to destruction, but O'Connor presents them through her own particular aesthetic, revealing their humanity, and their search for wholeness.*

A Good Man Is Hard to Find

FLANNERY O'CONNOR

THE GRANDMOTHER DIDN'T WANT to go to Florida. She wanted to visit some of her connections in east Tennessee and she was seizing every chance to change Bailey's mind. Bailey was the son she lived with, her only boy. He was sitting on the edge of his chair at the table, bent over the orange sports section of the *Journal.* "Now look here, Bailey," she said, "see here, read this," and she stood with one hand on her thin hip and the other rattling the newspaper at his bald head. "Here this fellow that calls himself The Misfit is aloose from the Federal Pen and headed toward Florida and you read here what it says he did to these people. Just you read it. I wouldn't take my children in any direction with the criminal like that aloose in it. I couldn't answer to my conscience if I did."

Bailey didn't look up from his reading so she wheeled around then and faced the children's mother; a young woman in slacks, whose face was as broad and innocent as a cabbage and was tied around with a green headkerchief that had two points on the top like rabbit's ears. She was sitting on the sofa, feeding the baby his apricots out of a jar. "The children have been to Florida before," the old lady said. "You all ought to take them somewhere else for a change so they would see different parts of the world and be broad. They never have been to east Tennessee."

The children's mother didn't seem to hear her, but the eight-year-old boy, John Wesley, a stocky child with glasses, said, "If you don't want to go to Florida, why dontcha stay at home?" He and the little girl, June Star, were reading the funny papers on the floor.

"She wouldn't stay at home to be queen for a day," June Star said without raising her yellow head.

"Yes, and what would you do if this fellow, The Misfit, caught you?" the grandmother asked.

"I'd smack his face," John Wesley said.

"She wouldn't stay at home for a million bucks," June Star said. "Afraid she'd miss something. She has to go everywhere we go."

"All right, Miss," the grandmother said. "Just remember that the next time you want me to curl your hair."

June Star said her hair was naturally curly.

The next morning the grandmother was the first one in the car, ready to go. She had her big black valise that looked like the head of a hippopotamus in one corner, and underneath it she was hiding a basket with Pitty Sing, the cat, in it. She didn't intend for the cat to be left alone in the house for three days because he would miss her too much and she was afraid he might brush against one of the gas burners and accidentally asphyxiate himself. Her son Bailey didn't like to arrive at a motel with a cat.

She sat in the middle of the back seat with John Wesley and June Star on either side of her. Bailey and the children's mother and the baby sat in the front and they left Atlanta at eight forty-five with the mileage on the car at 55890. The grandmother wrote this down because she thought it would be interesting to say how many miles they had been when they got back. It took them twenty minutes to reach the outskirts of the city.

The old lady settled herself comfortably, removing her white cotton gloves and putting them up with her purse on the shelf in front of the back window. The children's mother still had on slacks and still had her head tied up in a green kerchief, but the grandmother had on a navy blue straw sailor hat with a bunch of white violets on the brim and a navy blue dress with a small white dot in the print. Her collar and cuffs were white organdy trimmed with lace and at her neckline she had pinned a purple spray of cloth violets containing a sachet. In case of an accident, anyone seeing her dead on the highway would know at once that she was a lady.

She said she thought it was going to be a good day for driving, neither too hot nor too cold, and she cautioned Bailey that the speed limit was fifty-five miles an hour and that the patrolmen hid themselves behind billboards and small clumps of trees and sped out after you before you had a chance to slow down. She pointed out interesting details of the scenery: Stone Mountain; the blue granite that in some places came up to both sides of the highway; the brilliant red clay banks slightly streaked with purple; and the various crops that made rows of green lace-work on the ground. The trees were full of silverwhite sunlights and the meanest of them sparkled. The children were reading comic magazines and their mother had gone back to sleep.

"Let's go through Georgia fast so we don't have to look at it much," John Wesley said.

"If I were a little boy," said the grandmother, "I wouldn't talk about my native state that way. Tennessee has the mountains and Georgia has the hills."

"Tennessee is just a hillbilly dumping ground," John Wesley said, "and Georgia is a lousy state too."

"You said it," June Star said.

"In my time," said the grandmother, folding her thin veined fingers, "children were more respectful of their native states and their parents and everything else. People did right then. Oh look at the cute little pickaninny!" she said and pointed to a Negro child standing in the door of a shack. "Wouldn't that make a picture now?" she asked and they all turned and looked at the little Negro out of the back window. He waved.

"He didn't have any britches on," June Star said.

"He probably didn't have any," the grandmother explained. "Little niggers in the country don't have things like we do. If I could paint, I'd paint that picture," she said.

The children exchanged comic books.

The grandmother offered to hold the baby and the children's mother passed him over the front seat to her. She set him on her knee and bounced him and told him about the things they were passing. She rolled her eyes and screwed up her mouth and stuck her leathery thin face into his smooth bland one. Occasionally he gave her a faraway smile. They passed a large cotton field with five or six graves fenced in the middle of it, like a small island. "Look at the graveyard!" the grandmother said, pointing it out. "That was the old family burying ground. That belonged to the plantation."

"Where's the plantation?" John Wesley asked.

"Gone With the Wind," said the grandmother. "Ha. Ha."

When the children finished all the comic books they had brought, they opened the lunch and ate it. The grandmother ate a peanut butter sandwich and an olive and would not let the children throw the box and the paper napkins out the window. When there was nothing else to do they played a game by choosing a cloud and making the other two guess what shape it suggested. John Wesley took one the shape of a cow and June Star guessed a cow and John Wesley said, no, an automobile, and June Star said he didn't play fair, and they began to slap each other over the grandmother.

The grandmother said she would tell them a story if they would keep quiet. When she told a story, she rolled her eyes and waved her head and was very dramatic. She said once when she was a maiden lady she had been courted by a Mr. Edgar Atkins Teagarden from Jasper, Georgia. She said he was a very good-looking man and a gentleman and that he brought her a watermelon every Saturday afternoon with his initials cut in it, E.A.T. Well, one Saturday, she said, Mr. Teagarden brought the watermelon and there was nobody at home and he left it on the front porch and returned in his buggy to Jasper, but she never got the watermelon, she said, because a nigger boy ate it when he saw the initials, E.A.T.! This story tickled John Wesley's funny bone and he giggled and giggled but June Star didn't think it was any good. She said she wouldn't marry a man that just brought her a watermelon on Saturday.

The grandmother said she would have done well to marry Mr. Teagarden because he was a gentleman and had bought Coca-Cola stock when it first came out and that he had died only a few years ago, a very wealthy man.

They stopped at The Tower for barbecued sandwiches. The Tower was a part-stucco and part-wood filling station and dance hall set in a clearing outside of Timothy. A fat man named Red Sammy Butts ran it and there were signs stuck here and there on the building and for miles up and down the highway saying, TRY RED SAMMY'S FAMOUS BARBECUE. NONE LIKE FAMOUS RED SAMMY'S! RED SAM! THE FAT BOY WITH THE HAPPY LAUGH. A VETERAN! RED SAMMY'S YOUR MAN!

Red Sammy was lying on the bare ground outside The Tower with his head under a truck while a gray monkey about a foot high, chained to a small chinaberry tree, chattered nearby. The monkey sprang back into the tree and got on the highest limb as soon as he saw the children jump out of the car and run toward him.

Inside, The Tower was a long dark room with a counter at one end and tables at the other and dancing space in the middle. They all sat down at a broad table next to the nickelodeon and Red Sam's wife, a tall burnt-brown woman with hair and eyes lighter than her skin, came and took their order. The children's mother put a dime in the machine and played "The Tennessee Waltz," and the grandmother said that tune always made her want to dance. She asked Bailey if he would like to dance but he only glared at her. He didn't have a naturally sunny disposition like she did and trips made him nervous. The grandmother's brown eyes were very bright. She swayed her head from side to side and pretended she was dancing in her chair. June Star said play something she could tap to so the children's mother put in another dime and played a fast number and June Star stepped out onto the dance floor and did her tap routine.

"Ain't she cute?" Red Sam's wife said, leaning over the counter. "Would you like to come be my little girl?"

"No, I certainly wouldn't," June Star said. "I wouldn't live in a broken-down place like this for a million bucks!" and she ran back to the table.

"Ain't she cute?" the woman repeated, stretching her mouth politely.

"Aren't you ashamed?" hissed the grandmother.

Red Sam came in and told his wife to quit lounging on the counter and hurry up with these people's order. His khaki trousers reached just to his hip bones and his stomach hung over them like a sack of meal swaying under his shirt. He came over and sat down at a table nearby and let out a combination sigh and yodel. "You can't win," he said. "You can't win," and he wiped his sweating red face off with a gray handkerchief. "These days you don't know who to trust," he said. "Ain't that the truth?"

"People are certainly not nice like they used to be," said the grandmother.

"Two fellers come in here last week," Red Sammy said, "driving a Chrysler. It was an old beat-up car but it was a good one and these boys looked all right to me. Said they worked at the mill and you know I let them fellers charge the gas they bought? Now why did I do that?"

"Because you're a good man!" the grandmother said at once.

"Yes'm, I suppose so," Red Sam said as if he were struck with this answer.

His wife brought the orders, carrying the five plates all at once without a tray, two in each hand and one balanced on her arm. "It isn't a soul in this green world of God's that you can trust," she said. "And I don't count nobody out of that, not nobody," she repeated, looking at Red Sammy.

"Did you read about that criminal, The Misfit, that's escaped?" asked the grandmother.

"I wouldn't be a bit surprised if he didn't attack this place right here," said the woman. "If he hears about it being here, I wouldn't be none surprised to see him. If he hears it's two cent in the cash register, I wouldn't be a tall surprised if he . . ."

"That'll do," Red Sam said. "Go bring these people their Co'-Colas," and the woman went off to get the rest of the order.

"A good man is hard to find," Red Sammy said. "Everything is getting terrible. I remember the day you could go off and leave your screen door unlatched. Not no more."

He and the grandmother discussed better times. The old lady said that in her opinion Europe was entirely to blame for the way things were now. She said the way Europe acted you would think we were made of money and Red Sam said it was no use talking about it, she was exactly right. The children ran outside into the white sunlight and looked at the monkey in the lacy chinaberry tree. He was busy catching fleas on himself and biting each one carefully between his teeth as if it were a delicacy.

They drove off again into the hot afternoon. The grandmother took cat naps and woke up every few minutes with her own snoring. Outside of Toombsboro she woke up and recalled an old plantation that she had visited in this neighborhood once when she was a young lady. She said the house had six white columns across the front and that there was an avenue of oaks leading up to it and two little wooden trellis arbors on either side in front where you sat down with your suitor after a stroll in the garden. She recalled exactly which road to turn off to get to it. She knew that Bailey would not be willing to lose any time looking at an old house, but the more she talked about it, the more she wanted to see it once again and find out if the little twin arbors were still standing. "There was a secret panel in this house," she said craftily, not telling the truth but wishing that she were, "and the story went that all the family silver was hidden in it when Sherman came through but it was never found. . . ."

"Hey!" John Wesley said. "Let's go see it! We'll find it! We'll poke at the wood work and find it! Who lives there? Where do you turn off at? Hey Pop, can't we turn off there?"

"We never have seen a house with a secret panel!" June Star shrieked. "Let's go to the house with the secret panel! Hey, Pop, can't we go see the house with the secret panel!"

"It's not far from here, I know," the grandmother said. "It wouldn't take over twenty minutes."

Bailey was looking straight ahead. His jaw was as rigid as a horseshoe. "No," he said.

The children began to yell and scream that they wanted to see the house with the secret panel. John Wesley kicked the back of the front seat and June Star hung over her mother's shoulder and whined desperately into her ear that they never had any fun even on their vacation, that they could never do what THEY wanted to do. The baby began to scream and John Wesley kicked the back of the seat so hard that his father could feel the blows in his kidney.

"All right!" he shouted and drew the car to a stop at the side of the road. "Will you all shut up? Will you all just shut up for one second? If you don't shut up, we won't go anywhere."

"It would be very educational for them," the grandmother murmured.

"All right," Bailey said, "but get this. This is the only time we're going to stop for anything like this. This is the one and only time."

"The dirt road that you have to turn down is about a mile back," the grandmother directed. "I marked it when we passed."

"A dirt road," Bailey groaned.

After they had turned around and were headed toward the dirt road, the grandmother recalled other points about the house, the beautiful glass over the front doorway and the candle lamp in the hall. John Wesley said that the secret panel was probably in the fireplace.

"You can't go inside the house," Bailey said. "You don't know who lives there."

"While you all talk to the people in front, I'll run around behind and get in a window," John Wesley suggested.

"We'll all stay in the car," his mother said.

They turned onto the dirt road and the car raced roughly along in a swirl of pink dust. The grandmother recalled the times when there were no paved roads and thirty miles was a day's journey. The dirt road was hilly and there were sudden washes in it and sharp curves on dangerous embankments. All at once they would be on a hill, looking down over the blue tops of trees for miles around, then the next minute, they would be in a red depression with the dust-coated trees looking down on them.

"This place had better turn up in a minute," Bailey said, "or I'm going to turn around."

The road looked as if no one had traveled on it in months.

"It's not much further," the grandmother said and just as she said it, a horrible thought came to her. The thought was so embarrassing that she turned red in the face and her eyes dilated and her feet jumped up, upsetting her valise in the corner. The instant the valise moved, the newspaper top she had over the basket under it rose with a snarl and Pitty Sing, the cat, sprang onto Bailey's shoulder.

The children were thrown to the floor and their mother, clutching the baby, was thrown out the door onto the ground; the old lady was thrown into the front seat. The car turned over once and landed right-side-up in a gulch on the side of the road. Bailey remained in the driver's seat with the cat—gray-striped with a broad white face and an orange nose—clinging to his neck like a caterpillar.

As soon as the children saw they could move their arms and legs, they scrambled out of the car shouting, "We've had an ACCIDENT!" The grandmother was curled up under the dashboard, hoping she was injured so that Bailey's wrath would not come down on her all at once. The horrible thought she had had before the accident was that the house she had remembered so vividly was not in Georgia but in Tennessee.

Bailey removed the cat from his neck with both hands and flung it out the window against the side of a pine tree. Then he got out of the car and started looking for the children's mother. She was sitting against the side of the red gutted ditch, holding the screaming baby, but she only had a cut down her face and a broken shoulder. "We've had an ACCIDENT!" the children screamed in a frenzy of delight.

"But nobody's killed," June Star said with disappointment as the grandmother limped out of the car, her hat still pinned to her head but the broken front brim standing up at a jaunty angle and the violet spray hanging off the side. They all sat down in the ditch, except the children, to recover from the shock. They were all shaking.

"Maybe a car will come along," said the children's mother hoarsely.

"I believe I have injured an organ," said the grandmother, pressing her side, but no one answered her. Bailey's teeth were clattering. He had on a yellow sport shirt with bright parrots designed in it and his face was as yellow as the shirt. The grandmother decided that she would not mention that the house was in Tennessee.

The road was about ten feet above and they could see only the tops of the trees on the other side of it. Behind the ditch they were sitting in there were more woods, tall and dark and deep. In a few minutes they saw a car some distance away on top of a hill, coming slowly as if the occupants were watching them. The grandmother stood up and waved both arms dramatically to attract their attention. The car continued to come on slowly, disappeared around a bend and appeared again, moving even slower, on top of the hill they had gone over. It was a big black battered hearselike automobile. There were three men in it.

It came to a stop just over them and for some minutes, the driver looked down with a steady expressionless gaze to where they were sitting, and didn't speak. Then he turned his head and muttered something to the other two and they got out. One was a fat boy in black trousers and a red sweat shirt with a silver stallion embossed on the front of it. He moved around on the right side of them and stood staring, his mouth partly open in a kind of loose grin. The other had on khaki pants and a blue striped coat and a gray hat pulled down very low, hiding most of his face. He came around slowly on the left side. Neither spoke.

The driver got out of the car and stood by the side of it, looking down at them. He was an older man than the other two. His hair was just beginning to gray and he wore silver-rimmed spectacles that gave him a scholarly look. He had a long creased face and didn't have on any shirt or undershirt. He had on blue jeans that were too tight for him and he was holding a black hat and a gun. The two boys also had guns.

"We've had an ACCIDENT!" the children screamed.

The grandmother had the peculiar feeling that the bespectacled man was someone she knew. His face was as familiar to her as if she had known him all her life but she could not recall who he was. He moved away from the car and began to come down the embankment, placing his feet carefully so that he wouldn't slip. He had on tan and white shoes and no socks, and his ankles were red and thin. "Good afternoon," he said, "I see you all had you a little spill."

"We turned over twice!" said the grandmother.

"Oncet," he corrected. "We see it happen. Try their car and see will it run, Hiram," he said quietly to the boy with the gray hat.

"What you got that gun for?" John Wesley asked. "Whatcha gonna do with that gun?"

"Lady," the man said to the children's mother, "would you mind calling them children to sit down by you? Children make me nervous. I want all you all to sit down right together there where you're at."

"What are you telling us what to do for?" June Star asked.

Behind them the line of woods gaped like a dark open mouth. "Come here," said their mother.

"Look here now," Bailey began suddenly, "we're in a predicament! We're in . . ."

The grandmother shrieked. She scrambled to her feet and stood staring. "You're The Misfit!" she said. "I recognized you at once!"

"Yes'm," the man said, smiling slightly as if he were pleased in spite of himself to be known. "But it would have been better for all of you, lady, if you hadn't of reckernized me."

Bailey turned his head sharply and said something to his mother that shocked the children. The old lady began to cry and The Misfit reddened.

"Lady," he said, "don't you get upset. Sometimes a man says things he don't mean. I don't reckon he meant to talk to you thataway."

"You wouldn't shoot a lady, would you?" the grandmother said and removed a clean handkerchief from her cuff and began to slap at her eyes with it.

The Misfit pointed the toe of his shoe into the ground and made a little hole and then covered it up again. "I would hate to have to," he said.

"Listen," the grandmother almost screamed, "I know you're a good man. You don't look a bit like you have common blood. I know you must come from nice people!"

"Yes mam," he said, "finest people in the world." When he smiled he showed a row of strong white teeth. "God never made a finer woman than my mother and my daddy's heart was pure gold," he said. The boy with the red sweat shirt had come around behind them and was standing with his gun at his hip. The Misfit squatted down on the ground. "Watch them children, Bobby Lee," he said. "You know they make me nervous." He looked at the six of them huddled together in front of him and he seemed to be embarrassed as if he couldn't think of anything to say. "Ain't a cloud in the sky," he remarked, looking up at it. "Don't see no sun but don't see no cloud neither."

"Yes, it's a beautiful day," said the grandmother. "Listen," she said, "you shouldn't call yourself The Misfit because I know you're a good man at heart. I can just look at you and tell."

"Hush!" Bailey yelled. "Hush! Everybody shut up and let me handle this!" He was squatting in the position of a runner about to spring forward but he didn't move.

"I pre-chate that, lady," The Misfit said and drew a little circle in the ground with the butt of his gun.

"It'll take a half a hour to fix this here car," Hiram called, looking over the raised hood of it.

"Well, first you and Bobby Lee get him and that little boy to step over yonder with you," The Misfit said, pointing to Bailey and John Wesley. "The boys want to ask you something," he said to Bailey. "Would you mind stepping back in them woods there with them?"

"Listen," Bailey began, "we're in a terrible predicament! Nobody realizes what this is," and his voice cracked. His eyes were as blue and intense as the parrots in his shirt and he remained perfectly still.

The grandmother reached up to adjust her hat brim as if she were going to the woods with him but it came off in her hand. She stood staring at it and after a second she let it fall on the ground. Hiram pulled Bailey up by the arm as if he were assisting an old man. John Wesley caught hold of his father's hand and Bobby Lee followed. They went off toward the woods and just as they reached the dark edge, Bailey turned and supporting himself against a gray naked pine trunk, he shouted, "I'll be back in a minute, Mamma, wait on me!"

"Come back this instant!" his mother shrilled but they all disappeared into the woods.

"Bailey Boy!" the grandmother called in tragic voice but she found she was looking at The Misfit squatting on the ground in front of her. "I just know you're a good man," she said desperately. "You're not a bit common!"

"Nome, I ain't a good man," The Misfit said after a second as if he had considered her statement carefully, "but I ain't the worst in the world neither. My daddy said I was a different breed of dog from my brothers and sisters. 'You know,' Daddy said, 'it's some that can live their whole life out without asking about it and it's others has to know why it is, and this boy is one of the latters. He's going to be into everything!' " He put on his black hat and looked up suddenly and then away deep into the woods as if he were embarrassed again. "I'm sorry, I don't have on a shirt before you ladies," he said, hunching his shoulders slightly. "We buried our clothes that we had on when we escaped and we're just making do until we can get better. We borrowed these from some folks we met," he explained.

"That's perfectly all right," the grandmother said. "Maybe Bailey has an extra shirt in his suitcase."

"I'll look and see terrectly," The Misfit said.

"Where are they taking him?" the children's mother screamed.

"Daddy was a card himself," The Misfit said. "You couldn't put anything over on him. He never got in trouble with the Authorities though. Just had the knack of handling them."

"You could be honest too if you'd only try," said the grandmother. "Think how wonderful it would be to settle down and live a comfortable life and not have to think about somebody chasing you all the time."

The Misfit kept scratching in the ground with the butt of his gun as if he were thinking about it. "Yes'm, somebody is always after you," he murmured.

The grandmother noticed how thin his shoulder blades were just behind his hat because she was standing up looking down on him. "Do you ever pray?" she asked.

He shook his head. All she saw was the black hat wiggle between his shoulder blades. "Nome," he said.

There was a pistol shot from the woods, followed closely by another. Then silence. The old lady's head jerked around. She could hear the wind move through the tree tops like a long satisfied insuck of breath. "Bailey Boy!," she called.

"I was a gospel singer for a while," The Misfit said. "I been most everything. Been in the arm service, both land and sea, at home and abroad, been twict married, been an undertaker, been with the railroads, plowed Mother Earth, been in a tornado, seen a man burnt alive oncet," and he looked up at the children's mother and the little girl who were sitting close together, their faces white and their eyes glassy; "I even seen a woman flogged," he said.

"Pray, pray," the grandmother began, "pray, pray . . ."

"I never was a bad boy that I remember of," The Misfit said in an almost dreamy voice, "but somewheres along the line I done something wrong and got sent to the penitentiary. I was buried alive," and he looked up and held her attention to him by a steady stare.

"That's when you should have started to pray," she said. "What did you do to get sent to the penitentiary that first time?"

"Turn to the right, it was a wall," The Misfit said, looking up again at the cloudless sky. "Turn to the left, it was a wall. Look up it was a ceiling, look down it was a floor. I forgot what I done, lady. I set there and set there, trying to remember what it was I done and I ain't recalled it to this day. Oncet in a while, I would think it was coming to me, but it never come."

"Maybe they put you in by mistake," the old lady said vaguely.

"Nome," he said. "It wasn't no mistake. They had the papers on me."

"You must have stolen something," she said.

The Misfit sneered slightly. "Nobody had nothing I wanted," he said. "It was a head-doctor at the penitentiary said what I had done was kill my daddy but I known that for a lie. My daddy died in nineteen ought nineteen of the epidemic flu and I never had a thing to do with it. He was buried in the Mount Hopewell Baptist churchyard and you can go there and see for yourself."

"If you would pray," the old lady said, "Jesus would help you."

"That's right," The Misfit said.

"Well then, why don't you pray?" she asked trembling with delight suddenly.

"I don't want no hep," he said, "I'm doing all right by myself."

Bobby Lee and Hiram came ambling back from the woods. Bobby Lee was dragging a yellow shirt with bright blue parrots in it.

"Throw me that shirt, Bobby Lee," The Misfit said. The shirt came flying at him and landed on his shoulder and he put it on. The grandmother couldn't name what the shirt reminded her of. "No, lady," The Misfit said while he was buttoning it up, "I found out the crime don't matter. You can do one thing or you can do another, kill a man or take a tire off his car, because sooner or later you're going to forget what it was you done and just be punished for it."

The children's mother had begun to make heaving noises as if she couldn't get her breath. "Lady," he asked, "would you and that little girl like to step off yonder with Bobby Lee and Hiram and join your husband?"

"Yes, thank you," the mother said faintly. Her left arm dangled helplessly and she was holding the baby, who had gone to sleep, in the other. "Hep that lady up, Hiram," The Misfit said as she struggled to climb out of the ditch, "and Bobby Lee, you hold onto that little girl's hand."

"I don't want to hold hands with him," June Star said. "He reminds me of a pig."

The fat boy blushed and laughed and caught her by the arm and pulled her off into the woods after Hiram and her mother.

Alone with The Misfit, the grandmother found that she had lost her voice. There was not a cloud in the sky nor any sun. There was nothing around her but woods. She wanted to tell him that he must pray. She opened and closed her mouth several times before anything came out. Finally she found herself saying, "Jesus. Jesus," meaning, Jesus will help you, but the way she was saying it, it sounded as if she might be cursing.

"Yes'm," The Misfit said as if he agreed. "Jesus thown everything off balance. It was the same case with Him as with me except He hadn't committed any crime and they could prove I had committed one because they had the papers on me. Of course," he said, "they never shown me any papers. That's why I sign myself now. I said long ago, you get you a signature and sign everything you do and keep a copy of it. Then you'll know what you done and you can hold up the crime to the punishment and see do they match and in the end you'll have something to prove you ain't been treated right. I call myself The Misfit," he said, "because I can't make what all I done wrong fit with all I gone through in punishment."

There was a piercing scream from the woods, followed closely by a pistol report. "Does it seem right to you, lady, that one is punished a heap and another ain't punished at all?"

"Jesus!" the old lady cried. "You've got good blood! I know you wouldn't shoot a lady! I know you come from nice people! Pray! Jesus, you ought not to shoot a lady. I'll give you all the money I've got!"

"Lady," The Misfit said, looking beyond her far into the woods, "there was never a body that give the undertaker a tip."

There were two more pistol reports and the grandmother raised her head like a parched old turkey hen crying for water and called, "Bailey Boy, Bailey Boy!" as if her heart would break.

"Jesus was the only One that ever raised the dead," The Misfit continued, "and He shouldn't have done it. He thown everything off balance. If He did what He said, then it's nothing for you to do but thow away everything and follow Him, and if He didn't then it's nothing for you to do but enjoy the few minutes you got left the best way you can—by killing somebody or burning down his house or doing some other meanness to him. No pleasure but meanness," he said and his voice had become almost a snarl.

"Maybe He didn't raise the dead," the old lady mumbled, not knowing what she was saying and feeling so dizzy that she sank down in the ditch with her legs twisted under her.

"I wasn't there so I can't say He didn't," The Misfit said. "I wisht I had of been there," he said, hitting the ground with his fist. "It ain't right I wasn't there because if I had of been there I would of known. Listen lady," he said in a high voice, "if I had of been there I would of known and I wouldn't be like I am now." His voice seemed about to crack and the grandmother's head cleared for an instant. She saw the man's face twisted close to her own as if he were going to cry and she murmured, "Why, you're one of my babies. You're one of my own children!" She reached out and touched him on the shoulder. The Misfit sprang back as if a snake had bitten him and shot her three times through the chest. Then he put his gun down on the ground and took off his glasses and began to clean them.

Hiram and Bobby Lee returned from the woods and stood over the ditch, looking down at the grandmother who half sat and half lay in a puddle of blood with her legs crossed under her like a child's and her face smiling up at the cloudless sky.

Without his glasses, The Misfit's eyes were red-rimmed and pale and defenseless-looking. "Take her off and thow her where you thown the others," he said, picking up the cat that was rubbing itself against his leg.

"She was a talker, wasn't she?" Bobby Lee said, sliding down the ditch with a yodel.

"She would of been a good woman," The Misfit said, "if it had been somebody there to shoot her every minute of her life."

"Some fun!" Bobby Lee said.

"Shut up, Bobby Lee," The Misfit said. "It's no real pleasure in life."

[1953]

183

QUESTIONS

FLANNERY O'CONNOR, *A Good Man Is Hard to Find*

1. What does the grandmother do that causes the accident? What mistake about place does she make? How does her mistake fit with her personality?

2. The conversation with Red Sammy reveals many of the issues of the story. What does Red Sammy have to say about the nature of human beings?

3. The Misfit has been jailed for crimes he does not remember. How do we know that he really is a criminal? What should readers make of his claims about himself?

4. Is it true that no one can be trusted, as Red Sammy and the Grandmother say? What can be said about people who do not trust other people?

5. O'Connor took the idea of this story from a newspaper article about a criminal called The Misfit. What does society do with its misfits? How are they generally treated, and what does this treatment do to them?

6. O'Connor believed that people needed something to wake them up from their complacency. What do the grandmother's last words say about our need to recognize the needs of others?

7. O'Connor uses imagery and color to bring her ideas vividly to life. How does she use color in place, dress, and figure in this story? Note the descriptions of the monkey, the cat, Barleys shirt.

8. The story centers around the moment of the accident. What is the irony of the children's response to the accident? What clues tell the reader that someone will, indeed, be killed?

9. Sammy uses the words "a good man is hard to find," after his wife has said that she trusts no one, including him. Why are these words put in the mouth of a man like Sammy?

10. Find a newspaper article that interests you and write a story that includes the information in the article.

11. Read about the South of the past that the grandmother remembers. Write about life in that time and place. Consider race and class issues as you write.

12. What causes cruelty? What is the mind set of people who have lost their ability to identify with others? Write about this issue, using a particular event in past or current history (World War II, The Civil war, etc.).

Chinua Achebe
[1930–   ]

CHINUA ACHEBE'S Things Fall Apart *(1958), which was awarded the Margaret Wrong Memorial Prize, represents the arrival of a new voice in world literature. While the Nigerian-born writer's career flourished during the second half of the twentieth century, the publication of* Home and Exile *and his nomination for a Nobel Prize in literature in 2000 signifies the writer's presence in the field of contemporary literature in the twenty-first century. The critical reception of his works over the years marks a shift in contemporary writing, as Achebe has achieved prominence by blurring boundaries, bridging divides in aesthetics and politics. In all his work, Achebe draws on the cultural roots of oral storytelling in experimental prose. Between the past and the present, between old and new forms, Achebe's writing redefines borders, the balance among home and exile, articulating how things come together and fall apart.*

In the field of Nigerian literature—a field that has emerged and developed in the second half of the twentieth century during what critics dub the Nigerian Renaissance—Achebe occupies a central position. Things Fall Apart, *his first novel, was published two years before Nigeria gained its independence, and his entire body of work chronicles the country's history. Writing "from the inside," Achebe's works redefine the relationships between self and other, individuals and communities, as they tackle the complicated issues of survival in a contemporary (and postcolonial) world. Born in Ogidi, Nigeria, to a father who was a catechist for the Church Missionary Society, Achebe's early life was marked by his introduction to the study of Christianity. While Achebe rejected his given name "Albert" in favor of a traditional name "Chinua," in his writing Achebe returns to the dominant form of language, to the standard (and standardized) English that he began to study when he was eight years old. From his earlier education at the Church Mission Society School to his studies at the Government College and University College (B.A., 1953), Achebe studied English language and literature as he began to cultivate his writing. While working for the Nigerian Broadcasting Company after graduation, Achebe developed* Things Fall Apart. *Unlike his contemporaries, writers such as Ngugi wa Thiong'o, who reject standard English, Achebe embraces English to redefine the perceived "other." In this sense, Achebe's writing reflects the politics of this time period—the tumultuous period of civil wars at home in the 1960s and his divided loyalties and traditions.*

In his work Achebe radically calls the English language literary tradition into question, employing rich, evocative, and provocative language that melds the speech patterns of his native tongue with English lexicon. In his narratives these contradictory and complementary languages come together rather than fall apart. *Revisionary, even revolutionary, Achebe redefines the relationship between politics and aesthetics so that his novels examine how the colonial past is both a burden to and a source of Nigeria's present condition. In fiction and nonfiction, Achebe crosses borders, reexamining how home is redefined by language.*

—Lisa Perdigao, *Florida Institute of Technology*

Civil Peace

CHINUA ACHEBE

JONATHAN IWEGBU COUNTED HIMSELF extraordinarily lucky. "Happy survival!" meant so much more to him than just a current fashion of greeting old friends in the first hazy days of peace. It went deep to his heart. He had come out of the war with five inestimable blessings—his head, his wife Maria's head, and the heads of three out of their four children. As a bonus he also had his old bicycle—a miracle too but naturally not to be compared to the safety of five human heads.

The bicycle had a little history of its own. One day at the height of the war it was commandeered "for urgent military action." Hard as its loss would have been to him he would still have let it go without a thought had he not had some doubts about the genuineness of the officer. It wasn't his disreputable rags, nor the toes peeping out of one blue and one brown canvas shoe, nor yet the two stars of his rank done obviously in a hurry in biro[1] that troubled Jonathan; many good and heroic soldiers looked the same or worse. It was rather a certain lack of grip and firmness in his manner. So Jonathan, suspecting he might be amenable to influence, rummaged in his raffia bag and produced the two pounds with which he had been going to buy firewood which his wife, Maria, retailed to camp officials for extra stockfish and corn-meal, and got his bicycle back. That night he buried it in the little clearing in the bush where the dead of the camp, including his own youngest son, were buried. When he dug it up again a year later after the surrender all it needed was a little palm-oil greasing. "Nothing puzzles God," he said in wonder.

He put it to immediate use as a taxi and accumulated a small pile of Biafran money ferrying camp officials and their families across the four-mile stretch to the nearest tarred road. His standard charge per trip was six pounds and those who had the money were only glad to be rid of some of it in this way. At the end of a fortnight he had made a small fortune of one hundred and fifteen pounds.

---

[1]Ballpoint pen

Reprinted from *Girls at War and Other Stories*, by permission of Random House, Inc. and Harold Ober Associates. Copyright ● 1972 by Chinua Achebe.

Then he made the journey to Enugu and found another miracle waiting for him. It was unbelievable. He rubbed his eyes and looked again and it was still standing there before him. But, needless to say, even that monumental blessing must be accounted also totally inferior to the five heads in the family. This newest miracle was his little house in Ogui Overside. Indeed nothing puzzles God! Only two houses away a huge concrete edifice some wealthy contractor had put up just before the war was a mountain of rubble. And here was Jonathan's little zinc house of no regrets built with mud blocks quite intact! Of course the doors and windows were missing and five sheets off the roof. But what was that? And anyhow he had returned to Enugu early enough to pick up bits of old zinc and wood and soggy sheets of cardboard lying around the neighborhood before thousands more came out of their forest holes looking for the same things. He got a destitute carpenter with one old hammer, a blunt plane, and a few bent and rusty nails in his tool bag to turn this assortment of wood, paper, and metal into door and window shutters for five Nigerian shillings or fifty Biafran pounds. He paid the pounds, and moved in with his overjoyed family carrying five heads on their shoulders.

His children picked mangoes near the military cemetery and sold them to soldiers' wives for a few pennies—real pennies this time—and his wife started making breakfast akara balls[2] for neighbors in a hurry to start life again. With his family earnings he took his bicycle to the villages around and bought fresh palm wine which he mixed generously in his rooms with the water which had recently started running again in the public tap down the road, and opened up a bar for soldiers and other lucky people with good money.

At first he went daily, then every other day, and finally once a week, to the offices of the Coal Corporation where he used to be a miner, to find out what was what. The only thing he did find out in the end was that that little house of his was even a greater blessing than he had thought. Some of his fellow ex-miners who had nowhere to return at the end of the day's waiting just slept outside the doors of the offices and cooked what meal they could scrounge together in Bournvita tins. As the weeks lengthened and still nobody could say what was what, Jonathan discontinued his weekly visits altogether and faced his palm-wine bar.

But nothing puzzles God. Came the day of the windfall when after five days of endless scuffles in queues and counterqueues in the sun outside the Treasury he had twenty pounds counted into his palms as ex gratia award for the rebel money he had turned in. It was like Christmas for him and for many

---

[2]Fried dough

others like him when the payments began. They called it (since few could manage its proper official name) *egg-rasher.*[3]

As soon as the pound notes were placed in his palm Jonathan simply closed it tight over them and buried fist and money inside his trouser pocket. He had to be extra careful because he had seen a man a couple of days earlier collapse into near-madness in an instant before that oceanic crowd because no sooner had he got his twenty pounds than some heartless ruffian picked it off him. Though it was not right that a man in such an extremity of agony should be blamed yet many in the queues that day were able to remark quietly at the victim's carelessness, especially after he pulled out the innards of his pocket and revealed a hole in it big enough to pass a thief's head. But of course he had insisted that the money had been in the other pocket, pulling it out too to show its comparative wholeness. So one had to be careful.

Jonathan soon transferred the money to his left hand and pocket so as to leave his right free for shaking hands should the need arise, though by fixing his gaze at such an elevation as to miss all approaching human faces he made sure that the need did not arise, until he got home.

He was normally a heavy sleeper but that night he heard all the neighborhood noises die down one after another. Even the night watchman who knocked the hour on some metal somewhere in the distance had fallen silent after knocking one o'clock. That must have been the last thought in Jonathan's mind before he was finally carried away himself. He couldn't have been gone for long, though, when he was violently awakened again.

"Who is knocking?" whispered his wife lying beside him on the floor.

"I don't know," he whispered back breathlessly.

The second time the knocking came it was so loud and imperious that the rickety old door could have fallen down.

"Who is knocking?" he asked them, his voice parched and trembling.

"Na tief-man and him people," came the cool reply. "Make you hopen de door." This was followed by the heaviest knocking of all.

Maria was the first to raise the alarm, then he followed and all their children.

"*Police-o! Thieves-o! Neighbors-o! Police-o! We are lost! We are dead! Neighbors, are you asleep? Wake up! Police-o!*"

"You done finish?" asked the voice outside. "Make we help you small. Oya, everybody!"

"*Police-o! Tief-man-so! Neighbors-o! we done loss-o! Police-o! . . .*"

There were at least five other voices besides the leader's.

---

[3]Phonetic pronunciation of *ex gratia*, the official term for Nigerian currency. Given in exchange for worthless rebel currency.

Jonathan and his family were now completely paralyzed by terror. Maria and the children sobbed inaudibly like lost souls. Jonathan groaned continuously.

The silence that followed the thieves' alarm vibrated horribly. Jonathan all but begged their leader to speak again and be done with it.

"My frien," said he at long last, "we don try our best for call dem but I tink say dem all done sleep-o . . . So wetin we go do now? Sometaim you wan call soja? Or you wan make we call dem for you? Soja better pass police. No be so?"

"Na so!" replied his men. Jonathan thought he heard even more voices now than before and groaned heavily. His legs were sagging under him and his throat felt like sandpaper.

"My frien, why you no de talk again. I de ask you say you wan make we call soja?"

"No."

"Awrighto. Now make we talk business. We no be bad tief. We no like for make trouble. Trouble done finish. War done finish and all the katakata[4] wey de for inside. No Civil War again. This time na Civil Peace. No be so?"

"Na so!" answered the horrible chorus.

"What do you want from me? I am a poor man. Everything I had went with this war. Why do you come to me? You know people who have money. We . . ."

"Awright! We know say you no get plenty money. But we sef no get even anini.[5] So derefore make you open dis window and give us one hundred pound and we go commot. Otherwise we de come for inside now to show you guitar-boy like dis . . ."

A volley of automatic fire rang through the sky. Maria and the children began to weep aloud again.

"Ah, missisi de cry again. No need for dat. We done talk say we na good tief. We just take our small money and go nwayorly. No molest. Abi we de molest?"

"At all!" said the chorus.

"My friends," began Jonathan hoarsely. "I hear what you say and I thank you. If I had one hundred pounds . . ."

"Lookia my frien, no be play we come play for your house. If we make mistake and step for inside you no go like am-o. So derefore . . ."

"To God who made me; if you come inside and find one hundred pounds, take and shoot me and shoot my wife and children. I swear to God. The only

---

[4]Shit

[5]Penny

money I have in this life is this twenty-pounds *egg-rasher* they gave me today . . ."

"OK. Time de go. Make you open dis window and bring the twenty pound. We go manage am like dat."

There were now loud murmurs of dissent among the chorus: "Na lie de man de lie; e get plenty money . . . Make we go inside and search properly well . . . Wetin be twenty pound? . . ."

"Shurrup!" rang the leader's voice like a lone shot in the sky and silenced the murmuring at once. "Are you dere? Bring the money quick!"

"I am coming," said Jonathan fumbling in the darkness with the key of the small wooden box he kept by his side on the mat.

At the first sign of light as neighbors and others assembled to commiserate with him he was already strapping his five-gallon demijohn to his bicycle carrier and his wife, sweating in the open fire, was turning over akara balls in a wide clay bowl of boiling oil. In the corner his eldest son was rinsing out dregs of yesterday's palm wine from old beer bottles.

"I count it as nothing," he told his sympathizers, his eyes on the rope he was tying. "What is *egg-rasher?* Did I depend on it last week? Or is it greater than other things that went with the war? I say, let *egg-rasher* perish in the flames! Let it go where everything else has gone. Nothing puzzles God."

[1971]

QUESTIONS

1. Why does Jonathan Iwegbu consider himself so lucky? What does his joy convey regarding the severity of the war and its impact on the civilian population?

2. Why are those who take Jonathan's taxi anxious to rid themselves of Biafran money? What are the implications of their attitude toward money?

3. How does the Iwegbu family rebuild their lives after the war? How does their effort illustrate their resilience?

4. Jonathan's encounter with the gang of thieves is presented in an almost comic way. How does this presentation affect your response to the encounter? Why do you think Achebe relates the tale in this way?

5. Why does Jonathan repeat the phrase, "nothing puzzles God"? What does this phrase imply about his attitude toward the war, the peace, and life in general?

6. In explaining his demand for money, the leader of the thieves refers to the time as "Civil Peace." What are the implications of this term? How does Civil Peace differ from Civil War? In what ways are the two conditions similar?

7. Throughout the story, Jonathan and his family take action to reestablish themselves in their village. Which actions are effective, and which are not? To what extent are the Iwegbus capable of controlling their lives? To what extent do outside forces control them?

8. Write a character analysis of Jonathan Iwegbu, focusing on the ways in which his philosophy is illustrated in his words, his actions, and his reactions. In your essay, explain why you consider him primarily a survivor or a victim.

9. "Civil Peace" is set in 1970 Nigeria, a country emerging from a bloody three-year civil war; the country had been a British colony until 1963. Read about the colonial influences on Nigeria and write a paper analyzing the story as a commentary on the impact of European values on African culture. Keep in mind the question of how colonialism contributed to the economic, social, and political turmoil that followed independence.

Raymond Carver
[1938–1988]

RAYMOND CARVER *grew up in a working class family in Yakima, Washington.*
At nineteen he married Maryann Burk and soon found himself struggling to
make ends meet for his family of two children while he attended Yakima
Community College. With a growing interest in writing, Carver moved his small
family to Paradise, California so he could attend Chico State College where he
took creative writing classes taught by early mentor, novelist John Gardner. While
attending school Carver worked in saw mills and at other odd jobs to support his
growing family. In 1963 Carver earned a bachelor's degree and left California for
the Iowa Writers Workshop.

    Carver's work was acknowledged early on in his career, when his short sto-
ries and poetry appeared in various small literary magazines. His financial strug-
gles continued, however. Coupled with burgeoning alcoholism spurred on by the
death of his father in 1968, Carver was forced to declare bankruptcy. His growing
fame, however, lead to a number of academic creative writing appointments, and
in 1976 Carver's first short story collection, Will You Be Quiet, *was published by*
a mainstream publisher. In 1981 he published the collection What We Talk
About When We Talk About Love, *followed by* Where I'm Calling From *(1988).*
He received much acclaim for his fiction, including a National Endowment for
the Arts award and a Guggenheim Fellowship.

    Carver successfully quelled his alcoholism in 1977, and considered it a turn-
ing point in his life. His family life, however, was irreparably damaged. The
Carvers separated and in 1979 Carver took up residence with poet Tess Gallagher
whom he had met at a writer's conference. Carver and Maryann eventually
divorced in 1982 and Gallagher and Carver married in 1988, six weeks before he
died of lung cancer.

    Carver said, "Everything we write is, in some way, autobiographical." In his
stories he often depicts the lives of white- and blue-collar workers who struggle to
understand and to express themselves in their world. Carver's prose style is
clipped and precise, but lacks any sense of judgment of the characters or their
actions. The characters he portrays are shown complete: for example, petty jeal-
ousies, gluttonous addictions, or prejudices. In this way, Carver attempts to make
his characters lifelike. While appearing ordinary, his characters are not without
moments of growth and exacting self-awareness. In Carver's stories, reader get
the sense that he chooses his words very carefully so that the honesty of the
moment can emerge.

Cathedral

RAYMOND CARVER

THIS BLIND MAN, an old friend of my wife's, he was on his way to spend the night. His wife had died. So he was visiting the dead wife's relatives in Connecticut. He called my wife from his in-laws'. Arrangements were made. He would come by train, a five-hour trip, and my wife would meet him at the station. She hadn't seen him since she worked for him one summer in Seattle ten years ago. But she and the blind man had kept in touch. They made tapes and mailed them back and forth. I wasn't enthusiastic about his visit. He was no one I knew. And his being blind bothered me. My idea of blindness came from the movies. In the movies, the blind moved slowly and never laughed. Sometimes they were led by seeing-eye dogs. A blind man in my house was not something I looked forward to.

That summer in Seattle she had needed a job. She didn't have any money. The man she was going to marry at the end of the summer was in officers' training school. He didn't have any money, either. But she was in love with the guy, and he was in love with her, etc. She'd seen something in the paper: HELP WANTED—*Reading to Blind Man*, and a telephone number. She phoned and went over, was hired on the spot. She'd worked with this blind man all summer. She read stuff to him, case studies, reports, that sort of thing. She helped him organize his little office in the county social-service department. They'd become good friends, my wife and the blind man. How do I know these things? She told me. And she told me something else. On her last day in the office, the blind man asked if he could touch her face. She agreed to this. She told me he touched his fingers to every part of her face, her nose—even her neck! She never forgot it. She even tried to write a poem about it. She was always trying to write a poem. She wrote a poem or two every year, usually after something really important had happened to her.

When we first started going out together, she showed me the poem. In the poem, she recalled his fingers and the way they had moved around over her face. In the poem, she talked about what she had felt at the time, about what went through her mind when the blind man touched her nose and lips. I can remember I didn't think much of the poem. Of course, I didn't tell her that.

Maybe I just don't understand poetry. I admit it's not the first thing I reach for when I pick up something to read.

Anyway, this man who'd first enjoyed her favors, the officer-to-be, he'd been her childhood sweetheart. So okay. I'm saying that at the end of the summer she let the blind man run his hands over her face, said goodbye to him, married her childhood etc., who was now a commissioned officer, and she moved away from Seattle. But they'd kept in touch, she and the blind man. She made the first contact after a year or so. She called him up one night from an Air Force base in Alabama. She wanted to talk. They talked. He asked her to send him a tape and tell him about her life. She did this. She sent the tape. On the tape, she told the blind man about her husband and about their life together in the military. She told the blind man she loved her husband but she didn't like it where they lived and she didn't like it that he was a part of the military-industrial thing. She told the blind man she'd written a poem and he was in it. She told him that she was writing a poem about what it was like to be an Air Force officer's wife. The poem wasn't finished yet. She was still writing it. The blind man made a tape. He sent her the tape. She made a tape. This went on for years. My wife's officer was posted to one base and then another. She sent tapes from Moody AFB,[1] McGuire, McConnell, and finally Travis, near Sacramento, where one night she got to feeling lonely and cut off from people she kept losing in that moving-around life. She got to feeling she couldn't go it another step. She went in and swallowed all the pills and capsules in the medicine chest and washed them down with a bottle of gin. Then she got into a hot bath and passed out.

But instead of dying, she got sick. She threw up. Her officer—why should he have a name? he was the childhood sweetheart, and what more does he want?—came home from somewhere, found her, and called the ambulance. In time, she put it all on a tape and sent the tape to the blind man. Over the years she put all kinds of stuff on tapes and sent the tapes off lickety-split. Next to writing a poem every year, I think it was her chief means of recreation. On one tape, she told the blind man she'd decided to live away from her officer for a time. On another tape, she told him about her divorce. She and I began going out, and of course she told her blind man about it. She told him everything, or so it seemed to me. Once she asked me if I'd like to hear the latest tape from the blind man. This was a year ago. I was on the tape, she said. So I said okay, I'd listen to it. I got us drinks and we settled down in the living room. We made ready to listen. First she inserted the tape into the player and adjusted a couple of dials. Then she pushed a lever. The tape squeaked and someone began to talk in this loud voice. She lowered the volume. After a few minutes of

---

[1]Air force base.

harmless chitchat, I heard my own name in the mouth of this stranger, this blind man I didn't even know! And then this: "From all you've said about him, I can only conclude—" But we were interrupted, a knock at the door, something, and we didn't ever get back to the tape. Maybe it was just as well. I'd heard all I wanted to.

Now this same blind man was coming to sleep in my house.

"Maybe I could take him bowling," I said to my wife. She was at the draining board doing scalloped potatoes. She put down the knife she was using and turned around.

"If you love me," she said, "you can do this for me. If you don't love me, okay. But if you had a friend, any friend, and the friend came to visit, I'd make him feel comfortable." She wiped her hands with the dish towel.

"I don't have any blind friends," I said.

"You don't have *any* friends," she said. "Period. Besides," she said, "goddam it, his wife's just died! Don't you understand that? The man's lost his wife!"

I didn't answer. She'd told me a little about the blind man's wife. Her name was Beulah. Beulah! That's a name for a colored woman.

"Was his wife a Negro?" I asked.

"Are you crazy?" my wife said. "Have you just flipped or something?" She picked up a potato. I saw it hit the floor, then roll under the stove. "What's wrong with you?" she said. "Are you drunk?"

"I'm just asking," I said.

Right then my wife filled me in with more detail than I cared to know. I made a drink and sat at the kitchen table to listen. Pieces of the story began to fall into place.

Beulah had gone to work for the blind man the summer after my wife had stopped working for him. Pretty soon Beulah and the blind man had themselves a church wedding. It was a little wedding—who'd want to go to such a wedding in the first place?—just the two of them, plus the minister and the minister's wife. But it was a church wedding just the same. It was what Beulah had wanted, he'd said. But even then Beulah must have been carrying the cancer in her glands. After they had been inseparable for eight years—my wife's word, *inseparable*—Beulah's health went into a rapid decline. She died in a Seattle hospital room, the blind man sitting beside the bed and holding on to her hand. They'd married, lived and worked together, slept together—had sex, sure—and then the blind man had to bury her. All this without his having ever seen what the goddamned woman looked like. It was beyond my understanding. Hearing this, I felt sorry for the blind man for a little bit. And then I found myself thinking what a pitiful life this woman must have led. Imagine a woman who could never see herself as she was seen in the eyes of her loved one. A woman who could go on day after day and never receive the smallest compliment from her beloved. A woman whose husband could never read the expression on her face, be it misery or something better. Someone who could wear makeup or not—what difference to him? She could, if she wanted, wear green eye-shadow around one eye, a straight pin in her nostril, yellow slacks and purple shoes, no matter. And then to slip off into death, the blind man's hand on her hand, his blind eyes streaming tears—I'm imagining now—her last thought maybe this: that he never even knew what she looked like, and she on an express to the grave. Robert was left with a small insurance policy and half of a twenty-peso Mexican coin. The other half of the coin went into the box with her. Pathetic.

So when the time rolled around, my wife went to the depot to pick him up. With nothing to do but wait—sure, I blamed him for that—I was having a drink and watching the TV when I heard the car pull into the drive. I got up from the sofa with my drink and went to the window to have a look.

I saw my wife laughing as she parked the car. I saw her get out of the car and shut the door. She was still wearing a smile. Just amazing. She went around to the other side of the car to where the blind man was already starting to get out. This blind man, feature this, he was wearing a full beard! A beard on a blind man! Too much, I say. The blind man reached into the back seat and dragged out a suitcase. My wife took his arm, shut the car door, and, talking all the way, moved him down the drive and then up the steps to the front porch. I turned off the TV. I finished my drink, rinsed the glass, dried my hands. Then I went to the door.

My wife said, "I want you to meet Robert. Robert, this is my husband. I've told you all about him." She was beaming. She had this blind man by his coat sleeve.

The blind man let go of his suitcase and up came his hand.

I took it. He squeezed hard, held my hand, and then he let it go.

"I feel like we've already met," he boomed.

"Likewise," I said. I didn't know what else to say. Then I said, "Welcome. I've heard a lot about you." We began to move then, a little group, from the porch into the living room, my wife guiding him by the arm. The blind man was carrying his suitcase in his other hand. My wife said things like, "To your left here, Robert. That's right. Now watch it, there's a chair. That's it. Sit down right here. This is the sofa. We just bought this sofa two weeks ago."

I started to say something about the old sofa. I'd liked that old sofa. But I didn't say anything. Then I wanted to say something else, small-talk, about the scenic ride along the Hudson. How going *to* New York, you should sit on the right-hand side of the train, and coming *from* New York, the left-hand side.

"Did you have a good train ride?" I said. "Which side of the train did you sit on, by the way?"

"What a question, which side!" my wife said. "What's it matter which side?" she said.

"I just asked," I said.

"Right side," the blind man said. "I hadn't been on a train in nearly forty years. Not since I was a kid. With my folks. That's been a long time. I'd nearly forgotten the sensation. I have winter in my beard now," he said. "So I've been told, anyway. Do I look distinguished, my dear?" the blind man said to my wife.

"You look distinguished, Robert," she said. "Robert," she said. "Robert, it's just so good to see you."

My wife finally took her eyes off the blind man and looked at me. I had the feeling she didn't like what she saw. I shrugged.

I've never met, or personally known, anyone who was blind. This blind man was late forties, a heavy-set, balding man with stooped shoulders, as if he carried a great weight there. He wore brown slacks, brown shoes, a light-brown shirt, a tie, a sports coat. Spiffy. He also had this full beard. But he didn't use a cane and he didn't wear dark glasses. I'd always thought dark glasses were a must for the blind. Fact was, I wished he had a pair. At first glance, his eyes looked like anyone else's eyes. But if you looked close, there was something different about them. Too much white in the iris, for one thing, and the pupils seemed to move around in the sockets without his knowing it or being able to stop it. Creepy. As I stared at his face, I saw the left pupil turn in toward his nose while the other made an effort to keep in one place. But it was only an effort, for that eye was on the roam without his knowing it or wanting it to be.

I said, "Let me get you a drink. What's your pleasure? We have a little of everything. It's one of our pastimes."

"Bub, I'm a Scotch man myself," he said fast enough in this big voice.

"Right," I said. Bub! "Sure you are. I knew it."

He let his fingers touch his suitcase, which was sitting alongside the sofa. He was taking his bearings. I didn't blame him for that.

"I'll move that up to your room," my wife said.

"No, that's fine," the blind man said loudly. "It can go up when I go up."

"A little water with the Scotch?" I said.

"Very little," he said.

"I knew it," I said.

He said, "Just a tad. The Irish actor, Barry Fitzgerald?[2] I'm like that fellow. When I drink water, Fitzgerald said, I drink water. When I drink whiskey, I drink whiskey." My wife laughed. The blind man brought his hand up under his beard. He lifted his beard slowly and let it drop.

---

[2]Known for playing stock Irish figures in American films of the mid twentieth century.

I did the drinks, three big glasses of Scotch with a splash of water in each. Then we made ourselves comfortable and talked about Robert's travels. First the long flight from the West Coast to Connecticut, we covered that. Then from Connecticut up here by train. We had another drink concerning that leg of the trip.

I remembered having read somewhere that the blind didn't smoke because, as speculation had it, they couldn't see the smoke they exhaled. I thought I knew that much and that much only about blind people. But this blind man smoked his cigarette down to the nubbin and then lit another one. This blind man filled his ashtray and my wife emptied it.

When we sat down at the table for dinner, we had another drink. My wife heaped Robert's plate with cube steak, scalloped potatoes, green beans. I buttered him up two slices of bread. I said, "Here's bread and butter for you." I swallowed some of my drink. "Now let us pray," I said, and the blind man lowered his head. My wife looked at me, her mouth agape. "Pray the phone won't ring and the food doesn't get cold," I said.

We dug in. We ate everything there was to eat on the table. We ate like there was no tomorrow. We didn't talk. We ate. We scarfed. We grazed that table. We were into serious eating. The blind man had right away located his foods, he knew just where everything was on his plate. I watched with admiration as he used his knife and fork on the meat. He'd cut two pieces of meat, fork the meat into his mouth, and then go all out for the scalloped potatoes, the beans next, and then he'd tear off a hunk of buttered bread and eat that. He'd follow this up with a big drink of milk. It didn't seem to bother him to use his fingers once in a while, either.

We finished everything, including half a strawberry pie. For a few moments, we sat as if stunned. Sweat beaded on our faces. Finally, we got up from the table and left the dirty plates. We didn't look back. We took ourselves into the living room and sank into our places again. Robert and my wife sat on the sofa. I took the big chair. We had us two or three more drinks while they talked about the major things that had come to pass for them in the past ten years. For the most part, I just listened. Now and then I joined in. I didn't want him to think I'd left the room, and I didn't want her to think I was feeling left out. They talked of things that had happened to them—to them!—these past ten years. I waited in vain to hear my name on my wife's sweet lips: "And then my dear husband came into my life"—something like that. But I heard nothing of the sort. More talk of Robert. Robert had done a little of everything, it seemed, a regular blind jack-of-all-trades. But most recently he and his wife had had an Amway[3] distributorship, from which, I gathered, they'd earned their living, such as it was. The

---

[3] A retail business run from the home.

blind man was also a ham radio operator. He talked in his loud voice about con-
versations he'd had with fellow operators in Guam, in the Philippines, in Alaska,
and even in Tahiti. He said he'd have a lot of friends there if he ever wanted to
go visit those places. From time to time, he'd turn his blind face toward me, put
his hand under his beard, ask me something. How long had I been in my present position? (Three years.) Did I like my work (I didn't.) Was I going to stay
with it? (What were the options?) Finally when I thought he was beginning to
run down, I got up and turned on the TV.

My wife looked at me with irritation. She was heading toward a boil. Then
she looked at the blind man and said, "Robert, do you have a TV?"

The blind man said, "My dear, I have two TVs. I have a color set and a
black-and-white thing, an old relic. It's funny, but if I turn the TV on, and I'm
always turning it on, I turn on the color set. It's funny, don't you think?"

I didn't know what to say to that. I had absolutely nothing to say to that.
No opinion. So I watched the news program and tried to listen to what the
announcer was saying.

"This is a color TV," the blind man said. "Don't ask me how, but I can tell."

"We traded up a while ago," I said.

The blind man had another taste of his drink. He lifted his beard, sniffed
it, and let it fall. He leaned forward on the sofa. He positioned his ashtray on
the coffee table, then put the lighter to his cigarette. He leaned back on the sofa
and crossed his legs at the ankles.

My wife covered her mouth, and then she yawned. She stretched. She said,
"I think I'll go upstairs and put on my robe. I think I'll change into something
else. Robert, you make yourself comfortable," she said.

"I'm comfortable," the blind man said.

"I want you to feel comfortable in this house," she said.

"I am comfortable," the blind man said.

After she'd left the room, he and I listened to the weather report and then
to the sports roundup. By that time, she'd been gone so long I didn't know if
she was going to come back. I thought she might have gone to bed. I wished
she'd come back downstairs. I didn't want to be left alone with a blind man. I
asked him if he wanted another drink, and he said sure. Then I asked if he
wanted to smoke some dope with me. I said I'd just rolled a number. I hadn't,
but I planned to do so in about two shakes.

"I'll try some with you," he said.

"Damn right," I said. "That's the stuff."

I got our drinks and sat down on the sofa with him. Then I rolled us two
fat numbers. I lit one and passed it. I brought it to his fingers. He took it and
inhaled.

"Hold it as long as you can," I said. I could tell he didn't know the first thing.

My wife came back downstairs wearing her pink robe and her pink slippers.

"What do I smell?" she said.

"We thought we'd have us some cannabis," I said.

My wife gave me a savage look. Then she looked at the blind man and said, "Robert, I didn't know you smoked."

He said, "I do now, my dear. There's a first time for everything. But I don't feel anything yet."

"This stuff is pretty mellow," I said. "This stuff is mild. It's dope you can reason with," I said. "It doesn't mess you up."

"Not much it doesn't, bub," he said, and laughed.

My wife sat on the sofa between the blind man and me. I passed her the number. She took it and toked and then passed it back to me. "Which way is this going?" she said. Then she said, "I shouldn't be smoking this. I can hardly keep my eyes open as it is. That dinner did me in. I shouldn't have eaten so much."

"It was the strawberry pie," the blind man said. "That's what did it," he said, and he laughed his big laugh. Then he shook his head.

"There's more strawberry pie," I said.

"Do you want some more, Robert?" my wife said.

"Maybe in a little while," he said.

We gave our attention to the TV. My wife yawned again. She said, "Your bed is made up when you feel like going to bed, Robert. I know you must have had a long day. When you're ready to go to bed, say so." She pulled his arm. "Robert?"

He came to and said, "I've had a real nice time. This beats tapes, doesn't it?"

I said, "Coming at you," and I put the number between his fingers. He inhaled, held the smoke, and then let it go. It was like he'd been doing it since he was nine years old.

"Thanks, bub," he said. "But I think this is all for me. I think I'm beginning to feel it," he said. He held the burning roach out for my wife.

"Same here," she said. "Ditto. Me, too." She took the roach and passed it to me. "I may just sit here for a while between you two guys with my eyes closed. But don't let me bother you, okay? Either one of you. If it bothers you, say so. Otherwise, I may just sit here with my eyes closed until you're ready to go to bed," she said. "Your bed's made up, Robert, when you're ready. It's right next to our room at the top of the stairs. We'll show you up when you're ready. You wake me up now, you guys, if I fall asleep." She said that and then she closed her eyes and went to sleep.

The news program ended. I got up and changed the channel. I sat back down on the sofa. I wished my wife hadn't pooped out. Her head lay across the back of the sofa, her mouth open. She'd turned so that her robe had slipped away from her legs, exposing a juicy thigh. I reached to draw her robe back over her, and it was then that I glanced at the blind man. What the hell! I flipped the robe open again.

"You say when you want some strawberry pie," I said.

"I will," he said.

I said, "Are you tired? Do you want me to take you up to your bed? Are you ready to hit the hay?"

"Not yet," he said. "No, I'll stay up with you, bub. If that's all right. I'll stay up until you're ready to turn in. We haven't had a chance to talk. Know what I mean? I feel like me and her monopolized the evening." He lifted his beard and he let it fall. He picked up his cigarettes and his lighter.

"That's all right," I said. Then I said, "I'm glad for the company."

And I guess I was. Every night I smoked dope and stayed up as long as I could before I fell asleep. My wife and I hardly ever went to bed at the same time. When I did go to sleep, I had these dreams. Sometimes I'd wake up from one of them, my heart going crazy.

Something about the church and the Middle Ages was on the TV. Not your run-of-the-mill TV fare. I wanted to watch something else. I turned to the other channels. But there was nothing on them, either. So I turned back to the first channel and apologized.

"Bub, it's all right," the blind man said. "It's fine with me. Whatever you want to watch is okay. I'm always learning something. Learning never ends. It won't hurt me to learn something tonight. I got ears," he said.

We didn't say anything for a time. He was leaning forward with his head turned at me, his right ear aimed in the direction of the set. Very disconcerting. Now and then his eyelids drooped and then they snapped open again. Now and then he put his fingers into his beard and tugged, like he was thinking about something he was hearing on the television.

On the screen, a group of men wearing cowls was being set upon and tormented by men dressed in skeleton costumes and men dressed as devils. The men dressed as devils wore devil masks, horns, and long tails. This pageant was part of a procession. The Englishman who was narrating the thing said it took place in Spain once a year. I tried to explain to the blind man what was happening.

"Skeletons," he said. "I know about skeletons," he said, and he nodded.

The TV showed this one cathedral. Then there was a long, slow look at another one. Finally, the picture switched to the famous one in Paris, with its flying buttresses and its spires reaching up to the clouds. The camera pulled away to show the whole of the cathedral rising above the skyline.

There were times when the Englishman who was telling the thing would shut up, would simply let the camera move around over the cathedrals. Or else the camera would tour the countryside, men in fields walking behind oxen. I waited as long as I could. Then I felt I had to say something. I said, "They're showing the outside of this cathedral now. Gargoyles. Little statues carved to look like monsters. Now I guess they're in Italy. Yeah, they're in Italy. There's paintings on the walls of this one church."

"Are those fresco paintings, bub?" he asked, and he sipped from his drink.

I reached for my glass. But it was empty. I tried to remember what I could remember. "You're asking me are those frescoes?" I said. "That's a good question. I don't know."

The camera moved to a cathedral outside Lisbon. The differences in the Portuguese cathedral compared with the French and Italian were not that great. But they were there. Mostly the interior stuff. Then something occurred to me, and I said, "Something has occurred to me. Do you have any idea what a cathedral is? What they look like, that is? Do you follow me? If somebody says cathedral to you, do you have any notion what they're talking about? Do you know the difference between that and a Baptist church, say?"

He let the smoke dribble from his mouth. "I know they took hundreds of workers fifty or a hundred years to build," he said. "I just heard the man say that, of course. I know generations of the same families worked on a cathedral. I heard him say that, too. The men who began their life's work on them, they never lived to see the completion of their work. In that wise, bub, they're no different from the rest of us, right?" He laughed. Then his eyelids drooped again. His head nodded. He seemed to be snoozing. Maybe he was imagining himself in Portugal. The TV was showing another cathedral now. This one was in Germany. The Englishman's voice droned on. "Cathedrals," the blind man said. He sat up and rolled his head back and forth. "If you want the truth, bub, that's about all I know. What I just said. What I heard him say. But maybe you could describe one to me? I wish you'd do it. I'd like that. If you want to know, I really don't have a good idea."

I stared hard at the shot of the cathedral on the TV. How could I even begin to describe it? But say my life depended on it. Say my life was being threatened by an insane guy who said I had to do it or else.

I stared some more at the cathedral before the picture flipped off into the countryside. There was no use. I turned to the blind man and said, "To begin with, they're very tall." I was looking around the room for clues. "They reach way up. Up and up. Toward the sky. They're so big, some of them, they have to have these supports. To help hold them up, so to speak. These supports are called buttresses. They remind me of viaducts, for some reason. But maybe you don't know viaducts, either? Sometimes the cathedrals have devils and such carved into the front. Sometimes lords and ladies. Don't ask me why this is," I said.

He was nodding. The whole upper part of his body seemed to be moving back and forth.

"I'm not doing so good, am I?" I said.

He stopped nodding and leaned forward on the edge of the sofa. As he listened to me, he was running his fingers through his beard. I wasn't getting through to him, I could see that. But he waited for me to go on just the same. He nodded, like he was trying to encourage me. I tried to think what else to say. "They're really big," I said. "They're massive. They're built of stone. Marble, too, sometimes. In those olden days, when they built cathedrals, men wanted to be close to God. In those olden days, God was an important part of everyone's life. You could tell this from their cathedral building. I'm sorry," I said, "but it looks like that's the best I can do for you. I'm just no good at it."

"That's all right, bub," the blind man said. "Hey, listen. I hope you don't mind my asking you. Can I ask you something? Let me ask you a simple question, yes or no. I'm just curious and there's no offense. You're my host. But let me ask if you are in any way religious? You don't mind my asking?"

I shook my head. He couldn't see that, though. A wink is the same as a nod to a blind man. "I guess I don't believe in it. In anything. Sometimes it's hard. You know what I'm saying?"

"Sure, I do," he said.

"Right," I said.

The Englishman was still holding forth. My wife sighed in her sleep. She drew a long breath and went on with her sleeping.

"You'll have to forgive me," I said. "But I can't tell you what a cathedral looks like. It just isn't in me to do it. I can't do any more than I've done."

The blind man sat very still, his head down, as he listened to me.

I said, "The truth is, cathedrals don't mean anything special to me. Nothing. Cathedrals. They're something to look at on late-night TV. That's all they are."

It was then that the blind man cleared his throat. He brought something up. He took a handkerchief from his back pocket. Then he said, "I get it, bub. It's okay. It happens. Don't worry about it," he said. "Hey, listen to me. Will you do me a favor? I got an idea. Why don't you find us some heavy paper? And a pen. We'll do something. We'll draw one together. Get us a pen and some heavy paper. Go on, bub, get the stuff," he said.

So I went upstairs. My legs felt like they didn't have any strength in them. They felt like they did after I'd done some running. In my wife's room, I looked around. I found some ballpoints in a little basket on her table. And then I tried to think where to look for the kind of paper he was talking about.

Downstairs in the kitchen, I found a shopping bag with onion skins in the bottom of the bag. I emptied the bag and shook it. I brought it into the living room and sat down with it near his legs. I moved some things, smoothed the wrinkles from the bag, spread it out on the coffee table.

The blind man got down from the sofa and sat next to me on the carpet.

He ran his fingers over the paper. He went up and down the sides of the paper. The edges, even the edges. He fingered the corners.

"All right," he said. "All right, let's do her."

He found my hand, the hand with the pen. He closed his hand over my hand. "Go ahead, bub, draw," he said. "Draw. You'll see. I'll follow along with you. It'll be okay. Just begin now like I'm telling you. You'll see. Draw," the blind man said.

So I began. First I drew a box that looked like a house. It could have been the house I lived in. Then I put a roof on it. At either end of the roof, I drew spires. Crazy.

"Swell," he said. "Terrific. You're doing fine," he said. "Never thought anything like this could happen in your lifetime, did you, bub? Well, it's a strange life, we all know that. Go on now. Keep it up."

I put in windows with arches. I drew flying buttresses. I hung great doors. I couldn't stop. The TV station went off the air. I put down the pen and closed and opened my fingers. The blind man felt around over the paper. He moved the tips of his fingers over the paper, all over what I had drawn, and he nodded.

"Doing fine," the blind man said.

I took up the pen again, and he found my hand. I kept at it. I'm no artist. But I kept drawing just the same.

My wife opened up her eyes and gazed at us. She sat up on the sofa, her robe hanging open. She said, "What are you doing? Tell me, I want to know."

I didn't answer her.

The blind man said, "We're drawing a cathedral. Me and him are working on it. Press hard," he said to me. "That's right. That's good," he said. "Sure. You got it, bub. I can tell. You didn't think you could. But you can, can't you? You're cooking with gas now. You know what I'm saying? We're going to really have us something here in a minute. How's the old arm?" he said. "Put some people in there now. What's a cathedral without people?"

My wife said, "What's going on? Robert, what are you doing? What's going on?"

"It's all right," he said to her. "Close your eyes now," the blind man said to me.

I did it. I closed them just like he said.

"Are they closed?" he said. "Don't fudge."

"They're closed," I said.

"Keep them that way," he said. He said, "Don't stop now. Draw."

So we kept on with it. His fingers rode my fingers as my hand went over the paper. It was like nothing else in my life up to now.

Then he said, "I think that's it. I think you got it," he said. "Take a look. What do you think?"

But I had my eyes closed. I thought I'd keep them that way for a little longer. I thought it was something I ought to do.

"Well?" he said. "Are you looking?"

My eyes were still closed. I was in my house. I knew that. But I didn't feel like I was inside anything.

"It's really something," I said.

[1983]

RAYMOND CARVER, *Cathedral*

1. Why does the narrator dislike the blind man?

2. What is the importance of the drawing sessions at the end of the story?

3. List the stereotypes the narrator expresses about the blind. What do these beliefs tell you about the narrator?

4. Why is the narrator jealous of the relationship that his wife and the blind man have?

5. The narrator mentions that he dislikes the blind early in the story. What is the nature of his prejudice? Does he overcome it in the story?

6. What is the meaning of the cathedral in the story? How does that relate to the discussion and to the story's conclusion?

7. What role does alcohol, marijuana, and food play in the story? What is their effect on the characters? Is there a connection between their actions and consumption?

8. Write a brief essay in which you discuss the prejudices that the narrator expresses throughout the story. Where do these prejudices come from? Do you think the narrator has overcome them by the end of the story?

9. The wife at the end of the story asks twice what is going on. Write an essay in which you explain what is going on at the end of the story and what happens to the narrator as he slips into his reverie.

T. Coraghessan Boyle
[1948–   ]

Celebrated contemporary American fictionist T. CORAGHESSAN BOYLE *was born Thomas John Boyle on December 2, 1948, in Peekskill, New York. An alumnus of the State University of New York at Potsdam, Boyle taught for four years at his alma mater, Lakeland High School in Shrub Oak, New York. He had majored in English and History at SUNY and would eventually return to literary studies as a graduate student at the University of Iowa: he completed the M.F.A. in Fiction in 1974 and a Ph.D. in British Literature in 1977. Boyle has served as fiction editor for the* Iowa Review *and, since 1978, as a faculty member of the English Department at the University of Southern California, where he established that institution's Creative Writing program. He and his wife Karen have three children—Kerrie, Milo, and Spencer—and live near Santa Barbara, California.*

In 1979, Boyle published Descent of Man and Other Stories, *the first book in an impressive list that currently includes nineteen volumes translated into over fifteen languages. He has written eleven novels, among them* The Tortilla Curtain *(1995),* World's End *(1987),* Drop City *(2003), and* The Inner Circle *(2004); his novel* The Road to Wellville *(1993) was adapted for the 1994 motion picture directed by Alan Parker, and his latest novel* Talk Talk *(2006) is currently under production. His works have earned Boyle many honors, ranging from National Endowment for the Arts grants (1977, 1983) to a Guggenheim Fellowship (1988), the PEN/Faulkner Award (1988, for* World's End*), and Doctor of Humane Letters honorary degree from the State University of New York (1991). His short stories appear not only in collections such as* Descent of Man, Greasy Lake *(1986), and* Tooth and Claw *(2005), but also in numerous periodicals:* The New Yorker, Harper's, Esquire, The Atlantic Monthly, Playboy, The Paris Review, *and* Granta, *to name a few. Often adapting historical subject matter (as in* The Road to Wellville*), or creating plausible fictional settings like Greasy Lake, Boyle may be broadly associated with the tradition of literary realism. But while Boyle recognizes in his fiction the influence of realists such as John Cheever and Raymond Carver, he also makes clear his debt to the fantastical and even absurdist visions of Flannery O'Connor, Gabriel García Márquez, and Samuel Beckett. "In my own books," writes Boyle, "I've tried to keep a sort of Beckettian humor about the grim things of our world, while struggling toward the light."*

Greasy Lake

It's about a mile down on the dark side of Route 88.

—Bruce Springsteen

T.C. BOYLE

THERE WAS A TIME when courtesy and winning ways went out of style, when it was good to be bad, when you cultivated decadence like a taste. We were all dangerous characters then. We wore torn-up leather jackets, slouched around with toothpicks in our mouths, sniffed glue and ether and what somebody claimed was cocaine. When we wheeled our parents' whining station wagons out into the street we left a patch of rubber half a block long. We drank gin and grape juice, Tango, Thunderbird, and Bali Hai. We were nineteen. We were bad. We read André Gide[1] and struck elaborate poses to show that we didn't give a shit about anything. At night, we went up to Greasy Lake.

Through the center of town, up the strip, past the housing developments and shopping malls, street lights giving way to the thin streaming illumination of the headlights, trees crowding the asphalt in a black unbroken wall: that was the way out to Greasy Lake. The Indians had called it Wakan, a reference to the clarity of its waters. Now it was fetid and murky, the mud banks glittering with broken glass and strewn with beer cans and the charred remains of bonfires. There was a single ravaged island a hundred yards from shore, so stripped of vegetation it looked as if the air force had strafed it. We went up to the lake because everyone went there, because we wanted to snuff the rich scent of possibility on the breeze, watch a girl take off her clothes and plunge into the festering murk, drink beer, smoke pot, howl at the stars, savor the incongruous full-throated roar of rock and roll against the primeval susurrus of frogs and crickets. This was nature.

I was there one night, late, in the company of two dangerous characters. Digby wore a gold star in his right ear and allowed his father to pay his tuition at Cornell; Jeff was thinking of quitting school to become a painter/musician/

---

[1] André Gide (1869–1951): French author who was awarded the 1947 Nobel Prize for Literature. Gide's works treat the tension between social and moral constraints and the individual's drive for freedom and experience. In 1952, his works were placed on the Roman Catholic Church's "Index of Forbidden Books."

---

headshop proprietor. They were both expert in the social graces, quick with a sneer, able to manage a Ford with lousy shocks over a rutted and gutted blacktop road at eighty-five while rolling a joint as compact as a Tootsie Roll Pop stick. They could lounge against a bank of booming speakers and trade "man"s with the best of them or roll out across the dance floor as if their joints worked on bearings. They were slick and quick and they wore their mirror shades at breakfast and dinner, in the shower, in closets and caves. In short, they were bad.

I drove, Digby pounded the dashboard and shouted along with Toots & the Maytals while Jeff hung his head out the window and streaked the side of my mother's Bel Air with vomit. It was early June, the air soft as a hand on your cheek, the third night of summer vacation. The first two nights we'd been out till dawn, looking for something we never found. On this, the third night, we'd cruised the strip sixty-seven times, been in and out of every bar and club we could think of in a twenty-mile radius, stopped twice for bucket chicken and forty-cent hamburgers, debated going to a party at the house of a girl Jeff's sister knew, and chucked two dozen raw eggs at mailboxes and hitchhikers. It was 2:00 A.M.; the bars were closing. There was nothing to do but take a bottle of lemon-flavored gin up to Greasy Lake.

The taillights of a single car winked at us as we swung into the dirt lot with its tufts of weed and washboard corrugations; '57 Chevy, mint, metallic blue. On the far side of the lot, like the exoskeleton of some gaunt chrome insect, a chopper leaned against its kickstand. And that was it for excitement: some junkie half-wit biker and a car freak pumping his girlfriend. Whatever it was we were looking for, we weren't about to find it at Greasy Lake. Not that night.

But then all of a sudden Digby was fighting for the wheel.

"Hey, that's Tony Lovett's car! Hey!" he shouted, while I stabbed at the brake pedal and the Bel Air nosed up to the gleaming bumper of the parked Chevy. Digby leaned on the horn, laughing, and instructed me to put my brights on. I flicked on the brights. This was hilarious. A joke. Tony would experience premature withdrawal and expect to be confronted by grim-looking state troopers with flashlights. We hit the horn, strobed the lights, and then jumped out of the car to press our witty faces to Tony's windows; for all we knew we might even catch a glimpse of some little fox's tit, and then we could slap backs with red-faced Tony, roughhouse a little, and go on to new heights of adventure and daring.

The first mistake, the one that opened the whole floodgate, was losing my grip on the keys. In the excitement, leaping from the car with the gin in one hand and a roach clip in the other, I spilled them in the grass—in the dark, rank, mysterious nighttime grass of Greasy Lake. This was a tactical error, as damaging and irreversible in its way as Westmoreland's decision to dig in at

Khe Sanh.[2] I felt it like a jab of intuition, and I stopped there by the open door, peering vaguely into the night that puddled up round my feet.

The second mistake—and this was inextricably bound up with the first—was identifying the car as Tony Lovett's. Even before the very bad character in greasy jeans and engineer boots ripped out of the driver's door, I began to realize that this chrome blue was much lighter than the robin's-egg of Tony's car, and that Tony's car didn't have rear-mounted speakers. Judging from their expressions, Digby and Jeff were privately groping toward the same inevitable and unsettling conclusion as I was.

In any case, there was no reasoning with this bad greasy character—clearly he was a man of action. The first lusty Rockette's kick of his steel-toed boot caught me under the chin, chipped my favorite tooth, and left me sprawled in the dirt. Like a fool, I'd gone down on one knee to comb the stiff hacked grass for the keys, my mind making connections in the most dragged-out, testudineous way, knowing that things had gone wrong, that I was in a lot of trouble, and that the lost ignition key was my grail and my salvation. The three or four succeeding blows were mainly absorbed by my right buttock and the tough piece of bone at the base of my spine.

Meanwhile, Digby vaulted the kissing bumpers and delivered a savage kungfu blow to the greasy character's collarbone. Digby had just finished a course in martial arts for phys-ed credit and had spent the better part of the past two nights telling us apocryphal tales of Bruce Lee types and of the raw power invested in lightning blows shot from coiled wrists, ankles and elbows. The greasy character was unimpressed. He merely backed off a step, his face like a Toltec mask,[3] and laid Digby out with a single whistling roundhouse blow . . . but by now Jeff had got into the act, and I was beginning to extricate myself from the dirt, a tinny compound of shock, rage, and impotence wadded in my throat.

Jeff was on the guy's back, biting at his ear. Digby was on the ground, cursing. I went for the tire iron I kept under the driver's seat. I kept it there because bad characters always keep tire irons under the driver's seat, for just such an occasion as this. Never mind that I hadn't been involved in a fight since sixth grade, when a kid with a sleepy eye and two streams of mucus depending from his nostrils hit me in the knee with a Louisville slugger; never mind

---

[2] Westmoreland's ... Khe Sanh: The battle of Khe Sanh lasted 77 days and is considered one of the most controversial battles of the Vietnam war. American General William C. Westmoreland regarded Khe Sanh as an important strategic position from which to invade Laos.

[3] Toltec mask: The Toltecs are possibly mythical ancestors of the Aztecs; they may have existed in Ancient Mexico. Their masks are of monstrous, animalistic images.

that I'd touched the tire iron exactly twice before, to change tires: it was there. And I went for it.

I was terrified. Blood was beating in my ears, my hands were shaking, my heart turning over like a dirtbike in the wrong gear. My antagonist was shirtless, and a single cord of muscle flashed across his chest as he bent forward to peel Jeff from his back like a wet overcoat. "Motherfucker," he spat, over and over, and I was aware in that instant that all four of us—Digby, Jeff, and myself included—were chanting "motherfucker, motherfucker," as if it were a battle cry. (What happened next? the detective asks the murderer from beneath the turned-down brim of his porkpie hat. I don't know, the murderer says, something came over me. Exactly.)

Digby poked the flat of his hand in the bad character's face and I came at him like a kamikaze, mindless, raging, stung with humiliation—the whole thing, from the initial boot in the chin to this murderous primal instant involving no more than sixty hyperventilating, gland-flooding seconds—and I came at him and brought the tire iron down across his ear. The effect was instantaneous, astonishing. He was a stunt man and this was Hollywood, he was a big grimacing toothy balloon and I was a man with a straight pin. He collapsed. Wet his pants. Went loose in his boots.

A single second, big as a zeppelin, floated by. We were standing over him in a circle, gritting our teeth, jerking our necks, our limbs and hands and feet twitching with glandular discharges. No one said anything. We just stared down at the guy, the car freak, the lover, the bad greasy character laid low. Digby looked at me; so did Jeff. I was still holding the tire iron, a tuft of hair clinging to the crook like dandelion fluff, like down. Rattled, I dropped it in the dirt, already envisioning the headlines, the pitted faces of the police inquisitors, the gleam of handcuffs, clank of bars, the big black shadows rising from the back of the cell . . . when suddenly a raw torn shriek cut through me like all the juice in all the electric chairs in the country.

It was the fox. She was short, barefoot, dressed in panties and a man's shirt. "Animals!" she screamed, running at us with her fists clenched and wisps of blow-dried hair in her face. There was a silver chain round her ankle, and her toenails flashed in the glare of the headlights. I think it was the toenails that did it. Sure, the gin and the cannabis and even the Kentucky Fried may have had a hand in it, but it was the sight of those flaming toes that set us off—the toad emerging from the loaf in *Virgin Spring*,[4] lipstick smeared on a child: she was already tainted. We were on her like Bergman's deranged brothers—see no evil, hear none, speak none—panting, wheezing, tearing at her clothes,

---

[4] *Virgin Spring*: refers to Ingmar Bergman's film *The Virgin Spring* (1961), in which two herdsman rape and murder a virgin on her way to church.

grabbing for flesh. We were bad characters, and we were scared and hot and three steps over the line—anything could have happened.

It didn't.

Before we could pin her to the hood of the car, our eyes masked with lust and greed and the purest primal badness, a pair of headlights swung into the lot. There we were, dirty, bloody, guilty, dissociated from humanity and civilization, the first of the Ur-crimes behind us, the second in progress, shreds of nylon panty and spandex brassiere dangling from our fingers, our flies open, lips licked—there we were, caught in the spotlight. Nailed.

We bolted. First for the car, and then, realizing we had no way of starting it, for the woods. I thought nothing. I thought escape. The headlights came at me like accusing fingers. I was gone.

Ram-bam-bam, across the parking lot, past the chopper and into the feculent undergrowth at the lake's edge, insects flying up in my face, weeds whipping, frogs and snakes and red-eyed turtles splashing off into the night: I was already ankle-deep in muck and tepid water and still going strong. Behind me, the girl's screams rose in intensity, disconsolate, incriminating, the screams of the Sabine women,[5] the Christian martyrs, Anne Frank[6] dragged from the garret. I kept going, pursued by those cries, imagining cops and bloodhounds. The water was up to my knees when I realized what I was doing: I was going to swim for it. Swim the breadth of Greasy Lake and hide myself in the thick clot of woods on the far side. They'd never find me there.

I was breathing in sobs, in gasps. The water lapped at my waist as I looked out over the moon-burnished ripples, the mats of algae that clung to the surface like scabs. Digby and Jeff had vanished. I paused. Listened. The girl was quieter now, screams tapering to sobs, but there were male voices, angry, excited, and the high-pitched ticking of the second car's engine. I waded deeper, stealthy, hunted, the ooze sucking at my sneakers. As I was about to take the plunge—at the very instant I dropped my shoulder for the first slashing stroke—I blundered into something. Something unspeakable, obscene, something soft, wet, moss-grown. A patch of weed? A log? When I reached out to touch it, it gave like a rubber duck, it gave like flesh.

In one of those nasty little epiphanies for which we are prepared by films and TV and childhood visits to the funeral home to ponder the shrunken painted

---

[5] Sabine women: In early Roman history, Sabine women were supposedly abducted by Romans in order to populate the Roman state. The "Rape of Sabine Women" (in this sense the term rape is from the Latin word rapere that means abduction) is frequently depicted in classical art.

[6] Anne Frank: A Jewish child who wrote a diary while hiding from the Germans during World War II.

forms of dead grandparents, I understood what it was that bobbed there so inadmissibly in the dark. Understood, and stumbled back in horror and revulsion, my mind yanked in six different directions (I was nineteen, a mere child, an infant, and here in the space of five minutes I'd struck down one greasy character and blundered into the waterlogged carcass of a second), thinking, The keys, the keys, why did I have to go and lose the keys? I stumbled back, but the muck took hold of my feet—a sneaker snagged, balance lost—and suddenly I was pitching face forward into the buoyant black mass, throwing out my hands in desperation while simultaneously conjuring the image of reeking frogs and muskrats revolving in slicks of their own deliquescing juices. AAAAArrrgh! I shot from the water like a torpedo, the dead man rotating to expose a mossy beard and eyes cold as the moon. I must have shouted out, thrashing around in the weeds, because the voices behind me suddenly became animated.

"What was that?"

"It's them, it's them: they tried to, tried to . . . *rape* me!" Sobs.

A man's voice, flat, Midwestern accent. "You sons a bitches, we'll kill you!" Frogs, crickets.

Then another voice, harsh, *r*-less, Lower East Side: "Motherfucker!" I recognized the verbal virtuosity of the bad greasy character in the engineer boots. Tooth chipped, sneakers gone, coated in mud and slime and worse, crouching breathless in the weeds waiting to have my ass thoroughly and definitively kicked and fresh from the hideous stinking embrace of a three-days-dead-corpse, I suddenly felt a rush of joy and vindication: the son of a bitch was alive! Just as quickly, my bowels turned to ice. "Come on out of there, you pansy motherfuckers!" the bad greasy character was screaming. He shouted curses till he was out of breath.

The crickets started up again, then the frogs. I held my breath. All at once there was a sound in the reeds, a swishing, a splash: thunk-a-thunk. They were throwing rocks. The frogs fell silent. I cradled my head. Swish, swish, thunk-a-thunk. A wedge of feldspar the size of a cue ball glanced off my knee. I bit my finger.

It was then that they turned to the car. I heard a door slam, a curse, and then the sound of the headlights shattering—almost a good-natured sound, celebratory, like corks popping from the necks of bottles. This was succeeded by the dull booming of the fenders, metal on metal, and then the icy crash of the windshield. I inched forward, elbows and knees, my belly pressed to the muck, thinking of guerrillas and commandos and *The Naked and the Dead.*[7] I parted the weeds and squinted the length of the parking lot.

---

[7] *The Naked and the Dead:* This 1958 novel by Norman Mailer graphically depicts the horrors of World War II combat and celebrates the soldiers who attempt to survive and maintain their humanity.

The second car—it was a Trans-Am—was still running, its high beams washing the scene in a lurid stagy light. Tire iron flailing, the greasy bad character was laying into the side of my mother's Bel Air like an avenging demon, his shadow riding up the trunks of the trees. Whomp. Whomp. Whomp-whomp. The other two guys—blond types, in fraternity jackets—were helping out with tree branches and skull-sized boulders. One of them was gathering up bottles, rocks, muck, candy wrappers, used condoms, poptops, and other refuse and pitching it through the window on the driver's side. I could see the fox, a white bulb behind the windshield of the '57 Chevy. "Bobbie," she whined over the thumping, "come *on*." The greasy character paused a moment, took one good swipe at the left taillight, and then heaved the tire iron halfway across the lake. Then he fired up the '57 and was gone.

Blond head nodded at blond head. One said something to the other, too low for me to catch. They were no doubt thinking that in helping to annihilate my mother's car they'd committed a fairly rash act, and thinking too that there were three bad characters connected with that very car watching them from the woods. Perhaps other possibilities occurred to them as well—police, jail cells, justices of the peace, reparations, lawyers, irate parents, fraternal censure. Whatever they were thinking, they suddenly dropped branches, bottles, and rocks and sprang for their car in unison, as if they'd choreographed it. Five seconds. That's all it took. The engine shrieked, the tires squealed, a cloud of dust rose from the rutted lot and then settled back on darkness.

I don't know how long I lay there, the bad breath of decay all around me, my jacket heavy as a bear, the primordial ooze subtly reconstituting itself to accommodate my upper thighs and testicles. My jaws ached, my knee throbbed, my coccyx was on fire. I contemplated suicide, wondered if I'd need bridgework. scraped the recesses of my brain for some sort of excuse to give my parents—a tree had fallen on the car, I was blindsided by a bread truck, hit and run, vandals had got to it while we were playing chess at Digby's. Then I thought of the dead man. He was probably the only person on the planet worse off than I was: I thought about him, fog on the lake, insects chirring cerily, and felt the tug of fear, felt the darkness opening up inside me like a set of jaws. Who was he, I wondered, this victim of time and circumstance bobbing sorrowfully in the lake at my back. The owner of the chopper, no doubt, a bad older character come to this. Shot during a murky drug deal, drowned while drunkenly frolicking in the lake. Another headline. My car was wrecked; he was dead.

When the eastern half of the sky went from black to cobalt and the trees began to separate themselves from the shadows, I pushed myself up from the mud and stepped out into the open. By now the birds had begun to take over for the crickets, and dew lay slick on the leaves. There was a smell in the air, raw and sweet at the same time, the smell of the sun firing buds and opening blossoms. I contemplated the car. It lay there like a wreck along the highway, like a steel sculpture left over from a vanished civilization. Everything was still. This was nature.

I was circling the car, as dazed and bedraggled as the sole survivor of an air blitz, when Digby and Jeff emerged from the trees behind me. Digby's face was crosshatched with smears of dirt; Jeff's jacket was gone and his shirt was torn across the shoulder. They slouched across the lot, looking sheepish, and silently came up beside me to gape at the ravaged automobile. No one said a word. After a while Jeff swung open the driver's door and began to scoop the broken glass and garbage off the seat. I looked at Digby. He shrugged. "At least they didn't slash the tires," he said.

It was true: the tires were intact. There was no windshield, the headlights were staved in, and the body looked as if it had been sledge-hammered for a quarter a shot at the county fair, but the tires were inflated to regulation pressure. The car was drivable. In silence, all three of us bent to scrape the mud and shattered glass from the interior. I said nothing about the biker. When we were finished, I reached in my pocket for the keys, experienced a nasty stab of recollection, cursed myself, and turned to search the grass. I spotted them almost immediately, no more than five feet from the open door, glinting like jewels in the first tapering shaft of sunlight. There was no reason to get philosophical about it: I eased into the seat and turned the engine over.

It was at that precise moment that the silver Mustang with the flame decals rumbled into the lot. All three of us froze; then Digby and Jeff slid into the car and slammed the door. We watched as the Mustang rocked and bobbed across the ruts and finally jerked to a halt beside the forlorn chopper at the far end of the lot. "Let's go," Digby said. I hesitated, the Bel Air wheezing beneath me.

Two girls emerged from the Mustang. Tight jeans, stiletto heels, hair like frozen fur. They bent over the motorcycle, paced back and forth aimlessly, glanced once or twice at us, and then ambled over to where the reeds sprang up in a green fence round the perimeter of the lake. One of them cupped her hands to her mouth. "Al," she called. "Hey, Al!"

"Come on," Digby hissed. "Let's get out of here."

But it was too late. The second girl was picking her way across the lot, unsteady on her heels, looking up at us and then away. She was older—twenty-five or -six—and as she came closer we could see there was something wrong with her: she was stoned or drunk, lurching now and waving her arms for balance. I gripped the steering wheel as if it were the ejection lever of a flaming jet, and Digby spat out my name, twice, terse and impatient.

"Hi," the girl said.

We looked at her like zombies, like war veterans, like deaf-and-dumb pencil peddlers.

She smiled, her lips cracked and dry. "Listen," she said, bending from the waist to look in the window, "you guys seen Al?" Her pupils were pinpoints, her eyes glass. She jerked her neck. "That's his bike over there—Al's. You seen him?"

Al. I didn't know what to say. I wanted to get out of the car and retch, I wanted to go home to my parents' house and crawl into bed. Digby poked me in the ribs. "We haven't seen anybody," I said.

The girl seemed to consider this, reaching out a slim veiny arm to brace herself against the car. "No matter," she said, slurring the *t*'s, "he'll turn up." And then, as if she'd just taken stock of the whole scene—the ravaged car and our battered faces, the desolation of the place—she said: "Hey, you guys look like some pretty bad characters—been fightin', huh?" We stared straight ahead, rigid as catatonics. She was fumbling in her pocket and muttering something. Finally she held out a handful of tablets in glassine wrappers: "Hey, you want to party, you want to do some of these with me and Sarah?"

I just looked at her. I thought I was going to cry. Digby broke the silence. "No thanks," he said, leaning over me. "Some other time."

I put the car in gear and it inched forward with a groan, shaking off pellets of glass like an old dog shedding water after a bath, heaving over the ruts on its worn springs, creeping toward the highway. There was a sheen of sun on the lake. I looked back. The girl was still standing there, watching us, her shoulders slumped, hand outstretched.

[1981]

QUESTIONS

1. Consider the diverse and even contradictory meanings of the titular setting of Greasy Lake. In what ways does this place-name contribute to the story's tone and foreshadow its developments?

2. Early in the story, the narrator mentions an imaginary conversation with a detective figure in "a pork-pie hat." Why in your view does the narrator include this aside? What kinds of stories does Boyle evoke with this allusion?

3. "Greasy Lake" is structured around the escalation of a drunken brawl. Describe the various kinds of violence that pervade the story and discuss the ways in which this tale might serve as a parable of American life or the human condition in general.

4. Why does the narrator withhold the information of his discovery at Greasy Lake? On the other hand, what might motivate this character to share the episode with the reader? How does the tension between secrecy and disclosure affect the story's conclusion?

5. After conducting appropriate research into literary realism, compose an essay about the ways in which "Greasy Lake" conforms to and/or departs from realist conventions and thematics.

Amy Tan
[1952–   ]

Acclaimed author of The Joy Luck Club and several other books, **AMY TAN** was born in San Francisco to Chinese immigrant parents. Her father worked as a minister and electrical engineer; her mother was a vocational nurse who really did belong to a Joy Luck Club in China. After her father and brother died of brain cancer within six months of each other, Tan's mother brought the family to Europe, where the young Amy, according to her own accounts, ran wild. On returning to the United States, she defied her mother's wishes that she become a neurosurgeon and concert pianist, and earned a bachelor's degree in English and linguistics (1973) and a master's degree in linguistics (1974) from San Jose State. Tan has been married since 1974 to Lou DeMattei, a tax attorney. She began her creative writing career as therapy to distract her from her ninety-hour work weeks as a freelance technical writer.

Tan's first novel, The Joy Luck Club (1989), intertwines the stories of four aging Chinese immigrant women and their four Americanized daughters. Made into a feature film in 1993, the novel explores not only mother-daughter relationships, but the cultural conflict between immigrant parents and their American children. This novel, along with others including The Kitchen God's Wife (1991), The Hundred Secret Senses (1995), and The Bonesetter's Daughter (2001), draws heavily from stories Tan's mother recounted about her life in China. In 1992 Tan adapted one of the stories from The Joy Luck Club for a children's book, The Moon Lady; her second children's book, The Chinese Siamese Cat, was published in 1994 and is the basis for a long-running PBS cartoon.

Often compared to fellow Chinese-American writer Maxine Hong Kingston, Amy Tan populates her novels with strong, conflicted, oppressed, but often triumphant women, undercutting the powerful patriarchal structure of Chinese society. Critics compare her fiction to the work of Victorian novelist Jane Austen, noting her acute sense of the complex relationships within families strained by cultural clashes. Of The Joy Luck Club, critic Carolyn See observes, the mothers' "deepest wish is to pass their knowledge, their tales, on to their children, especially to their daughters, but those young women are undergoing a slow death of their own; drowning in American culture at the same time they starve for a past they can never fully understand." This novel remains her most acclaimed work, receiving the Commonwealth Club Gold Award; the Bay Area Book Reviewers Award; the American Library Association's best book for young adults award; and nominations for the National Book Critics Circle and the Los Angeles Times book awards.

Tan's mother died in 1999 of complications from Alzheimer's disease. In the dedication for The Bonesetter's Daughter, *the author writes, "On the last day that my mother spent on earth, I learned her real name, as well as that of my grandmother. This book is dedicated to them." This dedication reflects what Tan once told a reporter for the* Seattle Times, *"My books have amounted to taking [my mother's] stories—a gift to me—and giving them back to her. To me, it was the ultimate thing I ever could have done for myself and my mother."*

Two Kinds from The Joy Luck Club

AMY TAN

My MOTHER BELIEVED YOU could be anything you wanted to be in America. You could open a restaurant. You could work for the government and get good retirement. You could buy a house with almost no money down. You could become rich. You could become instantly famous.

"Of course you can be prodigy, too," my mother told me when I was nine. "You can be best anything. What does Auntie Lindo know? Her daughter, she is only best tricky."

America was where all my mother's hopes lay. She had come here in 1949 after losing everything in China: her mother and father, her family home, her first husband, and two daughters, twin baby girls. But she never looked back with regret. There were so many ways for thing to get better.

We didn't immediately pick the right kind of prodigy. At first my mother thought I could be a Chinese Shirley Temple. We'd watch Shirley's old movies on TV as though they were training films. My mother would poke my arm and say, "*Ni kan*"—You watch. And I would see Shirley tapping her feet, or singing a sailor song, or pursing her lips into a very round O while saying, "Oh my goodness."

"*Ni kan*," said my mother as Shirley's eyes flooded with tears. "You already know how. Don't need talent for crying!"

Soon after my mother got this idea about Shirley Temple, she took me to a beauty training school in the Mission district and put me in the hands of a student who could barely hold the scissors without shaking. Instead of getting big fat curls, I emerged with an uneven mass of crinkly black fuzz. My mother dragged me off to the bathroom and tried to wet down my hair.

"You look like Negro Chinese," she lamented, as if I had done this on purpose.

The instructor of the beauty training school had to lop off these soggy clumps to make my hair even again. "Peter Pan is very popular these days," the instructor assured my mother. I now had hair the length of a boy's, with straight-across bangs that hung at a slant two inches above my eyebrows. I liked the haircut and it made me actually look forward to my future fame.

In fact, in the beginning, I was just as excited as my mother, maybe even more so. I pictured this prodigy part of me as many different images, trying each one on for size. I was a dainty ballerina girl standing by the curtains, waiting to hear the right music that would send me floating on my tiptoes. I was like the Christ child lifted out of the straw manger, crying with holy indignity. I was Cinderella stepping from her pumpkin carriage with sparkly cartoon music filling the air.

In all of my imaginings, I was filled with a sense that I would soon become *perfect*. My mother and father would adore me. I would be beyond reproach. I would never feel the need to sulk for anything.

But sometimes the prodigy in me became impatient. "If you don't hurry up and get me out of here, I'm disappearing for good," it warned. "And then you'll always be nothing."

Every night after dinner, my mother and I would sit at the Formica kitchen table. She would present new tests, taking her examples from stories of amazing children she had read in *Ripley's Believe It or Not,* or *Good Housekeeping, Reader's Digest,* and a dozen other magazines she kept in a pile in our bathroom. My mother got these magazines from people whose houses she cleaned. And since she cleaned many houses each week, we had a great assortment. She would look through them all, searching for stories about remarkable children.

The first night she brought out a story about a three-year-old boy who knew the capitals of all the states and even most of the European countries. A teacher was quoted as saying the little boy could also pronounce the names of the foreign cities correctly.

"What's the capital of Finland?" my mother asked me, looking at the magazine story.

All I knew was the capital of California, because Sacramento was the name of the street we lived on in Chinatown. "Nairobi!" I guessed, saying the most foreign word I could think of. She checked to see if that was possibly one way to pronounce "Helsinki" before showing me the answer.

The tests got harder—multiplying numbers in my head, finding the queen of hearts in a deck of cards, trying to stand on my head without using my hands, predicting the daily temperatures in Los Angeles, New York, and London.

One night I had to look at a page from the Bible for three minutes and then report everything I could remember. "Now Jehoshaphat had riches and honor in abundance and . . . that's all I remember, Ma," I said.

And after seeing my mother's disappointed face once again, something inside of me began to die. I hated the tests, the raised hopes and failed expectations. Before going to bed that night, I looked in the mirror above the bathroom sink and when I saw only my face staring back—and that it would always be this ordinary face—I began to cry. Such a sad, ugly girl! I made high-pitched noises like a crazed animal, trying to scratch out the face in the mirror.

And then I saw what seemed to be the prodigy side of me—because I had never seen that face before. I looked at my reflection, blinking so I could see more clearly. The girl staring back at me was angry, powerful. This girl and I were the same. I had new thoughts, willful thoughts, or rather thoughts filled with lots of won'ts. I won't let her change me, I promised myself. I won't be what I'm not.

So now on nights when my mother presented her tests, I performed listlessly, my head propped on one arm. I pretended to be bored. And I was. I got so bored I started counting the bellows of the foghorns out on the bay while my mother drilled me in other areas. The sound was comforting and reminded me of the cow jumping over the moon. And the next day, I played a game with myself, seeing if my mother would give up on me before eight bellows. After a while I usually counted only one, maybe two bellows at most. At last she was beginning to give up hope.

Two or three months had gone by without any mention of my being a prodigy again. And then one day my mother was watching *The Ed Sullivan Show* on TV. The TV was old and the sound kept shorting out. Every time my mother got halfway up from the sofa to adjust the set, the sound would go back on and Ed would be talking. As soon as she sat down, Ed would go silent again. She got up, the TV broke into loud piano music. She sat down. Silence. Up and down, back and forth, quiet and loud. It was like a stiff embraceless dance between her and the TV set. Finally she stood by the set with her hand on the sound dial.

She seemed entranced by the music, a little frenzied piano piece with this mesmerizing quality, sort of quick passages and then teasing lilting ones before it returned to the quick playful parts.

"*Ni kan*," my mother said, calling me over with hurried hand gestures, "Look here."

I could see why my mother was fascinated by the music. It was being pounded out by a little Chinese girl, about nine years old, with a Peter Pan haircut. The girl had the sauciness of a Shirley Temple. She was proudly modest like a proper Chinese child. And she also did this fancy sweep of a curtsy, so that the fluffy skirt of her white dress cascaded slowly to the floor like the petals of a large carnation.

In spite of these warning signs, I wasn't worried. Our family had no piano and we couldn't afford to buy one, let alone reams of sheet music and piano lessons. So I could be generous in my comments when my mother bad-mouthed the little girl on TV.

"Play note right, but doesn't sound good! No singing sound," complained my mother.

"What are you picking on her for?" I said carelessly. "She's pretty good. Maybe she's not the best, but she's trying hard." I knew almost immediately I would be sorry I said that.

"Just like you," she said. "Not the best. Because you not trying." She gave a little huff as she let go of the sound dial and sat down on the sofa.

The little Chinese girl sat down also to play an encore of "Anitra's Dance" by Grieg. I remember the song, because later on I had to learn how to play it.

Three days after watching *The Ed Sullivan Show*, my mother told me what my schedule would be for piano lessons and piano practice. She had talked to Mr. Chong, who lived on the first floor of our apartment building. Mr. Chong was a retired piano teacher and my mother had traded housecleaning services for weekly lessons and a piano for me to practice on every day, two hours a day, from four until six.

When my mother told me this, I felt as though I had been sent to hell. I whined and then kicked my foot a little when I couldn't stand it anymore.

"Why don't you like me the way I am? I'm *not* a genius! I can't play the piano. And even if I could, I wouldn't go on TV if you paid me a million dollars!" I cried.

My mother slapped me. "Who ask you be genius?" she shouted. "Only ask you be your best. For you sake. You think I want you be genius? Hnnh! What for! Who ask you!"

"So ungrateful," I heard her mutter in Chinese. "If she had as much talent as she had temper, she would be famous now."

Mr. Chong, whom I secretly nicknamed Old Chong, was very strange, always tapping his fingers to the silent music of an invisible orchestra. He looked ancient in my eyes. He had lost most of the hair on top of his head and he wore thick glasses and had eyes that always looked tired and sleepy. But he must have been younger than I thought, since he lived with his mother and was not yet married.

I met Old Lady Chong once and that was enough. She had this peculiar smell like a baby that had done something in his pants. And her fingers felt like a dead person's, like an old peach I once found in the back of the refrigerator; the skin just slid off the meat when I picked it up.

I soon found out why Old Chong had retired from teaching piano. He was deaf. "Like Beethoven!" he shouted to me. "We're both listening only in our head!" And he would start to conduct his frantic silent sonatas.

Our lessons went like this. He would open the book and point to different things, explaining their purpose: "Key! Treble! Bass! No sharps or flats! So this is C major! Listen now and play after me!"

And then he would play the C scale a few times, a simple chord, and then, as if inspired by an old, unreachable itch, he gradually added more notes and running trills and a pounding bass until the music was really something quite grand.

I would play after him, the simple scale, the simple chord, and then I just played some nonsense that sounded like a cat running up and down on top of garbage cans. Old Chong smiled and applauded and then said, "Very good! But now you must learn to keep time!"

So that's how I discovered that Old Chong's eyes were too slow to keep up with the wrong notes I was playing. He went through the motions in half-time. To help me keep rhythm, he stood behind me, pushing down on my right shoulder for every beat. He balanced pennies on top of my wrists so I would keep them still as I slowly played scales and arpeggios. He had me curve my hand around an apple and keep that shape when playing chords. He marched stiffly to show me how to make each finger dance up and down, staccato like an obedient little soldier.

He taught me all these things, and that was how I also learned I could be lazy and get away with mistakes, lots of mistakes. If I hit the wrong notes because I hadn't practiced enough, I never corrected myself. I just kept playing in rhythm. And Old Chong kept conducting his own private reverie.

So maybe I never really gave myself a fair chance. I did pick up the basics pretty quickly, and I might have become a good pianist at that young age. But I was so determined not to try, not to be anybody different that I learned to play only the most ear-splitting preludes, the most discordant hymns.

Over the next year, I practiced like this, dutifully in my own way. And then one day I heard my mother and her friend Lindo Jong both talking in a loud bragging tone of voice so others could hear. It was after church, and I was leaning against the brick wall wearing a dress with stiff white petticoats. Auntie Lindo's daughter, Waverly, who was about my age, was standing farther down the wall about five feet away. We had grown up together and shared all the closeness of two sisters squabbling over crayons and dolls. In other words, for the most part, we hated each other. I thought she was snotty. Waverly Jong had gained a certain amount of fame as "Chinatown's Littlest Chinese Chess Champion."

"She bring home too many trophy," lamented Auntie Lindo that Sunday. "All day she play chess. All day I have no time do nothing but dust off her winnings." She threw a scolding look at Waverly, who pretended not to see her.

"You lucky you don't have this problem," said Auntie Lindo with a sigh to my mother.

And my mother squared her shoulders and bragged: "Our problem worser than yours. If we ask Jing-mei wash dish, she hear nothing but music. It's like you can't stop this natural talent."

And right then, I was determined to put a stop to her foolish pride.

A few weeks later, Old Chong and my mother conspired to have me play in a talent show which would be held in the church hall. By then, my parents had saved up enough to buy me a secondhand piano, a black Wurlitzer spinet with a scarred bench. It was the showpiece of our living room.

For the talent show, I was to play a piece called "Pleading Child" from Schumann's *Scenes from Childhood*. It was a simple, moody piece that sounded more difficult than it was. I was supposed to memorize the whole thing, playing the repeat parts twice to make the piece sound longer. But I dawdled over it, playing a few bars and then cheating, looking up to see what notes followed. I never really listened to what I was playing. I daydreamed about being somewhere else, about being someone else.

The part I liked to practice best was the fancy curtsy: right foot out, touch the rose on the carpet with a pointed foot, sweep to the side, left leg bends, look up and smile.

My parents invited all the couples from the Joy Luck Club to witness my debut. Auntie Lindo and Uncle Tin were there. Waverly and her two older brothers had also come. The first two rows were filled with children both younger and older than I was. The littlest ones got to go first. They recited simple nursery rhymes, squawked out tunes on miniature violins, twirled Hula Hoops, pranced in pink ballet tutus, and when they bowed or curtsied, the audience would sigh in unison, "Awww," and then clap enthusiastically.

When my turn came, I was very confident. I remember my childish excitement. It was as if I knew, without a doubt, that the prodigy side of me really did exist. I had no fear whatsoever, no nervousness. I remember thinking to myself, This is it! This is it! I looked out over the audience, at my mother's blank face, my father's yawn, Auntie Lindo's stiff-lipped smile, Waverly's sulky expression. I had on a white dress layered with sheets of lace, and a pink bow in my Peter Pan haircut. As I sat down I envisioned people jumping to their feet and Ed Sullivan rushing up to introduce me to everyone on TV.

And I started to play. It was so beautiful. I was so caught up in how lovely I looked at first I didn't worry how I would sound. So it was a surprise to me when I hit the first wrong note and I realized something didn't sound quite right. And then I hit another and another followed that. A chill started at the top of my head and began to trickle down. Yet I couldn't stop playing, as though my hands were bewitched. I kept thinking my fingers would adjust themselves back, like a train switching to the right track. I played this strange jumble through two repeats, the sour notes staying with me all the way to the end.

When I stood up, I discovered my legs were shaking. Maybe I had just been nervous and the audience, like Old Chong, had seen me go through the right motions and had not heard anything wrong at all. I swept my right foot out, went down on my knee, looked up and smiled. The room was quiet, except for Old Chong, who was beaming and shouting, "Bravo! Bravo! Well done!" But then I saw my mother's face, her stricken face. The audience clapped weakly, and as I walked back to my chair, with my whole face quivering as I tried not to cry, I heard a little boy whisper loudly to his mother, "That was awful," and the mother whispered back, "Well, she certainly tried."

And now I realized how many people were in the audience, the whole world it seemed. I was aware of eyes burning into my back. I felt the shame of my mother and father as they sat stiffly throughout the rest of the show.

We could have escaped during intermission. Pride and some strange sense of honor must have anchored my parents to their chairs. And so we watched it all: the eighteen-year-old boy with a fake mustache who did a magic show and juggled flaming hoops while riding a unicycle. The breasted girl with white makeup who sang from *Madama Butterfly* and got honorable mention. And the eleven-year-old boy who won first prize playing a tricky violin song that sounded like a busy bee.

After the show, the Hsus, the Jongs, and the St. Clairs from the Joy Luck Club came up to my mother and father.

"Lots of talented kids," Auntie Lindo said vaguely, smiling broadly.

"That was somethin' else," said my father, and I wondered if he was referring to me in a humorous way, or whether he even remembered what I had done.

Waverly looked at me and shrugged her shoulders. "You aren't a genius like me," she said matter-of-factly. And if I hadn't felt so bad, I would have pulled her braids and punched her stomach.

But my mother's expression was what devastated me: a quiet, blank look that said she had lost everything. I felt the same way, and it seemed as if everybody were now coming up, like gawkers at the scene of an accident, to see what parts were actually missing. When we got on the bus to go home, my father was humming the busy-bee tune and my mother was silent. I kept thinking she wanted to wait until we got home before shouting at me. But when my father unlocked the door to our apartment, my mother walked in and then went to the back, into the bedroom. No accusations. No blame. And in a way, I felt disappointed. I had been waiting for her to start shouting, so I could shout back and cry and blame her for all my misery.

I assumed my talent-show fiasco meant I never had to play the piano again. But two days later, after school, my mother came out of the kitchen and saw me watching TV.

"Four clock," she reminded me as if it were any other day. I was stunned, as though she were asking me to go through the talent-show torture again. I wedged myself more tightly in front of the TV.

"Turn off TV," she called from the kitchen five minutes later.

I didn't budge. And then I decided. I didn't have to do what my mother said anymore. I wasn't her slave. This wasn't China. I had listened to her before and look what happened. She was the stupid one.

She came out of the kitchen and stood in the arched entryway of the living room. "Four clock," she said once again, louder.

"I'm not going to play anymore," I said nonchalantly. "Why should I? I'm not a genius."

She walked over and stood in front of the TV. I saw her chest was heaving up and down in an angry way.

"No!" I said, and I now felt stronger, as if my true self had finally emerged. So this was what had been inside me all along.

"No! I won't!" I screamed.

She yanked me by the arm, pulled me off the floor, snapped off the TV. She was frighteningly strong, half pulling, half carrying me toward the piano as I kicked the throw rugs under my feet. She lifted me up and onto the hard bench. I was sobbing by now, looking at her bitterly. Her chest was heaving even more and her mouth was open, smiling crazily as if she were pleased I was crying.

"You want me to be someone that I'm not!" I sobbed. "I'll never be the kind of daughter you want me to be!"

"Only two kinds of daughters," she shouted in Chinese. "Those who are obedient and those who follow their own mind! Only one kind of daughter can live in this house. Obedient daughter!"

"Then I wish I wasn't your daughter. I wish you weren't my mother," I shouted. As I said these things I got scared. It felt like worms and toads and slimy things crawling out of my chest, but it also felt good, as if this awful side of me had surfaced, at last.

"Too late change this," said my mother shrilly.

And I could sense her anger rising to its breaking point. I wanted to see it spill over. And that's when I remembered the babies she had lost in China, the ones we never talked about. "Then I wish I'd never been born!" I shouted. "I wish I were dead! Like them."

It was as if I had said the magic words. Alakazam!—and her face went blank, her mouth closed, her arms went slack, and she backed out of the room, stunned, as if she were blowing away like a small brown leaf, thin, brittle, lifeless.

It was not the only disappointment my mother felt in me. In the years that followed, I failed her so many times, each time asserting my own will, my right to fall short of expectations. I didn't get straight As. I didn't become class president. I didn't get into Stanford. I dropped out of college.

For unlike my mother, I did not believe I could be anything I wanted to be. I could only be me.

And for all those years, we never talked about the disaster at the recital or my terrible accusations afterward at the piano bench. All that remained unchecked, like a betrayal that was now unspeakable. So I never found a way to ask her why she had hoped for something so large that failure was inevitable.

And even worse, I never asked her what frightened me the most: Why had she given up hope?

For after our struggle at the piano, she never mentioned my playing again. The lessons stopped. The lid to the piano was closed, shutting out the dust, my misery, and her dreams.

So she surprised me. A few years ago, she offered to give me the piano, for my thirtieth birthday. I had not played in all those years. I saw the offer as a sign of forgiveness, a tremendous burden removed.

"Are you sure?" I asked shyly. "I mean, won't you and Dad miss it?"

"No, this your piano," she said firmly. "Always your piano. You only one can play."

"Well, I probably can't play anymore," I said. "It's been years."

"You pick up fast," said my mother, as if she knew this was certain. "You have natural talent. You could been genius if you want to."

"No I couldn't."

"You just not trying," said my mother. And she was neither angry nor sad. She said it as if to announce a fact that could never be disproved. "Take it," she said.

But I didn't at first. It was enough that she had offered to me. And after that, every time I saw it in my parent's living room, standing in front of the bay windows, it made me feel proud, as if it were a shiny trophy I had won back.

Last week I sent a tuner over to my parents' apartment and had the piano reconditioned, for purely sentimental reasons. My mother had died a few months before and I had been getting things in order for my father, a little bit at a time. I put the jewelry in special silk pouches. The sweaters she had knitted in yellow, pink, bright orange—all the colors I hated—I put those in moth-proof boxes. I found some old Chinese silk dresses, the kind with little slits up the sides. I rubbed the old silk against my skin, then wrapped them in tissue and decided to take them home with me.

After I had the piano tuned, I opened the lid and touched the keys. It sounded even richer than I remembered. Really, it was a very good piano. Inside the bench were the same exercise notes with handwritten scales, the same secondhand music books with their covers held together with yellow tape.

I opened up the Schumann book to the dark little piece I had played at the recital. It was on the left-hand side of the page, "Pleading Child." It looked more difficult than I remembered. I played a few bars, surprised at how easily the notes came back to me.

And for the first time, or so it seemed, I noticed the piece on the right-hand side. It was called "Perfectly Contented." I tried to play this one as well. It had a lighter melody but the same flowing rhythm and turned out to be quite easy. "Pleading Child" was shorter but slower; "Perfectly Contented" was longer, but faster. And after I played them both a few times, I realized they were two halves of the same song.

[1989]

1. When Jing-Mei looks in the mirror after disappointing her mother yet one more time, she first sees "a sad, ugly girl" and then "the prodigy," who is "angry, powerful." What does she recognize in herself in this scene? How does this recognition affect her relationship with her mother?

2. Why is Jing-Mei "determined not to try" to play the piano well? What is she afraid of if she does try her best?

3. Why does her mother give up after Jing-Mei's hysterical reminder of the dead babies in China? How does this represent a defeat for her mother? For Jing-Mei?

4. How do the struggles between Jing-Mei and her mother contribute to the theme of the story? In what ways to these struggles reflect a clash of cultures as well as generations?

5. As Jing-Mei grows older, she often wonders why her mother "hoped for something so large that failure was inevitable," and more important, why she gave up that hope. How does her mother's offer of the piano as a thirtieth-birthday gift help to resolve those questions for Jing-Mei?

6. What is the significance of the piano lessons with Old Chong? What does he represent to Jing-Mei? Why are his deafness and his "private reveries" important?

7. "Two Kinds" is filled with contrasting pairs: Jing-Mei's mother and Auntie Lindo; Jing-Mei and Waverly; obedient and disobedient daughters; and at the center of the story, Jing-Mei and her mother. At the end of the story, Jing-Mei discovers that "Pleading Child," the piece from the talent show, and "Perfectly Contented" are not contrasting pairs, but rather "two halves of the same song." What is the significance of this revelation? How does it help to resolve the central conflict in Jing-Mei's life?

8. Write an essay analyzing "Two Kinds" as a coming-of-age story, in which a child experiences a revelation that results in a loss of innocence. Focus on such features as the cultural differences between mother and daughter, the significance of the musical pieces, and the internal struggles endured by Jing-Mei.

9. The promise of America figures largely in the aspirations of Jing-Mei's mother: She believes in the American dream, she focuses on American

icons such as Shirley Temple and Ed Sullivan in her quest to make Jing-Mei a prodigy, and she believes in the power of perseverance and hard work. Write an essay analyzing this story as a commentary on the cultural clashes that occur when immigrants adapt to American values.

Part 2: Poetry

William Shakespeare
[1564–1616]

WILLIAM SHAKESPEARE *was born in Stratford-upon-Avon, the son of a glove-maker and wool dealer. Though his father, John, held some status in the city, at some point the family lost its position and thus, though his eldest son William attended Stratford Grammar School and may have had hopes of attending university, he did not. When Shakespeare was eighteen years old, he married Anne Hathaway and had three children before his twenty-first birthday. By the early 1590s he was established in London as an actor and a playwright, as well as the part-owner and manager of a theater company. He was a prolific writer, having written (or, in a couple of cases, co-written) at the time of his death thirty-eight plays and several volumes of poetry—*The Sonnets *(1609),* Venus and Adonis *(1593), and* The Rape of Lucrece *(1593).*

Perhaps the most pored-over of all authors, Shakespeare fascinates in part because of the lack of detail known about his life. However, a good deal is discernable about the social milieu surrounding his life and work. By the time Shakespeare emerged as an actor and a playwright in the theater scene in London of the early 1590s, he must have spent some time as an apprentice actor, and tried his hand at playwriting. Theater-going at that time spanned all social classes. His earliest plays draw heavily on classical sources and models, suggesting something about his early education. Playwriting at that time was probably considered more a professional skill than an art. When theaters were shut down because of the plague (1592–1593), he wrote his narrative poems, probably dedicated to the Earl of Southampton, a patron. When Shakespeare retired to Stratford-upon-Avon, he had seen to the publication of the poems, though not his plays. Plays at that time were written for a fee, with the rights retained by production companies. Shakespeare owned a share of the theater company, which had Lord Chamberlain as its patron and was under the royal sponsorship of King James. The company built the Globe Theater, where many of the plays were produced. He was buried in the same parish church where he was baptized. Not until seven years after his death were most of the plays collected and published by two of his partners.

The sonnets have a special place in the Shakespeare oeuvre. They are still considered models of the form, and are part of a vibrant sonnet-writing tradition in the Renaissance. The kind of sonnet Shakespeare—and other Renaissance writers such as Sir Thomas Wyatt, Henry Howard, Earl of Surrey, Edmund Spenser, and Sir Philip Sidney—wrote is often called the Elizabethan or Shakespearean sonnet. Differing from the Italian or Petrarchan sonnet, the

Elizabethan sonnet was organized in quatrains, with a concluding couplet. (The Petrarchan sonnet had an octave and a sestet.) Typically, the quatrains created an argument of examples, with each set of four lines offering an instance or amplification of the poem's central idea.

My Mistress' Eyes are Nothing Like the Sun

WILLIAM SHAKESPEARE

My mistress' eyes are nothing like the sun;
Coral is far more red than her lips' red;
If snow be white, why then her breasts are dun;
If hairs be wires, black wires grow on her head.
I have seen roses damasked, red and white,   5
But no such roses see I in her cheeks;
And in some perfumes is there more delight
Than in the breath that from my mistress reeks.
I love to hear her speak, yet well I know
That music hath a far more pleasing sound;   10
I grant I never saw a goddess go:
My mistress, when she walks, treads on the ground.
   And yet, by heaven, I think my love as rare
   As any she belied with false compare.

[1609]

First published in the 1609 *Shake-speares sonnets.*

QUESTIONS

WILLIAM SHAKESPEARE, *My Mistress' Eyes are Nothing Like the Sun*

1. What strategies does the poet use to create comparisons? For instance, he negates extravagant comparisons—"... no such roses see I in her cheeks."

2. What words in this poem seem to have negative connotations to a reader today? What did those words mean when Shakespeare wrote them?

3. Divide the poem into its three quatrains. What ideas does each quatrain elaborate? What cumulative effect do they have by the time the poem reaches its concluding couplet?

4. This sonnet playfully satirizes the commonplaces of the courtly love tradition, wherein the beloved is praised in idealized terms. What role does the satiric impulse play in a love poem? Is it a love poem?

5. The concluding couplet contains an oath—"by heaven." Why does the poet swear by heaven? What effect does this gesture have? What is the tone of this oath?

6. Note the paradoxes in the poem—for instance, that by calling his mistress ordinary, the poet deems his love "rare." When a poem tries to advance its argument by means of contradictory impulses as this poem does, what is the effect on the reader?

7. In an exploratory essay compare this poem with another love poem, either another sonnet by Shakespeare or one by another writer. What strategies does each poem employ to describe the beloved? To what extent do love poems appear to praise themselves—their artistry, their own wit—in addition to praising the beloved?

8. In a brief essay, discuss the descriptive and argumentative resources of the sonnet form, using this poem as an exemplar. For what sorts of descriptions and arguments does the sonnet appear to be uniquely suited?

Shall I Compare Thee to a Summer's Day?

WILLIAM SHAKESPEARE

Shall I compare thee to a summer's day?
Thou art more lovely and more temperate.
Rough winds do shake the darling buds of May,
And summer's lease hath all too short a date.
Sometime too hot the eye of heaven shines,   5
And often is his gold complexion dimmed;
And every fair from fair sometimes declines,
By chance, or nature's changing course, untrimmed.
But thy eternal summer shall not fade,
Nor lose possession of that fair thou ow'st;   10
Nor shall death brag thou wand'rest in his shade,
When in eternal lines to time thou grow'st.
   So long as men can breathe or eyes can see,
   So long lives this, and this gives life to thee.

[1609]

First published in the 1609 *Shake-speares sonnets*.

QUESTIONS

WILLIAM SHAKESPEARE, *Shall I Compare Thee to a Summer's Day?*

1. Using a historical dictionary, such as the *Oxford English Dictionary*, look up the words "day," "lease," and "untrimm'd." How are the sixteenth century meanings connected to, and different from, the meanings these words have for us today?

2. Notice that the poem begins with a rhetorical question. As the poet answers his own question, what path does his logic take? How would you outline the argument of the poem?

3. Outline the poem's rhyme scheme. How do the rhymes serve to unify sections of the poem? How would you say the poem's sections become connected with one another—that is, what are the transitions of the poem?

4. The poem focuses on the act of comparing a beloved to something else. What does the poem seem to say about the value of comparison?

5. The poem offers itself as a substitute for physical beauty, which will fade. What does the poem seem to claim about the value of the work of art, in comparison to the experience it claims to immortalize?

6. The poem moves from asserting the greater loveliness of the beloved, to asserting that 'her loveliness, like all loveliness will fade—though not her "eternal summer." What is the nature of this eternal summer?

7. Write an essay in which you explore the poem as a sonnet. What ideas; requests to the reader; and relationship between the speaker and the beloved does the sonnet form enable?

8. Write an exploratory essay in which you consider the triangle the poem proposes between the lover/speaker, the beloved, and the idea of immortality.

Ben Jonson
[1572–1637]

BEN JONSON *was born in London, only one month after his clergyman father's death. He attended Westminster School, where he studied with the classical scholar William Camden. After completing his studies, he worked as a bricklayer for his stepfather, but he found the trade loathsome, and instead joined the army, and served in Flanders. He returned in 1592, and married Anne Lewis in 1594. Not long after, in 1597, he joined the theatrical company of Phillip Henslowe in London as an actor and playwright. In 1597, Jonson went to jail for his play* The Isle of Dogs, *considered dangerous to the government by the authorities. In 1598, he killed a fellow actor, Gabriel Spencer, in a duel, and was tried at Old Bailey for murder. He was again sent to jail, where he converted to Roman Catholicism, but he converted back to Anglicism a decade later. Jonson tended to move with the political winds, a trait that eventually facilitated his release from jail. His next play,* Every Man in His Humour, *was performed in 1598 by Lord Chamberlain's Men. It was during this production, at the Globe in London, where he met William Shakespeare, an actor in the play. Jonson's next play,* Every Man Out of His Humour *(1599), was followed by* Cynthia's Revels *(1600), both satirical comedies. In* The Poetaster *(1601) Jonson satirized other writers, especially playwrights Thomas Dekker and John Marston. A spat followed, but had obviously been reconciled by 1604 when Jonson collaborated with Dekker on* The King's Entertainment, *and with Marston on* Eastward Ho. *Jonson's next play, the classical tragedy* Sejanus, His Fall *(1603), criticized dictatorship and once more got Jonson in trouble with the authorities. By 1605, however, he was writing for the court of King James, and was appointed Court Poet after the performance of* The Satyr. *The* Masque of Blackness *(1605) was Jonson's first play written in collaboration with Inigo Jones, a noted English architect and set designer. The* Masque of Beauty *(1608) and* The Masque of Queens *(1609) followed. The plays for which Jonson is most famous are the comedies written between 1605 and 1614.* Volpone, or The Fox *was performed in 1605 and 1606, and was first published in 1607; it is regarded as his masterpiece. The play, though set in Venice, pokes fun at the rising merchant classes of Jacobean London.* Epicoene: or, The Silent Woman *(1609),* The Alchemist *(1610), and* Bartholomew Fair *(1614) continued to show Jonson's great wit. In 1618, Jonson walked to Scotland, the home of his ancestors. After his return, he was given a Master of Arts from Oxford University. He became a model for young poets, who called themselves the "sons" or "tribe" of Ben, but later became known as the Cavalier poets: Robert Herrick, Thomas Carew, Sir John Suckling, and Richard Lovelace. Jonson is buried in Westminster Abbey, under a stone which bears the words, "O Rare Ben Jonson!"*

That Women Are But Men's Shadows

BEN JONSON

Follow a shadow, it still flies you;
Seem to fly it, it will pursue:
So court a mistress, she denies you;
Let her alone, she will court you.
Say, are not women truly then,   5
Styled but the shadows of us men?
At morn and even, shades are longest;
At noon they are but short or none:
So men at weakest, they are strongest,
But grant us perfect, they're not known.   10
Say, are not women truly then,
Styled but the shadows of us men?

[1616]

Reprinted from *Seventeenth-Century Prose and Poetry*, Second Edition, edited by Alexander M
Witherspoon and Frank J Warnke (1633), Houghton Mifflin Harcourt Publishing.

QUESTIONS

BEN JONSON, *That Women Are But Men's Shadows*

1. What happens when a man chases a woman? What happens when he ceases to chase?

2. What happens to a shadow at noon? And what happens at evening? Is all life about waxing and waning? Is that what this poet and his Greek influences thought, too?

3. Poetry of the sixteen hundreds tended to deal with themes of love or of religion. In this case, love is the subject. What does this poem have to say about the problems of being in love?

4. The "battle of the sexes" seems to be a constant theme in literature, even in this era of equal advantages (and disadvantages). How is this ancient conflict a part of nature?

5. This poem is almost a sonnet (14 lines carefully rhymed and structured). How does the rhyme scheme add to the humor and wit of the poem? Read it aloud to emphasize the effects of the sounds of the words.

6. What happens psychologically when someone begins to pursue a lover? What is the appeal in the lover's running away (just a bit)? Write about the catch-me-if-you-can qualities to relationships. What has to happen, though, if a relationship continues?

7. Read about the Greek rhetorician, Philostratus, who wrote in the second and third centuries. Why are his ideas still read and discussed? Are poems still reflecting his ideas?

Jonathan Swift
[1667–1745]

Jonathan Swift's epitaph, which he wrote himself, reads

Swift sailed into his rest;
Savage indignation there
Cannot lacerate his breast.
Imitate him if you dare,
World-besotted traveler; he
Served human liberty.

In this epitaph, a translation from the Latin by W. B. Yeats, perhaps the expression "savage indignation" most captures the significance of Swift's life and writings. He was a true satirist in that he used humor and wit to critique humanity and its institutions for the purpose of holding people accountable for society's imperfections and in order to improve social conditions. At various times Swift used pseudonyms or published works anonymously to enhance his ends, such as with Gulliver's Travels *(1726) and* A Modest Proposal *(1729). By not using his actual name, readers of these great works were convinced of their authenticity. That is, for the satire to have its intended effect, readers had to accept the reality of Lemuel Gulliver's experiences. Further, they had to believe that the "modest" proposal of breeding infants as food for the wealthy was made in all sincerity— that the author of the pamphlet was an actual person. This famous essay was motivated by Swift's despair over England's mute response to the latest famine in Ireland. It was an unflinching indictment of England's policies toward Ireland.*

Swift was born in Dublin, received a degree from Trinity College in 1686 and furthered his studies at Oxford University, from which he earned a master of arts degree in 1692. In 1694 he returned to Ireland and in the following year was ordained in the Church of Ireland (Anglican), and eventually became Dean of St. Patrick's Cathedral. In 1704 Swift anonymously published A Tale of a Tub, *a satire on religious debates. Soon after, Swift published* The Battle of the Books *and* The Mechanical Operation of the Spirit. *The series of satirical pamphlets on church issues,* An Argument Against Abolishing Christianity, *appeared in 1708. Swift became the editor of the newspaper* The Examiner *siding with the Tories, (outlaw Irish), against the Whig party that supported English parliamentary rights. However, the Whigs gained power after the death of Queen Anne, which fueled Swift's sense of injustice experienced by the Irish people. By the time of* The Drapier's Letters *(1724), Swift was extremely popular in Ireland, having also donated much of his earnings to the establishment of St. Patrick's Hospital. Swift continued to resist English authority in* A Short View of the State of Ireland *(1728). By 1735 Swift's Ménière's disease became more pronounced, causing him bouts of dizziness and nausea. His memory was already beginning to fail, possibly due to Alzheimer's disease. Senility had set in by 1735 and eventually, after a stroke, he could no longer be deemed responsible to conduct his own affairs. When he died, Ireland mourned his passing.*

A Description of the Morning

JONATHAN SWIFT

Now hardly here and there an hackney-coach,
Appearing, showed the ruddy morn's approach.
Now Betty from her master's bed had flown
And softly stole to discompose her own.
The slipshod 'prentice from his master's door   5
Had pared the dirt, and sprinkled round the floor.
Now Moll had whirled her mop with dextrous airs,
Prepared to scrub the entry and the stairs.
The youth with broomy stumps began to trace
The kennel-edge, where wheels had worn the place.   10
The small-coal man was heard with cadence deep
Till drowned in shriller notes of chimneysweep,
Duns at his lordship's gate began to meet,
And Brickdust Moll had screamed through half the street.
The turnkey now his flock returning sees,   15
Duly let out a-nights to steal for fees;
The watchful bailiffs take their silent stands;
And schoolboys lag with satchels in their hands.

[1709]

First published in 1709.

QUESTIONS

JONATHAN SWIFT, *A Description of the Morning*

1. Boys' lesson books at that time often asked for assignments such as, "describe the morning or the evening." This poem addresses the typical assignment but with a rather nasty twist, since Swift was likely to see the worst in humanity. What images do you notice that criticize humanity and show its darker side?

2. Morning is usually thought to be a time of hope and promise, yet the morning in this poem tends to offer only dirt and work. Is the world in the eye of the beholder, and if so, what would you say about Swift's eye?

3. This poem consists of nine couplets, each rhymed in precise patterns and each indicating the mini-picture being presented. Trace the poem through its patterns, noting each place and person being described. What class of people is being shown? How can you tell?

4. Write a description of the morning in the world where you live. Use Swift's pattern of showing several people who make up the social world that you are describing, though you will have the luxury of describing each in more detail. Then comment on the world that you have described, noting the social and physical characteristics that strike you as important to an understanding of that world.

Alexander Pope
[1688–1744]

The Roman Catholic son of a draper, ALEXANDER POPE *began life in London with two strikes against him: a religion that prohibited him from public school and university, and a family of no high rank. He was trained by private tutors and through his own studies and hard work. At age twelve, he was dealt the third strike. He fell grievously ill and was left deformed by the disease. These hardships led to a sharp and spiteful disposition, but his education and talent led to some of the best satirical poetry and some of the most solid essay writing of his era or of any time, for that matter. His first published work was his* Pastorals *in 1709.* The Essay on Criticism *(1711),* The Rape of the Lock *(1712, 1714), and* Windsor Forest *(1713) followed. The first introduces many of the ideas of the classical era splendidly while* The Rape *introduces the delights of Pope's satirical abilities, as a silly young girl is outraged at the cutting of a sprig of hair by a suitor at a tea party. Some feminists might think the poem unfair for making fun of a serious problem, but no one with a poetic or satirical bent could fault the writing in the poem.* Windsor Forest *is less successful, for it displays a poet of the city and the political world writing about the woods, a subject better left to the Romantics. It did, however, set off a spat in* The Guardian *(the newspaper that succeeded* The Spectator, *famous conservative paper of its time). Pope spent a decade or so translating Homer's* Iliad *(1715–1720) and* Odyssey *(1725–1726), both translations having the same ring of falsity as* Windsor Forest: *Epic battle is best left to more Romantic writers. After this spate of translations, he restricted himself to his great talents, producing poems full of both wit and venom, assets of which he was well equipped.* The Dunciad *(1728–1743) is an epic of dunces in which Pope takes aim at every real and imagined literary enemy in the field. This work can only be described as malicious, but it is funny and even poetic. His* Moral Essays *and* Epistle to Dr. Arbuthnot *(1735) continue his satirical commentary. His* Essay on Man *(1733), however, is perhaps the finest statement of the philosophy and thinking of the neoclassical era. Literary history has not treated Pope well, but most critics agree that Pope was the unchallenged master of satire.*

A Little Learning is a dang'rous Thing

ALEXANDER POPE

A *little Learning* is a dang'rous Thing;
Drink deep, or taste not the *Pierian* Spring:
There *shallow Draughts* intoxicate the Brain,
And drinking *largely* sobers us again.
Fir'd at first Sight with what the *Muse* imparts,   5
In *fearless Youth* we tempt the Heights of Arts,
While from the bounded *Level* of our Mind,
Short Views we take, nor see the *Lengths behind*,
But *more advanc'd*, behold with strange Surprize
New, distant Scenes of *endless* Science rise!   10
So pleas'd at first, the towring *Alps* we try,
Mount o'er the Vales, and seem to tread the Sky;
Th'Eternal Snows appear already past,
And the first *Clouds* and *Mountains* seem the last:
But *those attain'd*, we tremble to survey   15
The growing Labours of the lengthen'd Way,
Th' *increasing* Prospect *tires* our wandring Eyes,
Hills peep o'er Hills, and *Alps* on *Alps* arise!

[1711]

First published in *The Essay on Criticism* in 1711.

ALEXANDER POPE, *A Little Learning is a dang'rous Thing*

1. The speaker in the poem uses a metaphor that compares learning to taking a drink from the fountain of wisdom and creativity. Why does he say that the reader should drink deeply if she or he is to drink at all? What does the speaker mean by saying that sips of knowledge "intoxicate" the brain but that deeper drinking will make one sober again? What happens when a person knows only a little about a subject and yet tries to sound knowledgeable? What happens when greater knowledge informs the person?

2. The word *sophomore* means wise fool: a sophomore has learned enough at the start of their educational career to feel confident and a bit cocky, but not quite enough to be truly well informed. Mark Twain said that when he went off to the river as a very young man, he thought his father rather stupid but when he later returned home, found that the old fellow had learned quite a bit. Find the places in Pope's poem that argue that a respect of knowledge is often relative.

3. In the middle of the poem, the speaker uses science to exemplify his argument. The era in which Pope lived was the time of the rise of scientific knowledge and method that dominates today. Is there any limit to scientific knowledge? How does the speaker in the poem feel about this expanding knowledge? In which lines of the poem can you locate the speaker's opinions?

4. Describe the first time you tried to learn a foreign language, a musical instrument, a sport, etc. How did you behave at first? Did you have any mishaps because of overconfidence? What happened to your confidence as you learned more and more? Why?

William Blake

[1757–1827]

WILLIAM BLAKE *was born in London to a middle class family, but his bent toward seeing the world in terms of visions quickly appeared. Blake saw more than the dirty world of a big city; rather he saw angels and other spiritual beings as he walked through life. He considered the world he lived in to be corrupted by its lack of imagination, and he set about creating his own Golden Age of art and poetry. Showing great artistic talent early in life, by age ten he began drawing in school and later became an engraver and design artist. He did not earn great sums as an artist, because his work was strange in an era that loved landscapes and careful representations of classic events such as Bible stories and historic battles. Blake's art illustrated more that could not be seen than that which could be seen.*

He married his wife, Catherine, in 1782. She was devoted to him though the story goes that she nearly fainted when she first saw him due to his fiery eyes and passionate presence. From that early era came his first collection of poetry, Poetical Sketches *(1783). When his younger brother Robert died, Blake's sense of connection to the spiritual world was strengthened. He wrote the* Songs of Experience *(1789) during this time of elation and spiritual growth, and these poems express his sense of the heavenly and spiritual. This bliss, however, was short-lived as Blake first followed and then rejected the Swedish theologian, Emanuel Swendenborg. Blake rejected Swendenborg's ideas about predestination, and wrote* The Marriage of Heaven and Hell *(1790–1793) as an attack on any such doctrine.*

Blake then became connected with the champions of the French Revolution, including William Godwin, Tom Paine, and the Romantic poets, William Wordsworth, Samuel Coleridge, Robert Southey, and William Hazlitt. His protest against those who interfere with the rights of their fellow humans expressed itself in the most famous of his collections, Songs of Experience *(1798–1794), and in* The French Revolution, America, *and the* Visions of the Daughters of Albion. *The last poem attacks marriage, which Blake disapproved of while he continued to be a faithful and devoted husband. The* Book of Thel *(1783) followed, a tale of a soul that refuses to be born into this wicked world. His mythology was elaborated and illustrated in* The Book of Urizen, The Song of Los, The Book of Ahania, *and* The Book of Los.

From 1800 to 1803, the Blakes lived in a small town called Felpham, supported by a patron and poet friend named William Hayley, but Blake and Hayley differed in the nature of the poetry the two wrote, Hayley's being simple and sentimental, Blake's being mystical and complex. While at Felpham, Blake finished

The Four Zoas *and* Milton; *upon returning to London, he wrote the third of his* "prophetic" *works*, Jerusalem. *After that he spent many years in poverty, even painting dishes for Wedgwood, but was finally rediscovered in 1818 by a younger generation of painters, John Linnell, Samuel Palmer, John Varley, and George Richmond. He began to illustrate Dante and the book of Job, but these remained unfinished at the time of his death in 1827.*

The Tyger

WILLIAM BLAKE

Tyger, Tyger, burning bright
In the forests of the night,
What immortal hand or eye
Could frame thy fearful symmetry?

In what distant deeps or skies   5
Burnt the fire of thine eyes?
On what wings dare he aspire?
What the hand dare seize the fire?

And what shoulder and what art
Could twist the sinews of thy heart?   10
And, when thy heart began to beat,
What dread hand and what dread feet?

What the hammer? What the chain?
In what furnace was thy brain?
What the anvil? What dread grasp   15
Dare its deadly terror clasp?

When the stars threw down their spears,
And watered heaven with their tears,
Did he smile his work to see?
Did he who made the Lamb make thee?   20

Tyger, Tyger, burning bright
In the forests of the night,
What immortal hand or eye
Dare frame thy fearful symmetry?

[1794]

First published in *Songs of Experience* in 1794.

QUESTIONS

WILLIAM BLAKE, *The Tyger*

1. What words describe the power of the tiger? What are his eyes like? His brain?

2. Notice the changes that occur throughout the poem. These are intentional, for Blake wrote many versions of this poem before deciding on this exact order. What changes occur, and where?

3. Humans have long wondered why life works the way that it does with predators and prey. Why do you think nature is so cruel?

4. Each lines ends with a question. Follow the sequence of the questions. Where do they lead?

5. Note the change from *could* in line four to *dare* in line twenty-four. What does this change indicate? What questions do the changed questions ask?

6. Consider the arguments of hunters in justification of their hunting. What do hunters give to nature? What do they take away? Write about this argument.

7. Is it possible to see the universe as finally benevolent toward life? Write about this philosophical question, tackling the same dilemma that Blake tackles in this poem.

John Keats
[1795–1821]

JOHN KEATS'S *father kept a London livery stable—not a very auspicious beginning for the Romantic poet of the sublimely beautiful. His father died when he was nine, and when he was fifteen, he lost his mother to tuberculosis. His brother died of the same disease a few years later, and it took Keats, too, at age twenty-six. Tuberculosis was common in the early 1800s, and was especially prevelant among those who lived in London's smoggy interior. Despite these challenges, and his early death, Keats produced a large volume of memorable poetry.*

He attended school at Enfield, but in 1810 was apprenticed to a surgeon. The medical profession did not have the status that it has today, and this change was not a social improvement for the young Keats. Despite his removal from school, he read and fell in love with Edmund Spenser's Faerie Queen, *and even as he finished his apprenticeship and began work in a London hospital, his heart and imagination were with Spenser's world of elves and knights. He met all the Romantic writers, including Percy Byssche Shelley and Samuel Taylor Coleridge, and became friends with Leigh Hunt, editor of* The Examiner, *which published some of his early sonnets. Keats dedicated his first volume of poems to Hunt in 1817. His first long poem,* Endymion, *appeared in 1818, but his friendship with Hunt, who was on the outs with the London critics, drew criticism of the poem. Keats was hurt, but continued to write, despite Shelley's later argument in* Adonais *that the critics had killed Keats with their reviews. At the same time he fell hopelessly in love with Fanny Brawne, whose social position would not allow her to marry a stable-boy-turned-physician, whatever poetic talents he possessed. These losses seemed to fuel his poetic passion. In 1819, he published* The Eve of St. Agnes, *arguably the signature poem of the sensuous and fanciful wing of the Romantic movement. This poem tells the story of a young knight who brings beautiful food to his lady's chamber, and appears to her as if in a dream to persuade her to run away with him, which she does. His next two poems,* La Belle Dame sans Merci (The Beautiful Woman Without Mercy), *a poem about a witch, and* Lamia, *a poem about a woman who can become a snake, followed in 1820.* Isabella, or The Pot of Basil, *followed, a tale taken from Boccaccio's* Decameron *about a woman who plants her unfaithful lover's head in a pot of herbs. His last poem, the unfinished* Hyperion, *recounts a classical myth, and throughout the last years of his life, he wrote the sonnets that have become the jewels of the Romantic movement.*

La Belle Dame sans Merci. A Ballad

JOHN KEATS

The Beautiful Woman without Mercy

I

O what can ail thee, knight-at-arms,
   Alone and palely loitering?
The sedge has withered from the lake,
   And no birds sing.

II

O what can ail thee, knight-at-arms,   5
   So haggard and so woe-begone?
The squirrel's granary is full,
   And the harvest's done.

III

I see a lily on thy brow
   With anguish moist and fever-dew,   10
And on thy cheeks a fading rose
   Fast withereth too.

IV

I met a lady in the meads,
   Full beautiful—a faery's child,
Her hair was long, her foot was light,   15
   And her eyes were wild.

Composed in 1819 and first published in *Lamia, Isabella, The Eve of St. Agnes, and Other Poems* in 1820.

V

I made a garland for her head,
    And bracelets too, and fragrant zone;
She looked at me as she did love,
    And made sweet moan.   *20*

VI

I set her on my pacing steed,
    And nothing else saw all day long,
For sidelong would she bend, and sing
    A faery's song.

VII

She found me roots of relish sweet,   *25*
    And honey wild, and manna-dew,
And sure in language strange she said—
    'I love thee true'.

VIII

She took me to her elfin grot,
    And there she wept and sighed full sore,   *30*
And there I shut her wild wild eyes
    With kisses four.

IX

And there she lullèd me asleep
    And there I dreamed—Ah! woe betide!—
The latest dream I ever dreamt   *35*
    On the cold hill side.

X

I saw pale kings and princes too,
    Pale warriors, death-pale were they all;
They cried—'La Belle Dame sans Merci
    Thee hath in thrall!'   *40*

XI

I saw their starved lips in the gloam,
  With horrid warning gapèd wide,
And I awoke and found me here,
  On the cold hill's side.

XII

And this is why I sojourn here   *45*
  Alone and palely loitering,
Though the sedge is withered from the lake,
  And no birds sing.

[1819]

QUESTIONS

JOHN KEATS, *La Belle Dame sans Merci*. A Ballad

1. This poem tells of a medieval knight wandering in a barren field, where he meets a beautiful woman. What happens to him next? What does she give him? Where do they go?

2. What do the speakers in the knight's dream tell him? What happens when he wakes up? How does he feel?

3. This poem is more about feeling than about reason. What effect is the poem meant to have? Why do we sometimes like to feel wistful and nostalgic?

4. The story of the seductress who appears and leads young men off to her fairy den is an old one. What is the appeal this creature? What part of the inner psyche does she symbolize?

5. Ballads are sure to have unhappy endings, and this one is no exception. How does the ballad form tell the reader from the beginning that things are not going to turn out well? What would happen if you sang this ballad? Would it be more powerful?

6. The first and last verses are almost the same. How does this complete the song? How does it also tell the listener that this is not a singular event, and that this story has happened over and over again?

7. Think about an experience you've had meeting someone who was appealing but not very good for you. What is appealing about dangerous people? Write about your experience, and analyze your response.

8. The world of knights and adventures exists in the psyches of all Westerners. These images appear in modern cinema, and in video and computer games. Write about the influence of the world of kings and knights on the world we know today.

Elizabeth Barrett Browning
[1806–1861]

ELIZABETH BARRETT BROWNING *was born in Durham, England, the daughter of an overly protective father who kept her at home and mostly indoors. The family moved to London where they lived quite unhappy lives. Fortunately for Browning, she had access to her brother's tutor and was allowed to learn and study alongside her sibling. In this way, she acquired the education of a wealthy young man of the early Victorian era. She was well schooled in Greek, Latin, and Hebrew and was well read in literature ranging from the classical texts of Greek and Rome, including Homer and Ovid; to the Romantics, poets including Lord Byron, Keats, Coleridge, and Wordsworth whose lives overlapped her own. At age thirteen, she published her first volume of poetry. She injured her spine at age fifteen, and her beloved brother Edward drowned in 1840. The combination of illness and depression provided ample reason for her father to keep her imprisoned at their house on Wimpole Street in London. When she met poet Robert Browning, she was a well-known essayist, poet, and scholar, having published* Essay on Mind, with Other Poems *in 1826, a translation of* Prometheus Bound *by Aeschylus in 1833 and* The Seraphim and Other Poems *in 1838. During their courtship, Elizabeth wrote sonnets to Browning that became her best-known work,* Sonnets from the Portuguese. *Browning referred to her as his little Portuguese because she was dark complexioned.*

In September 1846, the two poets ran away to Italy where they married and lived together until Elizabeth's death. They had one son, Pim. Their intellectual companionship yielded much writing on both their parts. She published two works on Italian political affairs, Casa Guidi Windows *(1951) and* Poems before Congress *(1860). Her longest poem,* Aurora Leigh *(1857), written in blank verse, covered biographical topics and expressed her beliefs on political, social, and economic issues. Her last book of poems,* Last Poems *(1862), was published after her death. Her physical problems returned as the great romance with Robert began to fade, leading to her death and burial in her beloved Florence. Though Elizabeth was originally more famous than her husband, for many decades after her death her work was considered less important than Robert's. Today she has regained critical interest among women scholars and has been rediscovered for the fine poet and social and political thinker that she was.*

Grief

ELIZABETH BARRETT BROWNING

I tell you, hopeless grief is passionless;
  That only men incredulous of despair,
  Half-taught in anguish, through the midnight air
Beat upward to God's throne in loud access
Of shrieking and reproach. Full desertness   5
  In souls, as countries, lieth silent-bare
  Under the blanching, vertical eye-glare
Of the absolute Heavens. Deep-hearted man, express
Grief for the Dead in silence like to death;
  Most like a monumental statue set   10
In everlasting watch and moveless woe
Till itself crumble to the dust beneath.
  Touch it: the marble eyelids are not wet—
If it could weep, it could arise and go.

[1850]

First published in 1850.

QUESTIONS

ELIZABETH BARRETT BROWNING, *Grief*

1. The poem claims that it is worse not to cry than to cry, that grief is worse when the bereft person is too shocked for tears. How does the speaker in the poem back up this claim?

2. This poem claims that people who have lost everything, for example people in war-torn cities or people whose families have died in disaster, sit quietly with blank faces. Why does this poem suggest that we are empty of emotion when we have lost all?

3. In the final couplet of this sonnet grief is compared to a marble statue that can neither cry nor move. What is the image of marble effective in expressing the meaning of the poem?

4. What makes you angry and what makes you cold, leaving you with little feeling? Describe a situation in which you felt one or both of these emotions. Help the reader to see the reasons for your emotions.

The Raven

EDGAR ALLAN POE

Once upon a midnight dreary, while I pondered, weak and
   weary,
Over many a quaint and curious volume of forgotten lore—
While I nodded, nearly napping, suddenly there came a tapping,
As of some one gently rapping, rapping at my chamber door.
"'Tis some visiter," I muttered, "tapping at my chamber door—   5
      Only this and nothing more."

Ah, distinctly I remember it was in the bleak December;
And each separate dying ember wrought its ghost upon the floor.
Eagerly I wished the morrow;—vainly I had sought to borrow
From my books surcease of sorrow—sorrow for the lost
   Lenore—   10
For the rare and radiant maiden whom the angels name
   Lenore—
      Nameless *here* for evermore.

And the silken, sad, uncertain rustling of each purple curtain
Thrilled me—filled me with fantastic terrors never felt before;
So that now, to still the beating of my heart, I stood repeating   15
"'Tis some visiter entreating entrance at my chamber door—
Some late visiter entreating entrance at my chamber door;—
      This it is and nothing more."

Presently my soul grew stronger; hesitating then no longer,
"Sir," said I, "or Madam, truly your forgiveness I implore;   20
But the fact is I was napping, and so gently you came rapping,
And so faintly you came tapping, tapping at my chamber door,
That I scarce was sure I heard you"—here I opened wide the
   door;——
      Darkness there and nothing more.

Deep into that darkness peering, long I stood there wondering,
    fearing,   *25*
Doubting, dreaming dreams no mortal ever dared to dream
    before;
But the silence was unbroken, and the stillness gave no token,
And the only word there spoken was the whispered word,
    "Lenore?"
This I whispered, and an echo murmured back the word,
    "Lenore!"
             Merely this and nothing more.   *30*

Back into the chamber turning, all my soul within me burning,
Soon again I heard a tapping somewhat louder than before.
"Surely," said I, "surely that is something at my window lattice;
Let me see, then, what thereat is, and this mystery explore—
Let my heart be still a moment and this mystery explore;—   *35*
            'Tis the wind and nothing more!"

Open here I flung the shutter, when, with many a flirt and
    flutter,
In there stepped a stately Raven of the saintly days of yore;
Not the least obeisance made he; not a minute stopped or
    stayed he;
But, with mien of lord or lady, perched above my chamber
    door—   *40*
Perched upon a bust of Pallas[1] just above my chamber door—
            Perched, and sat, and nothing more.

Then this ebony bird beguiling my sad fancy into smiling,
By the grave and stern decorum of the countenance it wore,
"Though thy crest be shorn and shaven, thou," I said, "art sure no
    craven,   *45*
Ghastly grim and ancient Raven wandering from the Nightly
    shore—
Tell me what thy lordly name is on the Night's Plutonian shore!"[2]
           Quoth the Raven "Nevermore."

---

[1] Pallas: Pallas Athene, Greek goddess of wisdom, arts, and war.
[2] Poe's speaker here associates the raven with Pluto, Roman god of death and the underworld.

Much I marvelled this ungainly fowl to hear discourse so plainly,
Though its answer little meaning—little relevancy bore; 50
For we cannot help agreeing that no living human being
Ever yet was blessed with seeing bird above his chamber door—
Bird or beast upon the sculptured bust above his chamber door,
    With such name as "Nevermore."

But the Raven, sitting lonely on the placid bust, spoke only 55
That one word, as if his soul in that one word he did outpour.
Nothing farther then he uttered—not a feather then he
  fluttered—
Till I scarcely more than muttered "Other friends have flown
  before—
On the morrow *he* will leave me, as my Hopes have flown
  before."
    Then the bird said "Nevermore." 60

Startled at the stillness broken by reply so aptly spoken,
"Doubtless," said I, "what it utters is its only stock and store
Caught from some unhappy master whom unmerciful Disaster
Followed fast and followed faster till his songs one burden
  bore—
Till the dirges of his Hope that melancholy burden bore 65
    Of 'Never—nevermore.'"

But the Raven still beguiling my sad fancy into smiling,
Straight I wheeled a cushioned seat in front of bird, and bust
  and door;
Then, upon the velvet sinking, I betook myself to linking
Fancy unto fancy, thinking what this ominous bird of yore— 70
What this grim, ungainly, ghastly, gaunt, and ominous bird of
  yore
    Meant in croaking "Nevermore."

This I sat engaged in guessing, but no syllable expressing
To the fowl whose fiery eyes now burned into my bosom's core;
This and more I sat divining, with my head at ease reclining 75
On the cushion's velvet lining that the lamp-light gloated o'er,
But whose velvet-violet lining with the lamp-light gloating o'er,
    She shall press, ah, nevermore!

Then, methought, the air grew denser, perfumed from an unseen
censer
Swung by seraphim[3] whose foot-falls tinkled on the tufted
floor.   *80*
"Wretch," I cried, "thy God hath lent thee—by these angels he
hath sent thee
Respite—respite and nepenthe[4] from thy memories of Lenore;
Quaff, oh quaff this kind nepenthe and forget this lost Lenore!"
            Quoth the Raven "Nevermore."

"Prophet!" said I, "thing of evil!—prophet still, if bird or
devil!—   *85*
Whether Tempter sent, or whether tempest tossed thee here
ashore,
Desolate yet all undaunted, on this desert land enchanted—
On this home by Horror haunted—tell me truly, I implore—
Is there—*is* there balm in Gilead?[5]—tell me—tell me, I implore!"
            Quoth the Raven "Nevermore."   *90*

"Prophet!" said I, "thing of evil!—prophet still, if bird or devil!
By that Heaven that bends above us—by that God we both
adore—
Tell this soul with sorrow laden if, within the distant Aidenn,[6]
It shall clasp a sainted maiden whom the angels name Lenore—
Clasp a rare and radiant maiden whom the angels name
Lenore."   *95*
            Quoth the Raven "Nevermore."

"Be that word our sign of parting, bird or fiend!" I shrieked,
upstarting—
"Get thee back into the tempest and the Night's Plutonian shore!
Leave no black plume as a token of that lie thy soul hath spoken!
Leave my loneliness unbroken!—quit the bust above my door!   *100*
Take thy beak from out my heart, and take thy form from off my
door!"
            Quoth the Raven "Nevermore."

---

[3] Seraphim: in Judeo-Christian tradition, seraphim are the highest order of angels; these
beings are known to inspire prophecy.
[4] Nepenthe: an ancient potion reputed to cure grief and sorrow.
[5] In the Hebrew Bible, the "balm of Gilead" is a healing ointment suggestive of God's power
to restore the soul.
[6] Aidenn: this is an alternate spelling for the biblical Garden of Eden.

And the Raven, never flitting, still is sitting, *still* is sitting
On the pallid bust of Pallas just above my chamber door;
And his eyes have all the seeming of a demon's that is dreaming,   *105*
And the lamp-light o'er him streaming throws his shadow on the
    floor;
And my soul from out that shadow that lies floating on the floor
            Shall be lifted—nevermore!

                                             [1845]

QUESTIONS

1. Describe the basic dramatic situation of "The Raven." Who is the speaker? Who is Lenore? What is his dilemma? What is the nature of the dialogue described in the text?

2. Discuss "The Raven" in terms of its setting. Where and when does the poem take place? To what extent do the colors, textures, and odors of the poem's setting contribute to its overall effects and meanings?

3. "The Raven" has been lauded as a masterpiece of poetic technique or "prosody." Consider the ways in which prosodic tactics such as rhyme, rhythm, assonance, and repetition are important to the work's overall effect.

4. What is the poetic genre of "The Raven"? Feel free to explore diverse possibilities.

5. Poe is often associated with the literary Gothic. Research this ethos and describe the ways in which Poe participates in or even invents Gothic conventions in "The Raven."

6. Compose an argument about the speaker's psychological condition. To what extent is this narrator reliable? What evidence— explicit and implicit—does he offer about his state of mind?

7. Various species of birds hold different meanings within different cultures. Research the significance of ravens within western culture and discuss the extent to which this context illuminates "The Raven."

Alfred, Lord Tennyson
[1809–1892]

ALFRED TENNYSON'S *life spans most of the years of Queen Victoria's reign. He was born in a Lincolnshire rectory into a talented and literate family, the fourth child and one of eight sons and four daughters. All the children were brought up as intellectuals. Tennyson's publication of poetry included the works of his two brothers, Frederick and Charles* (Poems by Two Brothers, 1827). *Tennyson looked the part of a poet, tall and slender with an elegant head, and he was quickly adopted by the artistic circle at school. At Trinity College, Cambridge, he became a member of the poets' club, The Apostles, where he met Arthur Henry Hallam, whose early death was to shape both Tennyson's temperament and his poetry. Before that event, however, Tennyson won the Chancellor's prize for a poem titled* Timbuctoo *and saw his first volume of poetry published in 1830,* Poems, Chiefly Lyrical. *His second volume appeared in 1832. In 1833, Hallam, by then engaged to Tennyson's sister, Emily, died in Vienna. Tennyson began his poem on faith and doubt,* In Memoriam, *that was eventually to make him famous. He worked on the poem for seventeen years. At the same time, he worked on* Idylls of the King, *a long work retelling the tales of King Arthur from Malory but molded into the Victorian mindset. In 1842, he published* Poems, *which included* Ulysses *and* Morte D'Arthur. *In 1847, his popular satire on women's place in the world,* Princess, *appeared. These were difficult times for Tennyson, despite the success of the latest poems. Then in 1850 he married Emily Sellwood and finally published* In Memoriam. *That year he was chosen to succeed Wordsworth as Poet Laureate. A long formal poem,* Ode on the Death of the Duke of Wellington *(1852) preceded* Maud *(1855), a romantic tale of love and death, followed by* Enoch Arden *and* Northern Farmer *(1964). He dedicated a new edition of* Idylls *to the memory of Queen Victoria's beloved husband Prince Albert, who had died in 1861, and became a great favorite of the queen. In 1884, he became Lord Tennyson and published* Becket, *a successful drama. In his last years, he wrote apace, publishing* Tiresias and Other Poems *in 1885,* Locksley Hall Sixty Years After *in 1886,* Demeter and Other Poems *in 1889, and* The Death of Oenone *in 1892, published just after his death. Assessments of Tennyson's work was, in turn, criticized and then praised in the past century. During most of the twentieth century, he was thought to be too ornate for most readers, but in time his poetic talent and his ability to bring sound and light to life were honored. Those who love a talented wordsmith and those who love a mythic vision of ancient England love Tennyson.*

Ulysses[1]

ALFRED, LORD TENNYSON

It little profits that an idle king,
By this still hearth, among these barren crags,
Matched with an agèd wife, I mete and dole
Unequal laws unto a savage race
That hoard, and sleep, and feed, and know not me.   5
I cannot rest from travel; I will drink
Life to the lees. All times I have enjoyed
Greatly, have suffered greatly, both with those
That loved me, and alone; on shore, and when
Through scudding drifts the rainy Hyades[2]   10
Vexed the dim sea. I am become a name;
For always roaming with a hungry heart
Much have I seen and known—cities of men
And manners, climates, councils, governments,
Myself not least, but honored of them all—   15
And drunk delight of battle with my peers,
Far on the ringing plains of windy Troy.
I am a part of all that I have met;
Yet all experience is an arch wherethrough
Gleams that untraveled world whose margin fades   20
Forever and forever when I move.
How dull it is to pause, to make an end,
To rust unburnished, not to shine in use!
As though to breathe were life! Life piled on life
Were all too little, and of one to me   25
Little remains; but every hour is saved

---

[1]Ulysses was the hero of the Trojan war. He left his wife Penelope, who wove a cloth to avoid her suitors, and then he returned to her and his son Telemachus after the war.

[2]Hyades was Atlas's daughters who became the stars.

First published in *English Idyls and Other Poems* in 1842.

From that eternal silence, something more,
A bringer of new things; and vile it were
For some three suns to store and hoard myself,
And this grey spirit yearning in desire   30
To follow knowledge like a sinking star,
Beyond the utmost bound of human thought.
    This is my son, mine own Telemachus,
To whom I leave the scepter and the isle—
Well-loved of me, discerning to fulfill   35
This labor, by slow prudence to make mild
A rugged people, and through soft degrees
Subdue them to the useful and the good.
Most blameless is he, centered in the sphere
Of common duties, decent not to fail   40
In offices of tenderness, and pay
Meet adoration to my household gods,
When I am gone. He works his work, I mine.
    There lies the port; the vessel puffs her sail;
There gloom the dark, broad seas. My mariners,   45
Souls that have toiled, and wrought, and thought with me—
That ever with a frolic welcome took
The thunder and the sunshine, and opposed
Free hearts, free foreheads—you and I are old;
Old age hath yet his honor and his toil.   50
Death closes all; but something ere the end,
Some work of noble note, may yet be done,
Not unbecoming men that strove with Gods.
The lights begin to twinkle from the rocks;
The long day wanes; the low moon climbs; the deep   55
Moans round with many voices. Come, my friends,
'Tis not too late to seek a newer world.
Push off, and sitting well in order smite
The sounding furrows; for my purpose holds
To sail beyond the sunset, and the baths   60
Of all the western stars, until I die.
It may be that the gulfs will wash us down;
It may be we shall touch the Happy Isles,
And see the great Achilles, whom we knew.
Though much is taken, much abides; and though   65
We are not now that strength which in old days

Moved earth and heaven, that which we are, we are—
One equal temper of heroic hearts,
Made weak by time and fate, but strong in will
To strive, to seek, to find, and not to yield.   *70*

[1833]

QUESTIONS

ALFRED, LORD TENNYSON, *Ulysses*

1. Ulysses has become an old man in this poem. How does he look back over his life? What has he done that he is proud of and what does he question?

2. Why does he take his men back to sea? What does he hope to find or do? Why not stay at home and relax? What's wrong with taking it easy?

3. What happens to people of action when they try to settle down? Why do human beings need to have a challenge?

4. In line 42 Ulysses explains the difference between him and his son. Why do fathers and sons often differ about what their goals should be? Why is Ulysses's solution a good one?

5. This is a monologue such as one might find in an Elizabethan play. Notice the blank verse and the internal address. What kind of a man is speaking?

6. Both the beginning and the end of this poem have become so much a part of the language that people quote it without knowing what they are quoting. What kinds of emotions does the last line evoke when it's read aloud?

7. Those who achieve much in their lives often seem less comfortable with growing old than those who led steady, unexciting lives. Read about the last few years of famous people such as Eleanor Roosevelt or Jacqueline Kennedy Onassis. What do these people do as life begins to wind down?

8. If you do any extreme sports or if you have ever taken an adventurous trip, write about your experiences. Would danger keep you from doing the same or similar things again? Why or why not?

Emily Brontë
[1818–1848]

EMILY BRONTË *was born at Thornton, near Bradford, Yorkshire in England. In 1820, the Brontë family moved to Haworth, and a year later Brontë's mother died. A few years later, Brontë enrolled at the Cowan Bridge School with her sister Charlotte. In 1824, another sister, Maria Brontë, died, and Charlotte and Emily left Cowan Bridge; shortly after, sister Elizabeth Brontë died as well. In 1826 Mr. Brontë brought home twelve wooden soldiers for his son Branwell; the soldiers became a part of stories and games the remaining children created for one another. In 1831, Emily and Anne began the Gondal saga, an elaborate story the two young girls created together. An early manuscript, dating from 1834, mentions Gondals discovering Caaldine. In 1836, Emily's first poem appeared, and a year later she went to teach at Law Hill School, near Halifax, where she remained for about six months. By 1842, most of Brontë's poetry was completed. That same year, she was at school in Brussels with Charlotte, studying music and foreign languages, and writing essays in French. By 1843, she was back at Haworth with her father, working on her poetry collection, and dividing the Gondalan and non-Gondalan material. The Brontë sisters were hoping to set up their own school but by 1845 had given up that idea. In the meantime, Branwell was writing a novel, and Emily decided to try her hand at the task as well, when Branwell assured her there was money in novel writing. She began* Wuthering Heights *in December of 1845. By 1846, the poems were published by Currer Ellis and Acton Bell, with the Brontës paying publishing costs, and* Wuthering Heights *was finished and sent to publishers. In 1847, T. C. Newby accepted* Wuthering Heights, *and it was published it the same year. In September of 1848, Branwell died. Emily caught a severe cold at his funeral service, developed pneumonia, and died in December. Brontë is best known for the haunting novel* Wuthering Heights, *a story of convoluted family relationships, which hints at strange connections among the family members, and evil not quite explained but always suggested. The novel has been wildly popular with young women almost since its publication. Critical responses to the work have varied over the decades, sometimes dismissing the book as a girl's story, and more recently regarding the book as an intense investigation of the complexities of gender interactions within and around families. Brontë's poetry, like the novel, expresses intense emotion and perhaps a sense of her own impending early death.*

The Night-Wind

EMILY BRONTË

In summer's mellow midnight,
A cloudless moon shone through
Our open parlor window
And rosetrees wet with dew.

I sat in silent musing,   5
The soft wind waved my hair:
It told me Heaven was glorious,
And sleeping Earth was fair.

I needed not its breathing
To bring such thoughts to me,   10
But still it whispered lowly,
"How dark the woods will be!

"The thick leaves in my murmur
Are rustling like a dream,
And all their myriad voices   15
Instinct with spirit seem."

I said, "Go, gentle singer,
Thy wooing voice is kind,
But do not think its music
Has power to reach my mind.   20

"Play with the scented flower,
The young tree's supple bough,
And leave my human feelings
In their own course to flow."

"The Night-Wind" was written in 1840.

The wanderer would not leave me;   25
Its kiss grew warmer still—
"O come," it sighed so sweetly,
"I'll win thee 'gainst thy will.

"Have we not been from childhood friends?
Have I not loved thee long?   30
As long as thou hast loved the night
Whose silence wakes my song.

"And when thy heart is laid at rest
Beneath the church-yard stone
I shall have time enough to mourn   35
And thou to be alone."

[1840]

QUESTIONS

EMILY BRONTË, *The Night-Wind*

1. The girl in the poem is having a conversation with the night wind on a warm summer night. What is the wind asking her to do? Why does she refuse? What is she tempted to do? What argument does the wind use?

2. Why is death romantic to the young? What language in the poem suggests the temptations of heaven?

3. What does the speaker mean when she says that "the wanderer would not leave" her? What kind of temptation is she expressing? Is there an erotic hint in the poem? What evidence do you see?

4. Youngsters, from Romeo and Juliet to the latest terrorist bomber, are constantly flirting with the idea of dying for love or duty. Write about your reaction to this idea. What do you think of this romantic idea? How do you assess the judgment of those who fancy a beautiful death?

Walt Whitman
[1819–1892]

WALT WHITMAN *was born in New York to Walter Whitman, a housebuilder, and Louisa Van Velsor. Both his parents descended from early settlers of Long Island. In Whitman's early childhood, his parents moved to Brooklyn, where he attended public school. As an adolescent, he worked as an office boy and learned the printing trade at the* Patriot *and* Star *newspapers in Brooklyn. He worked as a printer until 1836 until a fire destroyed much of the printing district, and he then took up school teaching on Long Island. In 1838 he founded a weekly newspaper,* Long-Islander, *which he published and edited. During this period, he wrote poetry and literary prose.*

During the 1840s, Whitman worked for various newspapers as an editor, writer, and compositor, while he continued to write in various genres, including a novel, stories, sketches, and poetry. He briefly edited a New Orleans newspaper in 1848, the Daily Crescent, *though the job was short-lived (he resigned just months after he arrived). He traveled back to Brooklyn via the Mississippi, the Great Lakes, and the Hudson River. Around this time, he wrote and published several poems that later appeared in the first edition of* Leaves of Grass. *Much of that work, however, existed only as fragments until it was collected and published in 1855. The first edition was 795 copies, and consisted of twelve untitled poems and a preface. A subsequent edition the next year contained thirty-three poems. Whitman added to and altered* Leaves of Grass *many times—in 1860, 1867, 1870, 1876, 1881, and 1891.*

The book achieved recognition almost immediately. Ralph Waldo Emerson sent Whitman a letter shortly after the book's publication, saying, "I greet you at the beginning of a great career." Many literary and other public figures hailed the work, and his writing was published in various well-known periodicals such as Harper's Magazine, Galaxy, *and* The Radical. *William Michael Rossetti published a selection of Whitman's work in London under the title* Poems of Walt Whitman *in 1868, which brought him to the attention of the literary lights of England, including Tennyson and Swinburne.*

During the Civil War, Whitman worked as a freelance journalist and as a visitor—a "wound-dresser"—in different hospitals. After the war, he worked in various government offices, and was fired from at least one of those positions, in part because some of the poems in Leaves of Grass *were considered obscene. In later years, his health was not good, though he continued writing, lecturing on diverse topics including Thomas Paine and Abraham Lincoln, and editing his own work. In 1884, he purchased a small house—a "little old shanty of my own"—on Mickle Street in Camden, New Jersey. Friends and admirers helped him financially and otherwise. Active as a writer and lecturer till nearly the end of his life, Whitman died in 1892 and was buried in the Harleigh Cemetery.*

Whitman is one of the great original poets, certainly of America but almost as certainly of all writers in English. His work is marked by the long exclamatory line, the oratorical, hortatory power of his voice, and the democratic inclusiveness of his subjects. In the preface to the first edition of Leaves of Grass, *Whitman wrote, "The messages of great poets to each man and woman are, Come to us on equal terms, Only then can you understand us, We are no better than you, What we enclose you enclose, What we enjoy you may enjoy. Did you suppose there could be only one Supreme?" In his every gesture as a poet, Whitman's ardor, and the genuineness of this invitation, reach out afresh to the reader.*

I Hear America Singing

WALT WHITMAN

I hear America singing, the varied carols I hear,
Those of mechanics, each one singing his as it should be
   blithe and strong,
The carpenter singing his as he measures his plank or beam,
The mason singing his as he makes ready for work, or leaves
   off work,
The boatman singing what belongs to him in his boat, the deckhand
   singing on the steamboat deck,   5
The shoemaker singing as he sits on his bench, the hatter
   singing as he stands,
The wood-cutter's song, the ploughboy's on his way in the
   morning, or at noon intermission or at sundown,
The delicious singing of the mother, or of the young wife at
   work, or of the girl sewing or washing,
Each singing what belongs to him or her and to none else,
The day what belongs to the day—at night the party of
   young fellows, robust, friendly,   10
Singing with open mouths their strong melodious songs.

[1860]

From *Leaves of Grass*, 1867.

QUESTIONS

WALT WHITMAN, *I Hear America Singing*

1. How would you describe the movement of the poem—does it turn or take a different direction at any point?

2. What means does Whitman use to distinguish among the various songs? How are the songs different from one another?

3. What overall disposition does Whitman have toward the differing songs? Is there an overall judgment or perspective that the speaker takes toward the songs he hears?

4. How does Whitman construct the lines of this poem? Are there any devices of repetition, for instance, that give the poem a kind of form?

5. Why do you suppose Whitman uses the kind of work the singers do as the tag by which he identifies them? What statement, if any, does he wish to make about work? What kinds of work does the poem seem to value? To what extent does work appear to be segregated by gender?

6. How does the poem end? Does that ending deviate from the rest of the poem? In what ways? Does the "party of young fellows" singing at night differ from the songs of the day?

8. The poem uses the construction "what belongs to him" several times: "The boatman singing what belongs to him in his boat"; "Each singing what belongs to him"; "The day what belongs to the day." In an exploratory essay, consider the idea of a song as a possession in the poem. What does it mean to a laborer to have or possess a song? What seems to be the nature of this possession?

9. In an essay, consider the poem as a particularly American statement. Whitman begins by saying "I hear America singing"—why is this a peculiarly American song? If you like, you could compare this poem with another American song form—the blues. How is Whitman's representation of America's song different from the song of the blues?

Matthew Arnold
[1822–1888]

MATTHEW ARNOLD *was born in a small town outside of London, Laleham on Themes. His family moved to Rugby School where his father, Thomas Arnold, was headmaster and where Arnold received his early education. He matriculated at Balliol College, Oxford, in 1841 where his poem "Cromwell, A Prize Poem" won a poetry award. He was a lively youth in college, sometimes thought by his friends to be less than serious, an unlikely beginning for a poet and critic who was to become known for his weighty thought. He even managed to graduate with less than top honors. He moved to Paris where he met female author George Sand, and his close friend the poet Arthur Clough, and tasted the sophisticated life of the Paris literary elite. In 1847 he became Lord Lansdowne's secretarial assistant, a post that gave him financial advantages, and in 1951 he received an appointment as school inspector, a post that allowed him enough funds to marry Frances Wightman, a prominent judge's daughter. In 1847 he published* The Tragic Reveler and Other Poems *and in 1852* Empedocles on Etna and Other Poems. *Both books lacked literary acclaim and soon disappeared from the scene, but the preface to the latter—with affinities to Greek thought, Goethe's romanticism, and the ideas of Wordsworth—began his career as a critic. Two volumes of poetry,* Poems: A New Edition *(1853–1854) and* New Poems *(1867) established him as a poet. In 1857 he was appointed at Oxford as professor of poetry where he wrote and published* Essays on Criticism *(1865, 1888) and* Culture and Anarchy *(1869). These essays reflect his ideas about romanticism and about those he called Philistines (those who do not appreciate fine art and fine literature, a concept he adopted from Scottish philosopher and critic Thomas Carlisle). At this point he turned to theology in* Literature and Dogma *(1872) and with* Last Essay on Church and Religion *(1877). His theology argued for the existence of a God who seemed to give his creatures more questions than answers. These ideas met with some resistance by his peers.*

In 1883 he received a pension and was able to leave teaching and the university life to become a man of leisure and to travel and lecture widely throughout Europe and America, where he lectured as far west as St. Louis. He wrote Discourses in America, *the book for which he said he would most like to be remembered. His daughter married an American, so he traveled back to America with some frequency. He died, during one of her visits to England, as he ran for a tram car. He is remembered for embodying the Romantic tradition that characterized the last part of the Victorian era and for his dark vision of the century to come.*

Dover Beach

MATTHEW ARNOLD

The sea is calm to-night.
The tide is full, the moon lies fair
Upon the straits;—on the French coast the light
Gleams and is gone; the cliffs of England stand,
Glimmering and vast, out in the tranquil bay.   *5*
Come to the window, sweet is the night-air!

Only, from the long line of spray
Where the sea meets the moon-blanch'd land,
Listen! you hear the grating roar
Of pebbles which the waves draw back, and fling,   *10*
At their return, up the high strand,
Begin, and cease, and then again begin,
With tremulous cadence slow, and bring
The eternal note of sadness in.

Sophocles long ago   *15*
Heard it on the Aegean, and it brought
Into his mind the turbid ebb and flow
Of human misery; we
Find also in the sound a thought,
Hearing it by this distant northern sea.   *20*

The Sea of Faith
Was once, too, at the full, and round earth's shore
Lay like the folds of a bright girdle furl'd.
But now I only hear
Its melancholy, long, withdrawing roar,   *25*
Retreating, to the breath
Of the night-wind, down the vast edges drear
And naked shingles of the world.

First published in *New Poems* in 1867.

Ah, love, let us be true
To one another! for the world, which seems 30
To lie before us like a land of dreams,
So various, so beautiful, so new,
Hath really neither joy, nor love, nor light,
Nor certitude, nor peace, nor help for pain;
And we are here as on a darkling plain 35
Swept with confused alarms of struggle and flight,
Where ignorant armies clash by night.

[1867]

QUESTIONS

MATTHEW ARNOLD, *Dover Beach*

1. What is the setting for the poem? Why does the sea evoke such sadness in the speaker of the poem? The speaker talks to a lover. What are the requests at the beginning and end of the poem?

2. What is the Sea of Faith? What does the speaker say about the nature of faith in the modern world? Why has it ebbed?

3. Who are the armies? Do we know? Are there always armies clashing somewhere?

4. Lovers usually feel that they are alone against the world, especially young lovers. How does the poem express this feeling of isolation?

5. The end of the nineteenth century hinted at the devastation to come in the twentieth century. How does this poem express that anticipation of conflict?

6. Scientists say that all humans came from the sea and long to return. How does the poem play with that idea?

7. This poem follows no particular metric form or rhyme pattern, yet it leans heavily on the use of rhymes and sounds. Look at the vowel sounds at the ends of lines in each stanza. Note that they are the same in the stanzas. What does each collection of sounds do to carry the meaning of the poem, especially the last rhyme of *fight* and *night*?

8. Note that the poem itself ebbs and flows like the waves and that the sound moves as waves move. How does this motion affect the reading of the poem?

9. Why is "Sea of Faith" in the middle of the poem capitalized? Can you propose some reasons why this might be?

10. Describe a moment you spent alone with someone who is significant to you. Let the reader understand the ideas that were communicated in that moment.

11. Research the end of the nineteenth century. Then write about the kinds of attitudes and energies that were expressed at that time, especially the rise of nationalism and threats of war.

12. Compare a place that you enjoy, as Arnold does the cliffs at Dover, with some social or political event in the world.

Emily Dickinson
[1830–1886]

Born to an Amherst, Massachusetts, family in the early Victorian era,
EMILY DICKINSON *has been analyzed and reanalyzed for nearly two hundred
years. She was one of three children of Edward and Emily Norcross Dickinson.
Both her parents encouraged her education, sending her to Amherst Academy
and Mount Holyoke Female Seminary, which she attended until her homesick-
ness sent her home to stay. Her father served a term in Congress, giving Dickinson
the opportunity to visit Washington, D.C. briefly, and an eye problem sent her to
Boston to stay with cousins during treatment. Otherwise, she spent nearly all her
life in Amherst. Her brother, Austin, was a justice of the peace and then succeeded
his father as treasurer of Amherst College, while her sister Lavinia (Vinnie) led a
lively social life in the town. Neither Emily or Vinnie married, both living in the
family home, called the Evergreens, until their deaths.*

*Dickinson has often been described as a reclusive poet whose fame came only
after her death, but she actually lived an exciting life of the mind, corresponding
with many of the poets and intellectuals of her day and discussing world events
and poetry with friends and family in the rich intellectual circle surrounding the
family. Austin married Susan Gilbert and built a stately house, the Homestead,
next door to the Evergreens. Emily and Susan became close friends and writing
collaborators, Susan reading and responding to Dickinson's poems throughout
their lives. Dickinson also exchanged correspondence with Samuel Bowles, editor
of the* Springfield Republican; *Josiah Holland, editor at Scribner's publishing
company; poet and novelist Helen Hunt Jackson; and Thomas Wentworth
Higginson, poet and critic. She lived the life of a private intellectual whose letters
recount a rich life of the mind.*

*Dickinson wrote throughout her life, but dating her poems can be done only
through analysis of her handwriting and though analysis of booklets of her poems
she called fascicles. Also, references to current events sometimes give clues to the
timing of her writing. For example, her most productive time seems to have been
from 1858 to 1865 when the Civil War provided her with both motivation and
topic for many a poem. Some have noted that she wrote about death and sadness,
but these Civil War poems clearly reflect the tragic times through which she lived.
She continued to produce poetry until her death, completing over 1,800 poems. In
1890, after her death, a family friend, Mabel Loomis Todd, and Higginson published* Poems, *followed by a second volume in 1890, and a third in 1896. No other
editors saw her manuscripts until Ralph W. Franklin was given access to them and
produced a version,* Poems in 1998, *which followed her particular punctuation*

and spelling patterns. These patterns give her poetry an extremely postmodern feel and flavor, for Dickinson was experimental in a variety of ways, using complex ideas in simple styles and creating new metaphors that challenge and intrigue readers as much in this century as in the last.

Because I could not stop for Death–

EMILY DICKINSON

Because I could not stop for Death–
He kindly stopped for me–
The Carriage held but just Ourselves–
And Immortality.

We slowly drove–He knew no haste   5
And I had put away
My labor and my leisure too,
For His Civility–

We passed the School, where Children strove
At Recess–in the Ring–   10
We passed the Fields of Gazing Grain–
We passed the Setting Sun–

Or rather–He passed Us–
The Dews drew quivering and Chill–
For only Gossamer, my Gown–   15
My Tippet–only Tulle–[1]

We paused before a House that seemed
A Swelling of the Ground–
The Roof was scarcely visible–
The Cornice–in the Ground–   20

Since then–'tis Centuries–and yet
Feels shorter than the Day
I first surmised the Horses' Heads
Were toward Eternity–

[C. 1862]

---

[1]A tippet is a cape, and tulle is fine, filmy material.

EMILY DICKINSON, *Because I could not stop for Death–*

1. Death is compared to a carriage driver who picks up the speaker in a carriage. What route does the carriage take, and what is its destination?

2. What has time become for the speaker? What does it mean that the horse's heads were "turned toward Eternity"?

3. The speaker accepts death calmly. What view of the afterlife is presented in this poem? Is it a comforting view?

4. Some writers have speculated that people who live in small towns or in the country live closer to life and death, closer to nature. Are country people better able to deal with the reality of death? Why might this be?

5. Many of Dickinson's poems could be sung as hymns. Try singing this poem or at least reading it aloud. What is the effect of the lilting tone of the words? How does it blend with the meaning of the poem?

6. The poem begins with Death and ends with Eternity. These are both grand concepts. How does framing the poem this way link the death and the afterlife?

7. Visit an old cemetery. Read the tomb stones and then write about the lives of the people who are buried in the tombs.

8. Walk through a familiar place, and write down a description as you might see it if you were a ghost wandering through the town. What is precious? What would be best remembered? Write a description of what you see and think.

Lewis Carroll
[1832–1898]

Charles Lutwidge Dodgson, who wrote under the pen name **LEWIS CARROLL,** *was a scholarly and erudite Oxford lecturer whose specialty was mathematics. He was known in this field for his scholarly texts,* An Elementary Treatise on Determinants *(1867) and* Symbolic Logic *(1896). These are only the best known of his sober and edifying theoretical works. Dodgson, however, was a person who delighted in the company of children, and he was in fact rather shy and retiring in the adult world. He loved children whose imaginations carried them beyond the real world of accounting and proper bedtimes. He was friends with the Liddell family, and often played with the children, particularly Alice, their charming and imaginative small daughter. Dodgson wrote the character of a whimsical friend of Alice who recounts her dream experiences in the world of the imagination. The first of these works appeared in 1865 as* Alice in Wonderland. *The work was colorfully illustrated by the famous artist John Tenniel so that not only did Carroll provide a wonderful world of words; he also provided, through his illustrator, images that live in the minds of children to this day. The fanciful cast includes Queen of Hearts and the Cheshire Cat, as well as the Mad Hatter (who was likely truly mad—hatters in the Victorian era worked with mind-altering chemicals when dying the hats) and the March Hare. In the book, Alice first meets the White Rabbit and then falls down a deep rabbit hole. The dream quality of the tale is obvious right from the start when Alices sees that the rabbit is wearing a waistcoat and carrying a pocket watch. Soon the ominous nature of this imaginary world becomes clear when the queen's tendency to order beheadings becomes a part of the story. Fortunately, the king quickly and politely regularly countermands his wife's decrees. This world portrays the way that the adult world must look to a child: completely mad and inexplicable. Perhaps the best part of the books are Carroll's satires of instructional poetry that were so popular in the Victorian period for teaching children proper behavior. By the time that Alice and her acquaintances finish with the poetry, it has become both satirical and silly, a fine end for pious instructional verse.*

The second volume, Through the Looking-Glass *(1871) features another dream that begins with a fall through a mirror into a room that only vaguely resembles the world of mundane reality. Alice ends up on a chessboard with a variety of pseudo-military animals and creatures but most especially with the Red Queen who assures her that you have to keep running as fast as you can to stay in place, rather like the academia that was Dodgson's working world. Carroll was clearly the master of parody and satire that still both amuses children and delights adults. Two other works, though not as widely read and loved,* The Hunting of the Snark *(1876)—yes, snark hunts were Carroll's idea—and* Silvie and Bruno *(1889–1993). Many twentieth-century adults would not be who they are today without nineteenth-century Lewis Carroll.*

Jabberwocky[1]

LEWIS CARROLL

'Twas brillig, and the slithy toves
Did gyre and gimble in the wabe:
All mimsy were the borogoves,
And the mome raths outgrabe.

"Beware the Jabberwock, my son!   5
The jaws that bite, the claws that catch!
Beware the Jubjub bird, and shun
The frumious Bandersnatch!"

He took his vorpal sword in hand;
Long time the manxome foe he sought—   10
So rested he by the Tumtum tree
And stood awhile in thought.

And, as in uffish thought he stood,
The Jabberwock, with eyes of flame,
Came whiffling through the tulgey wood,   15
And burbled as it came!

One, two! One, two! And through and through
The vorpal blade went snicker-snack!
He left it dead, and with its head
He went galumphing back.   20

"And hast thou slain the Jabberwock?
Come to my arms, my beamish boy!
O frabjous day! Callooh, Callay!"
He chortled in his joy.

---

[1]Carroll provides a glossary to the poem that is just as silly as the poem, maybe even sillier.

First published in *Through the Looking Glass and What Alice Saw There* in 1872.

'Twas brillig, and the slithy toves 25
Did gyre and gimble in the wabe:
All mimsy were the borogoves,
And the mome raths outgrabe.

[1871]

QUESTIONS

1. What happens to the dragon creature in the poem? How can you tell when the words are nonsense words?

2. This poem demonstrates that the logic of grammar works even when the words are nonsense. How do you know what the nonsense words mean? What grammatical clues are there in the poem?

3. The Victorians loved tales of knightly valor and bravery. The tales of King Arthur were very popular, especially the battle stories of his knights. This knight kills a dragon. How is his father's joy expressed? Does that seem quite proper? Why is the first stanza repeated at the end? What does it mean when a song repeats a chorus?

4. Compare the bravery of the "beamish boy" to the super heroes of modern television and cinema. Write about the cartoon character of the superhero and his (or her) roots in this poem.

Thomas Hardy
[1840–1928]

THOMAS HARDY *was born on June 2, 1840, the first child of Thomas and Jemima Hardy. He would be followed by two sisters and a brother. The family lived at Higher Bockhampton, Dorset, England—a hamlet consisting of some ten houses situated in a wooded area on the edge of Puddletown Heath (which Hardy was later to christen Edgon Heath). As a young boy, Hardy memorized large swatches of the* Book of Common Prayer, *and on wet Sundays, he would wrap himself in a tablecloth and lead the family in the Service for Morning Prayer.*

Hardy's mother, not necessarily taken with the religious life, enrolled her son in a nonconformist school, and within a year or two had secured him additional tuition in Latin. He left school at sixteen, with a good grounding in Latin, drawing, ancient history, and various branches of mathematics. The same year he was apprenticed to the local architect in Dorchester, John Hicks. Five years later, in 1861, he set off for London to practice architecture on a larger scale.

In London, he worked at his architectural career while reading English literature and taking advantage of the city's museums, opera-houses, and concert halls. He began to write poems ("Hap" and "The Ruined Maid" date from this period). Desperate to find his way into print, he wrote a first novel, The Poor Man and the Lady, *which was rejected. But the publisher's reader, George Meredith, encouraged Hardy to write another, which resulted in his first published book,* Desperate Remedies *(1871). During this time, he read Darwin's* The Origin of Species *and became an agnostic, adopting a scientific world view touched with a sense of beauty and nostalgia.*

By 1870, he returned to Dorset where he continued to write fiction. His first major hit was Far From the Madding Crowd *(1874). On the strength of this success, he was able to marry Emma Lavinia Gifford, a woman he had met and fallen in love with in 1870. For the next 22 years he wrote and published fiction and became one of England's leading novelists, famous as the sexually frank and socially challenging author of* Return of the Native *(1878),* The Mayor of Casterbridge *(1885),* The Woodlanders *(1887),* Tess of the d'Urbervilles *(1891), and* Jude the Obscure *(1895).*

In 1898, after the stormy success of Jude the Obscure, *Hardy surprised his readers by presenting them with not another novel but instead,* Wessex Poems, *his first collection of verse—a collection that included a good number of those early poems rejected by editors in the 1860s. This book was followed by seven more,* Poems of the Past and the Present *(1901—which included "The Darkling Thrush"),* Time's Laughingstocks *(1909),* Satires of Circumstance *(1914—*

which included "The Convergence of the Twain"), Moments of Vision *(1917),* Late Lyrics and Earlier *(1922),* Human Shows *(1925), and* Winter Words *(posthumous, 1928). He died at age 87 on January 11, 1928, equally famous as novelist and poet.*

—Bill Morgan, *Illinois State University*

Hap

THOMAS HARDY

If but some vengeful god would call to me
From up the sky, and laugh: "Thou suffering thing,
Know that thy sorrow is my ecstasy,
That thy love's loss is my hate's profiting!"

Then would I bear it, clench myself, and die,   *5*
Steeled by the sense of ire unmerited;
Half-eased in that a Powerfuller than I
Had willed and meted me the tears I shed.

But not so. How arrives it joy lies slain,
And why unblooms the best hope ever sown?   *10*
—Crass Casualty obstructs the sun and rain,
And dicing Time for gladness casts a moan . . .
These purblind Doomsters had as readily strown
Blisses about my pilgrimage as pain.

[1866]

First published in 1866.

QUESTIONS

THOMAS HARDY, *Hap*

1. The "dicing Time" of Casualty (cause and effect) in this poem suggests a throwing of dice randomly to see what will happen. If this is the case what does this poem say about hard work and ambition?

2. Hardy says that it would be better if there were a vengeful god than an indifferent universe; everything is just happening, not planned. How does he construct this argument?

3. Is "Hap" more concerned with the order of the cosmos or the unhappiness of the individual? What evidence do you find?

4. The speaker in the poem is angry at the universe for refusing him all his whims and wishes; does the poet agree or is he criticizing the speaker?

5. "Hap" is an English sonnet with an irregular rhyme scheme (ending *efeffe*, instead of the conventional *efefgg*); what purpose does this variation in the rhyme scheme serve?

6. The sonnet form sets up an argument and then responds to that argument. What is the response in the last six lines of this sonnet?

7. In "Hap," Hardy describes a cosmos without predictable order, but the poem itself is rigorously ordered in sonnet form. Write about the relationship of form to theme in the poem.

8. Choose a news story that demonstrates the seeming unfairness of the universe. Write about the possible causes and effects in the event.

William Butler Yeats
[1865–1939]

Like many of the upper class in Ireland, WILLIAM BUTLER YEATS *came from an Anglo-Irish background. His father was a noted artist, a portrait painter, and member of the Royal Hibernian Academy. Yeats was born near Dublin, attended school in both London and Dublin, and university at Dublin University. There he began to publish poems and articles in the* Dublin University Review. *By 1888 he moved to London and was initiated into the Rhymers' Club. In 1889 his first volume of verse appeared,* The Wanderings of Oisin and Other Poems. *His early work owes much to the pre-Raphaelites, to the Romantic poets Percy Bysshe Shelley and William Blake, and even to his father's painting. In these early years he helped organize Irish literary societies in both London and Dublin, as well as the Irish Literary Theater, later the Abbey Theater. In his youth he fell in love with a political activist and writer, Maude Gonne, with whom he worked but never married. Many of his most poignant poems are written to and about her. In 1895* Poems *appeared, the first of his lyric volumes, and a collection of prose legends and tales (*The Secret Rose*) followed in 1897. In 1899 another lyric volume,* The Wind among the Reeds *appeared. These lyric poems express much of the Celtic psyche and has a certain elfin charm, always with a touch of melancholy for the age of magic that has passed. At the same time, he was making his mark on the theater with* The Countess Cathleen *(1892) and* The Land of Heart's Desire *(1894). Many more volumes of poetry followed including* The Green Helmet and Other Poems *(1910),* Michael Robartes and the Dancer, *and* Reveries over Childhood and Youth *(1915), but in the 1920s he burst forth into greater public awareness. He became a senator in the new Irish Free State in 1922; in 1923 he received the Noble Prize for Literature, followed by his autobiographical* A Vision *and his greatest poetic work,* The Tower *(1928).*

Yeats's poetry and drama reflect his interest in Irish history and Irish politics, as well as his love for the beauty of the Irish landscape. He was also concerned with the tumult of the early twentieth century, often speaking as a prophet about the war that was to come in the middle of the century, though he did not live to see it. In 1918 he wrote a piece called Per Amica Silentia Lunae *(Friend of the Silent Moon), a volume of philosophical essays that suggested the later interests of his life. He was always a kind of mystic, and in later life he became more and more interested in magic, astrology, and a complex philosophy called Theosophy. The* Silentia Lunae *categorizes humanity according to the phases of the moon, an interest that was a part of the thinking of Jungians and other psychological and philosophical thinkers of the time. Whatever the influences on his thinking, he continued to express the plaintive feelings that are distinctly Irish. Yeats was buried first at Roquebrune but his body was later moved to County Sligo.*

The Second Coming

WILLIAM BUTLER YEATS

Turning and turning in the widening gyre   1
The falcon cannot hear the falconer;
Things fall apart; the center cannot hold;
Mere anarchy is loosed upon the world,
The blood-dimmed tide is loosed, and everywhere   5
The ceremony of innocence is drowned;
The best lack all conviction, while the worst
Are full of passionate intensity.
Surely some revelation is at hand;
Surely the Second Coming is at hand.   10
The Second Coming! Hardly are those words out
When a vast image out of *Spiritus Mundi*
Troubles my sight: somewhere in sands of the desert
A shape with lion body and the head of a man,
A gaze blank and pitiless as the sun,   15
Is moving its slow thighs, while all about it
Reel shadows of the indignant desert birds.
The darkness drops again; but now I know
That twenty centuries of stony sleep
Were vexed to nightmare by a rocking cradle,   20
And what rough beast, its hour come round at last,
Slouches toward Bethlehem to be born?

[1921]

Composed in 1921.

QUESTIONS

WILLIAM BUTLER YEATS, *The Second Coming*

1. In "The Second Coming" Yeats prophesies about the thing that was to come in the twentieth century. Religious people talked about the beast that would come. What beast did come in the middle of the twentieth century?

2. The literal beast in this poem is the Sphinx that guards the Pyramids, but it is far more too. What was lost when paganism replaced Christianity? What natural inclinations of human nature did Christianity suppress? What beast began to come alive in 1914 (World War I)?

4. Why is that so many people hope for a Second Coming? Consider all the popular books on the subject. Why does each generation have groups who thought the time had arrived? Write about your reactions to this phenomenon.

Paul Laurence Dunbar
[1872–1906]

The son of former Kentucky slaves, **PAUL LAURENCE DUNBAR** *became one of the first African-American writers to achieve national prominence. As a student in Dayton, Ohio High School, Dunbar saw several of his poems published in the* Dayton Herald; *pervasive race discrimination, however, prevented him from obtaining a job in journalism after graduation, despite having been voted class poet and president of his graduating class. Nonetheless, his first collection of poems,* Oak and Ivy, *appeared in 1893 when Dunbar was only twenty-one years old. Working as an elevator operator at the time, Dunbar enlisted the help of friends Wilbur Wright and Orville Wright (the brothers famous for their flying machine) to publish the volume privately. His reputation was enhanced by the recognition of the Western Association of Writers and prominent orator Frederick Douglass, who hired Dunbar to work in the Haitian Pavilion at the World Columbian Exposition in Chicago in 1893. In 1896 Dunbar's second collection,* Majors and Minors, *was published—and reviewed favorably (if condescendingly) by renowned critic William Dean Howells, who later that year convinced the publishing house of Dodd, Mead to publish* Lyrics of Lowly Life, *with an introduction by Howells himself. It was the publication of this collection that established Dunbar's reputation as a man of letters.*

Dunbar's most popular poems were written using African-American vernacular, while his more formal work in standard English received far less critical and popular attention. He expressed his frustration with this situation in "The Poet," who sings "serenely sweet," only to discover that the world praises not this "deep" verse but rather the "jingle in a broken tongue." In other poems, such as "We Wear the Mask," Dunbar unveils the "torn and bleeding hearts" hiding behind "the mask that grins and lies." Similar themes can be found in his short stories, particularly those in the 1898 volume Folks from Dixie, *in which he chronicled the myriad abuses heaped on African Americans both before and after emancipation. Throughout his work in fiction, nonfiction, and poetry, Dunbar reflects on the struggles of his race.*

In 1898, after a reading tour of England, Dunbar married fellow African-American poet Alice Ruth Moore and published another collection, Lyrics from the Hearthside. *By this time, however, his health was failing badly. He had suffered from tuberculosis for some time, and in the ensuing years he fought several bouts of pneumonia and other related illnesses. Dunbar's illness placed a strain on the marriage, and in 1902 he and his wife separated. He continued writing, however, publishing a highly acclaimed volume of poetry,* Lyrics of Love and Laughter, *the following year. This collection, appearing after several poorly reviewed novels, revived the poet's reputation, but not his health. An increasing dependence on alcohol exacerbated his condition, and Dunbar died in 1906 at the age of thirty-three. His legacy remains strong, however, particularly among African-American writers. Contemporary poet Nikki Giovanni calls Dunbar "a natural resource of our people," and the final line of his 1899 poem "Sympathy" became internationally famous when Maya Angelou selected it as the title for the first volume of her autobiography: "I know why the caged bird sings."*

Sympathy

PAUL LAURENCE DUNBAR

I know what the caged bird feels, alas!
   When the sun is bright on the upland slopes;
When the wind stirs soft through the springing grass,
And the river flows like a stream of glass;
   When the first bird sings and the first bud opes,   5
And the faint perfume from its chalice steals—
I know what the caged bird feels!

I know why the caged bird beats his wing
   Till its blood is red on the cruel bars;
For he must fly back to his perch and cling   10
When he fain would be on the bough a-swing;
   And a pain still throbs in the old, old scars
And they pulse again with a keener sting—
   I know why he beats his wing!

I know why the caged bird sings, ah me,   15
   When his wing is bruised and his bosom sore,—
When he beats his bars and he would be free;
It is not a carol of joy or glee,
   But a prayer that he sends from his heart's deep core,
But a plea, that upward to Heaven he flings—   20
I know why the caged bird sings!

[1896]

First published in *Lyrics of Lowly Life* in 1896.

QUESTIONS

PAUL LAURENCE DUNBAR, *Sympathy*

1. What feelings do the images in the first stanza convey? What is suggested by the image of the bud opening, "the faint perfume from its chalice steals"? Why is the perfume faint?

2. The caged bird is the extended metaphor of the poem. As such, it could stand for a variety of experiences. What does the caged bird metamorphize?

3. How does Dunbar represent the purpose of song in the poem? How does his approach in the poem reflect African-American traditions?

4. As an African-American writer in the late nineteenth century, what personal or professional experiences might have informed this poem?

5. What is the significance of the poem's title? How does the metaphor of the caged bird lend greater emotional intensity to the poem and great pathos to its message?

6. How does life impose limitations on people? How is poetry, or art in general, a response to such circumstances?

7. Write a biographical essay on the literary career of Dunbar. What burdened him as an artist? How did his career influence the movement Harlem Renaissance? What is Dunbar's significance to American letters?

8. Write an essay explaining your perspective on racial injustice in America. What is the effect of racism on the individuals who are subjected to it?

Robert Frost
[1874–1963]

The son of a journalist who died when **ROBERT FROST** *was only eleven, the now well-known poet lived with his mother in Lawrence, Massachusetts, where he worked at many jobs while finishing high school, where he was co-valedictorian of his class. While in school, he wrote for the* Lawrence High School Bulletin. *He married his co-valedictorian, Elinor White, and began his college career. Frost attended Dartmouth and Harvard, but dropped out of both shortly before the deaths of his three-year-old son and his mother. In search of financial stability, Frost bought a farm in Derry, New Hampshire, where he and Elinor had four more children while he wrote poetry and taught at the Pinkerton Academy. His first book,* A Boy's Will *appeared in 1913. Frost then sold the farm and moved his family to London where he met Ezra Pound who viewed Frost as a follower and composer of "Imagist" poems—poems of vivid pictoral language and minimal sentiment. However, Frost developed his own theory of the sound of poetry, that is, catching the word as it is heard and spoken. His* North of Boston *(1914) poems characterize his particular view of the purpose and practice of poetry. These poems use dramatic monologues to capture the realities of human life and words.*

Frost returned to the United States in 1915 and bought another farm in New Hampshire, but this time he was not dependent on farm income and minimal teaching. While in Europe, Frost had become friends with powerful editors and publishers, including Ellery Sedgwick editor of the Atlantic Monthly *and Henry Holt of the* New Republic. *He also became friends with the powerful poet and critic Louis Untermeyer. Frost taught at Amherst College and published his third book,* Mountain Interval *(1916). His fourth book,* New Hampshire, *won the Pulitzer Prize, followed by* West-Running Brook *in 1928, and* Collected Poems *in 1930, which won a second Pulitzer. Frost refused to join the political literary movements of the thirties but chose to write another personal and individual book,* A Further Range *(1936), which the critics attacked for lack of social relevance. In spite of its critics, the book also won a Pulitzer. In the late thirties, he suffered the deaths of two children and his wife, and he collapsed for a time. By 1942, however, he completed* A Witness Tree, *winner of yet another Pulitzer. This book was followed by* The Steeple Bush *in 1947 and* In the Clearing *in 1962. Frost spoke to the nation by reading "The Gift Outright" at President Kennedy's inauguration in 1961. He died two years later, a poet whose characters questioned their own comfortable assumptions about the world. With many well-wrought poems that demonstrate effective revisions of years of working and reworking, Frost was above all a craftsman.*

Stopping by Woods on a Snowy Evening

ROBERT FROST

Whose woods these are I think I know.
His house is in the village though;
He will not see me stopping here
To watch his woods fill up with snow.

My little horse must think it queer   5
To stop without a farmhouse near
Between the woods and frozen lake
The darkest evening of the year.

He gives his harness bells a shake
To ask if there is some mistake.   10
The only other sound's the sweep
Of easy wind and downy flake.

The woods are lovely, dark and deep,
But I have promises to keep,
And miles to go before I sleep,   15
And miles to go before I sleep.

[1923]

QUESTIONS

ROBERT FROST, *Stopping by Woods on a Snowy Evening*

1. This poem is famous in many ways, because it asks questions about life and death. What does snow seem to represent here?

2. The poet is lost in musing about death and life, but the horse is having none of it. What does the horse do for the narrator?

3. Everyone has "miles to go" every day, and sometimes the road is not easy. Why should we not end our lives? What lines in Frost's poem suggest his opinion on the subject?

4. The horse's body is life and warmth for the man, as well as company. A cowboy saying is that there is nothing so good for the inside of a man as the outside of a horse. How does Frost personify the horse in this poem? What is the effect of this poetic technique?

5. The quatrains in this poem link with an aaba, bbcb, ccdc pattern until the end when the pattern is dddd, not an easy rhyme to write. How does the repetition of the *eep* sound help to settle the poem's statement about life?

6. How do the words "lovely, dark, and deep" work together to suggest the temptations in the poem?

7. Psychologists sometimes describe moments of despair or sadness as "going into the woods" to discover something about ourselves. In this poem the poet discovers that he has obligations that will keep him alive and working for many years to come. Talk to older friends or family members about how they made it through rough times in their lives. Write about their trials and their solutions and triumphs.

Rupert Brooke
[1887–1915]

RUPERT BROOKE *was born at Rugby School, in Rugby Warwickshire, England, where his father was a housemaster, but it was Brooke's mother who was an important influence in his early life. She could not resist being involved in the world of her handsome and dashing son. She encouraged him in his studies, and assured him the advantages of the best schooling. Well educated and well supervised, Brooke completed his thesis,* John Webster and the Elizabethan Drama, *in 1912, which won him a fellowship at King's College, Cambridge. Brooke cut a dashing figure in the literary world; W. B. Yeats proclaimed Brooke "the handsomest young man in England." After school, Brooke traveled to North America and roamed the South Seas for the* Westminster Gazette, *sending back narratives and poems. Brooke had thus became a well-known essayist and poet when Britain entered World War I. Brooke died before entering the war, but his sonnet, "The Soldier," was read from the pulpit of Saint Paul's, forever tying the young poet to the war poet category. He was celebrated not for his bravery in war but for his ability to encapsulate the feelings of the nation at the outset of the Great War. In fact, he died from blood poisoning in the Aegean Sea, while sailing toward the battle at Gallipoli, and was buried on the Island of Skyros rather than being returned to his home in England. Brooke was thus a pre-war poet who was connected with the war he almost fought, but who actually wrote most of his poems about life before the war began. His reputation as a war poet comes from five war sonnets, but his military experience entailed only one day of limited action during the evacuation of Antwerp. Thus, the sonnets of Brooke are not about war at all but about the feelings of a young man about to embark on a great adventure. He never suffered the real horrors of war that led other war poets to write, not romantically, but graphically and tragically about war. It was natural that Brooke would have written about brave soldiers dying still beautiful and young, innocent and brave. That is exactly what he did.*

The Soldier

RUPERT BROOKE

If I should die, think only this of me;
   That there's some corner of a foreign field
That is for ever England. There shall be
   In that rich earth a richer dust concealed;
A dust whom England bore, shaped, made aware,   5
   Gave, once, her flowers to love, her ways to roam,
A body of England's breathing English air,
   Washed by the rivers, blest by suns of home.
And think, this heart, all evil shed away,
   A pulse in the eternal mind, no less   10
     Gives somewhere back the thoughts by England given;
Her sights and sounds; dreams happy as her day;
   And laughter, learnt of friends; and gentleness,
     In hearts at peace, under an English heaven.

[1915]

First published in *Collected Poems* in 1915.

QUESTIONS

1. This sonnet expresses the feelings of a young man about to go to war, who is naive of the realities he faces. How is his innocence made clear in the poem?

2. Imagined bravery is always far better than facing real dangers, and loving one's country is quite easy to do when one is sitting comfortably at a desk, writing a sonnet. What tensions lie between the dream of battle and the reality?

3. The sextet of this sonnet talks of the friends at home who will remember the dead soldier. Would those friends be laughing? Would they be at peace?

4. Read about the experiences of soldiers who are currently fighting in war, or who have fought in other wars. If possible, interview someone who has returned from war. Write about the real experiences of men and women in combat.

Langston Hughes
[1902–1967]

A major figure of the Harlem Renaissance, LANGSTON HUGHES *was born in Joplin, Missouri. His father left for Mexico in 1903, and after traveling for a time with his mother, Hughes moved to Lawrence, Kansas to live with his grandmother. He graduated from high school in Cleveland—again living with his mother—and then spent fifteen months with his father in Mexico and a year at Columbia University before he shipped on a merchant vessel abroad traveling to Africa. He worked for a year in Paris and Venice before returning to the United States.*

Hughes became interested in literature while still young, and published some of his most important poems before his trip abroad. In fact, by the time he was "discovered," working as a busboy, by poet Vachel Lindsay in 1925, he had already established himself as one of the central poets of the Harlem Renaissance. In 1921 The Crisis, *an important journal of African-American letters edited by W. E. B. Du Bois, was published. "The Negro Speaks of Rivers," and "The Weary Blues" appeared two years later in the* Amsterdam News *(a journal published in New York).*

Hughes worked in many genres, including drama, prose fiction, and journalism. He also edited literary anthologies, and offered support and encouragement for emerging writers such as Alice Walker and Gwendolyn Brooks. His first book of poetry, The Weary Blues, *was published in 1926, and his first novel,* Not Without Laughter, *appeared in 1930. He also collaborated for many years writing children's books with novelist Arna Bontemps. Besides the widely anthologized poems mentioned here, Hughes was also widely known for his sketches in the* Chicago Defender *featuring Harlem sage Jesse B. Semple. With Semple, Hughes created a persona through which he could humorously but pointedly address issues of race relations and the condition of African Americans.*

As a member of the Harlem Renaissance and a noted black man of letters, Hughes created controversy with his rejection of the bourgeois aspirations of upper-middle class African Americans, whose value systems he saw as a slavish imitation of white society. He worked toward a literature that was uniquely African American, rather than one that derived its structures and standards from the literatures of Europe. In poems such as "The Weary Blues" he sought to reproduce the rhythms of the blues and to focus on the realities of African-American life. His was a dominant voice in African-American literature, and he shed light on the concerns of black America far beyond the dissolution of the Harlem Renaissance.

—David L. G. Arnold, *University of Wisconsin, Stevens Point*

Dream Variations

LANGSTON HUGHES

To fling my arms wide
In some place of the sun,
To whirl and to dance
Till the white day is done.
Then rest at cool evening   5
Beneath a tall tree
While night comes on gently,
    Dark like me–
That is my dream!

To fling my arms wide   10
In the face of the sun,
Dance! Whirl! Whirl!
Till the quick day is done.
Rest at pale evening . . .
A tall, slim tree . . .   15
Night coming tenderly
    Black like me.

[1924]

QUESTIONS

LANGSTON HUGHES, *Dream Variations*

1. What is the significance of color imagery in "Dream Variations"?

2. Each stanza of "Dream Variations" imagines the course of a day. Describe the contrast between diurnal and nocturnal imagery in this poem.

3. "Dream Variations" is clearly divided into two stanzas. How do the stanzas differ from one another? What formal and thematic changes transpire as the poem progresses?

4. In poems such as "Danse Africaine" and "Juke Box Love Song," Hughes describes dancing as an ecstatic, liberating activity. Describe the significance of dancing in "Dream Variations" Why does the speaker dance only during the day in this poem?

5. In Hughes's "The Negro Speaks of Rivers," the speaker envisions the African-American experience in terms of the many rivers with which blacks have been associated, concluding "My soul has grown deep like the rivers." With what aspects of nature does the speaker identify in "Dream Variations"? Write a comparative essay about these poems, emphasizing the role of nature in each text.

Harlem [2]

LANGSTON HUGHES

What happens to a dream deferred?

    Does it dry up
    like a raisin in the sun?
    Or fester like a sore—
    And then run?   5
    Does it stink like rotten meat?
    Or crust and sugar over—
    like a syrupy sweet?

    Maybe it just sags
    like a heavy load.   10

    Or does it explode?

[1951]

Reprinted from *The Collected Poems of Langston Hughes,* by permission of Alfred A. Knopf, a division of Random House, Inc. Copyright © 1994 by The Estate of Langston Hughes.

1. Describe your experience of reading or listening to "Harlem." Which of the poem's images are shocking or disturbing? Why, in your opinion, might Hughes attempt to affect the reader in this way?

2. In this poem Hughes describes the mood of a community through a series of similes. Discuss the significance of these comparisons, and speculate about the last line, where the poet seems to stop short before making the final comparison.

3. What is the connection between this poem's title and its subject matter?

4. In what ways does Hughes use the device of repetition in "Harlem"?

5. Research and compose an essay about the ways in which "Harlem" treats the history of African-American experience.

6. Compare and contrast "Harlem" with either "Lenox Avenue: Midnight" or "The Weary Blues." What setting do these poems share? How does the poet emphasize different experiences of that setting in each poem?

7. Write a comparative essay about "Harlem" and Chester Himes's short story "Marihuana and a Pistol." What do these treatments of the black urban experience have in common? Do the texts share any themes, images, or rhetorical strategies? How do they differ in their handling of similar issues?

Elizabeth Bishop
[1911–1979]

ELIZABETH BISHOP *was born in Worcester, Massachusetts. Before her first birthday, her father died, and by the time she was five, her mother had been committed to a mental hospital, after a series of nervous collapses. Elizabeth was raised by her mother's family in Great Village, Nova Scotia until she was six, after which her father's family, who lived in Worcester and Boston, took her in. She attended Vassar; through a connection with the Vassar librarian, she met the poet Marianne Moore, twenty-four years her senior, and they became lifelong friends. Moore's was the first of many literary friendships for Bishop—she had a lasting friendship with Robert Lowell, and she had acquaintances and admirers such as Randall Jarrell, Donald Hall, James Merrill, and many others in the literary world.*

Bishop's earliest publications were in the Vassar undergraduate magazine, which she helped to found, along with novelist Mary McCarthy and others. Moore also published several of Bishop's poems in an anthology called Trial Balances *in 1935. She worked slowly; some of poems, such as "The Map" and "The Man-Moth," written when she lived in New York in 1936, did not see publication until her first volume,* North and South, *came out in 1946. A second volume,* A Cold Spring, *was published in 1955—this book won the Pulitzer Prize in 1956. In the intervening years, she lived in both Europe and Key West, Florida. In 1951, she began a long residency of about eighteen years in Brazil, with her lover Lota de Macedo Soares; she lived in Rio de Janeiro and, later, Ouro Prêto. Many poems in* Questions of Travel *(1965) take as their subject matter these years in Brazil.*

In 1967, Soares died of an overdose of tranquilizers, a loss that was devastating to Bishop, but she persisted to write and publish. A volume titled Complete Poems *was published in 1969, which included all her previously published poems as well as several new pieces; this book won the National Book Award of 1970. She accepted a teaching position at Harvard, where she taught for several years. Her last collection,* Geography III, *was published in 1976, and won the Book Critics Circle Award for 1977. She was at work on another volume, tentatively titled "Grandmother's Glass Eye," along with a book-length poem,* Elegy, *when she died in 1979. Four poems that were to be a part of the new collection—"Santarem," "North Haven," "Pink Dog," and "Sonnet"—were finished at that point; these poems were included in* The Complete Poems, 1927–1979, *published in 1983.*

Bishop's poems are cherished by generations of readers for their fresh, unstudied diction and their directness and warmth. Reviewing Geography III, *poet Alfred Corn noted that Bishop's work exhibited "a radiant patience few people ever achieve and few writers ever successfully render. The poems are works of philosophic beauty and calm, illuminated by that 'laughter in the soul' that belongs to the best part of the comic genius." James Merrill noted in his review of the posthumous* The Complete Poems 1927–1979 *that most of Bishop's poems are in the first person, and often that "I" is someone else—"the Riverman, or Robinson Crusoe." Merrill goes on to remark that "because [Bishop] is to no least degree concerned with making herself any more remarkable than, as the author of these poems, she already is, hers is a purified, transparent 'I,' which readers may take as their virtual own." These remarks suggest something of the high critical esteem in which Bishop's work is held, but also the reason why so many readers treasure the poems—for their playfulness, their matter-of-factness, their modesty, and for the marvels they introduce.*

The Fish

ELIZABETH BISHOP

I caught a tremendous fish
and held him beside the boat
half out of water, with my hook
fast in a corner of his mouth.
He didn't fight.   5
He hadn't fought at all.
He hung a grunting weight,
battered and venerable
and homely. Here and there
his brown skin hung in strips   10
like ancient wallpaper,
and its pattern of darker brown
was like wallpaper:
shapes like full-blown roses
stained and lost through age.   15
He was speckled with barnacles,
fine rosettes of lime,
and infested
with tiny white sea-lice,
and underneath two or three   20
rags of green weed hung down.
While his gills were breathing in
the terrible oxygen
—the frightening gills,
fresh and crisp with blood,   25
that can cut so badly—
I thought of the coarse white flesh
packed in like feathers,
the big bones and the little bones,
the dramatic reds and blacks   30
of his shiny entrails,

and the pink swim-bladder
like a big peony.
I looked into his eyes
which were far larger than mine   35
but shallower, and yellowed,
the irises backed and packed
with tarnished tinfoil
seen through the lenses
of old scratched isinglass.   40
They shifted a little, but not
to return my stare.
—It was more like the tipping
of an object toward the light.
I admired his sullen face,   45
the mechanism of his jaw,
and then I saw
that from his lower lip
—if you could call it a lip—
grim, wet, and weaponlike,   50
hung five old pieces of fish-line,
or four and a wire leader
with the swivel still attached,
with all their five big hooks
grown firmly in his mouth.   55
A green line, frayed at the end
where he broke it, two heavier lines,
and a fine black thread
still crimped from the strain and snap
when it broke and he got away.   60
Like medals with their ribbons
frayed and wavering,
a five-haired beard of wisdom
trailing from his aching jaw.
I stared and stared   65
and victory filled up
the little rented boat,
from the pool of bilge
where oil had spread a rainbow
around the rusted engine   70
to the bailer rusted orange,
the sun-cracked thwarts,

the oarlocks on their strings,
the gunnels—until everything
was rainbow, rainbow, rainbow!   *75*
And I let the fish go.

[1940]

QUESTIONS

1. What can you say about the speaker of the poem, based on the poem? Focus not only on the outcome of the poem, but also on the particular moments of attention the speaker pays to the fish.

2. The poem tells a brief narrative, and generally stories have a moment where events turn—where something changes. Does this poem have such a moment? If so, where would you locate that moment?

3. Most of the lines hover around six or seven syllables; the lines generally have either two or three stresses per line. Read the poem aloud, with a brief pause at the end of each line. Do the lines feel regular or irregular to you? How does this aspect of the poem's form affect your reading of it?

4. The poem describes a moment where the human world meets the animal world. What happens at this meeting? How does it resolve?

5. In what ways does the speaker of the poem invest the fish with human qualities? In what way does she preserve the fish's other-ness? How does this fit into the overall movement of the poem?

6. Does the poem ever explicitly make reference to the idea of beauty? For instance, when the speaker notes, "victory filled up / the little rented boat, / from the pool of bilge / where oil had spread a rainbow / around the rusted engine," is she smuggling in an image of beauty in the midst of images of corrosion and filth? To what effect? How does the idea of beauty play out in the poem's ending?

7. One might say of this poem that it is concerned with a moment of seeing—perhaps even a moment of vision: The speaker catches the fish, then holds it half in the water, beholding him in order to describe him. It's long poem, and the narrator frankly acknowledges that the fish, by taking in oxygen, is on the verge of death. In an essay, analyze and discuss what this speaker's gaze signifies, and what it shows her.

8. In an exploratory essay, compare this poem with another poem that illustrates a similar collision with the natural world or an animal, such as Wallace Stevens's "Thirteen Ways of Looking at a Blackbird," or Robert Frost's "The Most of It." In the poems you examine, what does the animal world seem to say to human beings?

Dylan Thomas
[1914–1953]

A popular image of the poet is, perhaps, as a hard-drinking, womanizing, rabble-rousing, egotistic, irresponsible, and ultimately tragic figure. No poet more conformed to this image than **DYLAN THOMAS.** *Born in the town of Swansea, Wales, Thomas attended Swansea Grammar School, dropped out of school at sixteen, and became a reporter for* The South Wales Daily Post. *By the age of twenty, he published his first book of poems, drawing high praise. Between 1936 and 1946 he published several more books of poems and prose, made radio broadcasts for the BBC, and by 1950 embarked on the first of his legendary reading tours of the United States. These readings captivated American audiences who were entranced by the force of Thomas's personality, his theatrical performances, and the emotional, lyrical intensity of his poetry.*

Thomas was, as another poet described him, "the maddest of the word-mad poets." Consistent with the Romantic, self-destructive image he cast, Thomas died at thirty-nine after a heavy bout of drinking at the renowned White Horse Tavern in New York City. Always productive, Thomas published In Country Sleep, And Other Poems *and his* Collected Poems *in 1952. In 1954 he published the memoir of his Welsh childhood,* A Child's Christmas in Wales *and a radio play,* Under Milk Wood, *which also recalls memories of the coastal town where he was raised.*

Do Not Go Gentle into That Good Night

DYLAN THOMAS

Do not go gentle into that good night,
Old age should burn and rave at close of day;
Rage, rage against the dying of the light.

Though wise men at their end know dark is right,
Because their words had forked no lightning they   5
Do not go gentle into that good night.

Good men, the last wave by, crying how bright
Their frail deeds might have danced in a green bay,
Rage, rage against the dying of the light.

Wild men who caught and sang the sun in flight,   10
And learn, too late, they grieved it on its way,
Do not go gentle into that good night.

Grave men, near death, who see with blinding sight
Blind eyes could blaze like meteors and be gay,
Rage, rage against the dying of the light.   15

And you, my father, there on the sad height,
Curse, bless, me now with your fierce tears, I pray.
Do not go gentle into that good night.
Rage, rage against the dying of the light.

[1952]

QUESTIONS

DYLAN THOMAS, *Do Not Go Gentle into That Good Night*

1. This poem is one of the most famous examples of a *villanelle*. Examine the form carefully for its structure and rhythm; summarize how it is designed. Does your examination influence your appreciation of the poem? How does the form lend it emotional intensity?

2. Thomas wrote this poem during his father's final illness. What is the poet's mood or frame of mind as reflected in the poem?

3. Name the different kinds of men described in the poem. How does each of them confront death? What is the poet attempting to convey to his father?

4. The lines "Do not go gentle into that good night" and "Rage, rage against the dying of the light" are each repeated twice. Why? How is the meaning enhanced the second time?

5. What does Thomas suggest about regret and how people confront it? What is the connection between regret and the reasons why death is resented?

6. How does the poem treat social concepts of illness, death, and grief?

7. What is the poet's perspective on the role of spirituality in the lives of humans? Does the poem make an argument for a particular point of view?

8. Write an essay explaining how each man in the poem stands in contrast to forces larger than himself. What does the poem have to say about human agency and fate?

9. Write an essay in which you explore cultural views of grief and death. What is our attitude about them? How is that attitude reflected in the various rituals or practices, and expressions that surround them?

Maya Angelou
[1928–   ]

Born Marguerite Johnson in St. Louis, Missouri, **MAYA ANGELOU** *was reared in rural Arkansas, which she portrays in her autobiography* I Know Why the Caged Bird Sings *(1970). After being violently attacked as a child, she refused to speak for several years, but she eventually found a voice that would influence millions during her lifetime. She grew up with a respected uncle and was a part of a larger Southern community that gave her both a voice and the ambition to change the lives of oppressed children and adults around the world. She married a South African freedom fighter and moved to Cairo, Egypt, where she edited the only English news source, the* Arab Observer. *She also began a career as an actor and dancer at this stage in her life. Next she moved to Ghana where she taught at the University of Ghana and edited the* African Review. *Upon her return to the United States Angelou was persuaded by Dr. Martin Luther King, Jr. to become the Northern leader of the Southern Christian Leadership Conference during the unrest of the sixties. She lent her powerful voice to the American civil rights movement and opened many doors for African Americans through her powerful presence and careful diplomacy. President Carter appointed her to the National Commission on the Observance of International Women's Year, and President Ford appointed her to the Bicentennial Commission so that she used her voice to speak for women around the world. During the seventies she was recipient of the* Ladies Home Journal Woman of the Year *Award. In 1981 she was nominated for the Pulitzer Prize and the National Book award. She received the Golden Eagle award for her PBS series* Afro-Americans in the Arts *and an Emmy for her performance in the acclaimed TV series* Roots. *She wrote the screenplay* Georgia *and was the first black woman to see her play filmed. She also produced, directed, and starred in* Cabaret for Freedom, *a political review.*

Angelou's career has included writing poetry, drama, and prose; acting, producing, and directing drama for both television and the theater; and civil rights activism at home and abroad. At the same time, she has thrilled audiences around the world with her brilliant readings and lectures and has moved many to follow her lead toward a positive advocacy for civil rights for all. She speaks French, Spanish, Italian, and West African Fanti. In 1993 she read at President Clinton's inauguration. She is currently Reynolds Professor of English at Wake Forest University in North Carolina and continues to travel widely, generously giving of her time and energy for political causes, poetry readings, and human rights.

Africa

MAYA ANGELOU

Thus she had lain
sugar cane sweet
deserts her hair
golden her feet
mountains her breasts   5
two Niles her tears
Thus she has lain
Black through the years.

Over the white seas
rime white and cold   10
brigands ungentled
icicle bold
took her young daughters
sold her strong sons
churched her with Jesus   15
bled her with guns.
Thus she has lain.

Now she is rising
remember her pain   20
remember the losses
her screams loud and vain
remember her riches
her history slain
now she is striding   25
although she had lain.

[1975]

Reprinted from *Oh, Pray My Wings Are Gonna Fit Me Well,* by permission of Random House, Inc. Copyright © 1975 by Maya Angelou.

MAYA ANGELOU, *Africa*

1. What is the basic nature of Africa? How does it look, and what has been its position in relationship to the world?

2. What mistreatment have Africans experienced, and how are they now responding?

3. How have Euro-centric countries treated Africa? What themes of colonization and exploitation are expressed in this poem?

4. The call for freedom of all oppressed Third World countries has been a theme of the late twentieth century. How does this poem express that theme?

5. The poem rolls like the ocean. How do the rhymes and rhythm contribute to the rolling effect of the poem? What is the purpose of that effect?

6. The last stanza turns the meaning of the poem. How is African personified? How are women, the women of Africa especially, changing like Africa?

7. If there are African students on your campus, ask them about their experiences in their country. Learn about Africa as it is today, and write about what you learn.

8. Discuss the effects of the personification and comparisons in this poem. Write about how this female imagery affects your reading of the poem.

Sylvia Plath
[1932–1963]

SYLVIA PLATH *was born in Boston to academic parents. Her father, Otto, was a professor of entomology at Boston College while her mother taught high school German and English. Plath's father became ill in 1936 with diabetes and died in 1940 from complications after surgery. Plath's mother supported the family by teaching, but Plath herself suffered at her father's loss and began cycles of depression early in life. The cycles were eventually to lead to her own much-publicized suicide as a young mother. While still in high school she published poems in* The Boston Globe, Seventeen, *and* The Christian Science Monitor. *In 1950 she began school at Smith College where she earned prizes in poetry and fiction, becoming an intern in the summer of 1953 for* Mademoiselle. *She wrote a feature called "Poets on Campus" in which she interviewed important poets such as Elizabeth Bowen and Richard Wilbur. This hard work contributed to her first collapse, sending her to a hospital for treatments, which at the time meant electro-shock therapy. She healed and returned to Smith where she graduated with honors in 1955. In the meantime, Plath published poems in* Harpers, Atlantic Monthly, Mademoiselle, *and* The Nation. *After graduation, she moved to England to study literature at Newnham College, Cambridge. There she met Ted Hughes, the poet, and married within four months. She took a teaching job at Smith back in the United States to support Hughes while his career was on the rise. By the summer of 1958, she was publishing poems regularly in the* New Yorker, The Nation, *and the* Sewanee Review. *In the summer of 1959 Plath and Hughes moved to the artist colony at Yaddo where she was able to write, collect, and publish her first book of poems,* The Colossus and Other Poems *(1960).*

At this point the poets moved to London where difficulties followed. Plath worked on her autobiography The Bell Jar *(1961) and Hughes also continued to write. The tale of her life described her early struggles with her father's death and her desperate efforts to adjust to a world where talented women were expected to live the housewife life of the 1950s. The book, like Plath's poems, spoke to intellectual and educated women of the time, being read by the sixties women's advocates as a cry for change. Plath gave birth to a daughter in 1960 and a son in 1962. The marriage, however, crumbled as Hughes became interested in another woman and Plath spiraled into anger and despair. Out of this despair grew some of her most powerful poetry, including "Daddy" and "Lady Lazarus." These poems speak about women's feelings in a world where talented women stay at home with dishes and children while men make their ways in the wider world. Alone in a small London flat with two toddlers, she committed suicide in the winter of 1963. Hughes collected her poems into* Ariel, *published in 1968. In 1982, after her works sold over 120,000 copies, she was awarded a posthumous Pulitzer Prize.*

Lady Lazarus[1]

SYLVIA PLATH

I have done it again.
One year in every ten
I manage it—

A sort of walking miracle, my skin
Bright as a Nazi lampshade,   5
My right foot

A paperweight,
My face a featureless, fine
Jew linen.

Peel off the napkin   10
O my enemy.
Do I terrify?—

The nose, the eye pits, the full set of teeth?
The sour breath
Will vanish in a day.   15

Soon, soon the flesh
The grave cave ate will be
At home on me

And I a smiling woman.
I am only thirty.   20
And like the cat I have nine times to die.

---

[1]Lazarus was the friend of Jesus who died and was raised to life by him.

This is Number Three.
What a trash
To annihilate each decade.

What a million filaments.   25
The peanut-crunching crowd
Shoves in to see

Them unwrap me hand and foot—
The big strip tease.
Gentlemen, ladies   30

These are my hands
My knees.
I may be skin and bone,

Nevertheless, I am the same, identical woman.
The first time it happened I was ten.   35
It was an accident.

The second time I meant
To last it out and not come back at all.
I rocked shut

As a seashell.   40
They had to call and call
And pick the worms off me like sticky pearls.

Dying
Is an art, like everything else.
I do it exceptionally well.   45

I do it so it feels like hell.
I do it so it feels real.
I guess you could say I've a call.

It's easy enough to do it in a cell.
It's easy enough to do it and stay put.   50
It's the theatrical

Comeback in broad day
to the same place, the same face, the same brute
Amused shout:

"A miracle!" 55
That knocks me out.
There is a charge

For the eyeing of my scars, there is a charge
For the hearing of my heart—
It really goes. 60

And there is a charge, a very large charge
For a word or a touch
Or a bit of blood

Or a piece of my hair or my clothes.
So, so, Herr Doktor. 65
So, Herr Enemy.

I am your opus,
I am your valuable,
The pure gold baby

That melts to a shriek. 70
I turn and burn.
Do not think I underestimate your great concern.

Ash, ash—
You poke and stir.
Flesh, bone, there is nothing there— 75

A cake of soap,
A wedding ring,
A gold filling.

Herr God, Herr Lucifer
Beware 80
Beware.

Out of the ash
I rise with my red hair
And I eat men like air.

[1962]

QUESTIONS

1. Plath draws her images from the remains of humans found in Nazi concentration camps. At the time of the poem's composition, the war was not long over, and the images of death were still vivid for society. What images does she use in this poem?

2. Plath tried to kill herself twice and succeeded on the third try. What is her description of the first two attempts?

3. How does the speaker feel each time she comes back from death (L. 46)? What does she mean in lines 57 and 58 when she says, "there is a charge . . ."? Why are people so fascinated by grotesques?

4. Why did Jesus raise Lazarus from the dead? Was it for Lazarus's sisters who were friends of Jesus? Was it because Lazarus was Jesus' friends? Was it to amaze people with a miracle? Why do all these questions have importance for this poem?

5. Why do people make numerous attempts at suicide? Why also are most suicides either quite young people or quite sick people? Do you think that Plath really intended to die on this third attempt? What does the poem seem to say?

6. People either project their anger outward onto others or inward onto themselves. Plath appears to be angry at the men in her life, but who receives the brunt of her anger? Why?

7. How do the short three-line stanzas work to create an impression of a drum pounding out the message of the poem? What happens in the next-to-last stanza when lines 80 and 81 chant "Beware/Beware"?

8. In the middle of the poem, the speaker says, "Dying/Is an art, like everything else." Why does this line work well as the turning point in the poem? What changes in the second half of the poem?

9. What is the image that ends the poem? Has Plath herself become the devil she hates (red hair indicates the devil)?

10. Why are young people sometimes tempted to commit suicide? Read about the causes of suicide, write about what might cause a young woman in her prime to kill herself.

11. People who hate other people often are hating what they have repressed in themselves. Consider some of the villains in the modern world. What

caused their hatred and cruelty or violence? What were they saying about themselves?

12. Read or reread the story of Lazarus in the Bible. Speculate about what it would have been like for him after Jesus resurrected him? What would his life have been like? What would he have done? What is to be gained by having a second chance?

Leonard Cohen
[1934–   ]

Born the son of a wealthy clothing store owner, LEONARD COHEN was a rich nine-year-old boy when his father died. He had great freedom in the sixties, when great freedom was a prized commodity. He moved to the Greek island of Hydra when he was twenty-six and wrote the novels Beautiful Losers *(1964),* Flowers for Hitler *(1964), and* Parasites of Heaven *(1966). He then moved to New York, where he joined the great experiment of the sixties counter-culture. His friends included writers Jack Kerouac and Allen Ginsberg and singers Bob Dylan and Joan Baez. In 1968, he received the Governor General's award for his* Selected Poems *(1968). At the same time, he was making his name as a songwriter with* Songs of Leonard Cohen *(1967). Many of these songs were debuted at the Newport Folk Festival in 1967. By 1972, Cohen's work had taken a negative turn in* The Energy of Slaves, *in which many poems find salvation in personal degradation. More recently, Cohen has become spiritual through his studies with a Buddhist master, Old Roshi. His poems and music continue to influence other poets, since so much of his work asks what it means to be a poet in society.*

A Kite Is a Victim

LEONARD COHEN

A kite is a victim you are sure of.
You love it because it pulls
gentle enough to call you master,
strong enough to call you fool;
because it lives   5
like a desperate trained falcon
in the high sweet air,
and you can always haul it down
to tame it in your drawer.

A kite is a fish you have already caught   10
in a pool where no fish come,
so you play him carefully and long,
and hope he won't give up,
or the wind die down.

A kite is the last poem you've written,   15
so you give it to the wind,
but you don't let it go
until someone finds you
something else to do.

A kite is a contract of glory   20
that must be made with the sun,
so you make friends with the field
the river and the wind,
then you pray the whole cold night before,
under the travelling cordless moon,   25
to make you worthy and lyric and pure.

[1961]

Reprinted from *Stranger Music: Selected Poems and Songs* (1993), by permission of Cooke Agency International.

QUESTIONS

LEONARD COHEN, *A Kite Is a Victim*

1. How is a kite a victim? Why does the speaker in the poem like the disputed control that a kite offers? Then, how is a kite like a caught fish? The fun of fishing is the struggle, not the catching. Why is the struggle with the kite so exciting?

2. In the second half of the poem, Cohen turns to the problem of writing poetry. He compares the struggle with the kite to the struggle of the writer who strains to find out where the poem will go. How does the ending express the joy of writing (and of playing with a kite)?

3. Writers love to write about writing because it brings them great joy, but also causes them great anxiety. How does Cohen address this dilemma in his kite/fish metaphor?

4. An almost sinister undertone dominates this poem until the end. Why would the speaker want a victim? What does the end of the poem suggest about letting the victim go?

5. Who is the "you" in the poem? Is the poet using "you" to mean the speaker of the poem, or is the poem really about the reader as poet and creator, too? Who would want to read this poem and identify with it?

6. The poem shifts from daytime kite flying to nighttime moon watching as the speaker becomes one with nature. What is he saying about the experience of writing when it is good and satisfying?

7. Cohen makes clear in his life story that poems are songs, for he is a famous composer as well as poet. Find a few of his songs to discover how his work has been recorded. Then write about the quality of his music and about the effect of poetry when it is sung.

8. Write about your own writing. Do you write for pleasure, or do you write as a part of your school and work life? Make a brief history of the pieces you have written, then discuss how you see yourself and your creations.

Margaret Atwood

[1939–   ]

Born in Ottawa, Canada, **MARGARET ATWOOD** *grew up in northern Ontario, Quebec, and Toronto. She is by far the best-known Canadian writer, with works published in over thirty languages, including such varied and disparate languages as Farsi, Japanese, Turkish, Finnish, Korean, Icelandic, and Estonian. Her career began when she received her undergraduate degree from Victoria College at the University of Toronto; she went on to receive her Master of Arts from Radcliffe College in Massachusetts. She has published more than twenty-five volumes of poetry, fiction, and nonfiction, won numerous awards, and been granted a multitude of honorary degrees. Her writing is haunting, and she sometimes appears to anticipate the issues and crises of the world before they drastically affect society. Her first novel,* The Edible Woman *(1970), entered the early world of feminism, before its great debates and struggles had a firm hold in the culture. The* Handmaid's Tale *(1983) perhaps her best-known work, raises many of the issues of power and patriarchy that later came to the surface with the growth of the struggles in the Middle East, predicting a world of religious fundamentation, where women were nearly slaves to the male head of the household. This haunting story depicts a world, not far in the future, where few women can conceive, and make fertile women become breeding stock for the wealthy and elite. The* Handmaid's Tale *was made into a movie in 1990; it chillingh suggests the dark quality of Atwood's invented future world, a world which might not be so very far from the world of the early twenty-first century. The Robber Bride, written in 1994, continues to investigate questions of feminism and nationalism. Alias* Grace *(1996), too, continues the social commentary, and brings the issues of women's lives to the reading public's attention. These novels are not comfortable, but they move the reader to think about what cannot be thought or said, and to imagine what might happen in a world that continues to careen in the direction it seems already to be heading.*

The Blind Assassin *was published in 2000, and won the prestigious Booker Prize, and the non-fiction work,* Negotiations with Death: A Writer on Writing, *followed in 2002, indicating the level of her scholarly as well as literary acclaim. Her latest novel,* Oryx and Crake *(2003), continues the prediction and investigation of social issues and popular concerns. Atwood currently lives in Toronto with novelist Graeme Gibson, but continues to travel constantly, presenting readings and speeches about both her fiction and her ideas. She writes prodigously, demonstrating that she leads other living writers in both productivity and in that powerful significance of her work to the critical reading public.*

—Lisa Perdigao, *Florida Institute of Technology*

Siren Song¹

MARGARET ATWOOD

This is the one song everyone
would like to learn: the song
that is irresistible:

the song that forces men
to leap overboard in squadrons   *5*
even though they see the beached skulls

the song nobody knows
because anyone who has heard it
is dead, and the others can't remember.

Shall I tell you the secret   *10*
and if I do, will you get me
out of this bird suit?

I don't enjoy it here
squatting on this island
looking picturesque and mythical   *15*

with these two feathery maniacs,
I don't enjoy singing
this trio, fatal and valuable.

I will tell the secret to you,
to you, only to you.   *20*
Come closer. This song

¹The Sirens were half women, half bird-water nymphs, who sang mysteriously beautiful songs to
sailors, whose ships then sailed into the rocks and were destroyed on the shore.

Reprinted from *Selected Poems 1966-1984,* by permission of Oxford University Press
Canada. Copyright © Margaret Atwood.

is a cry for help: Help me!
Only you, only you can,
you are unique

at last. Alas   25
it is a boring song
but it works every time.

[1974]

QUESTIONS

MARGARET ATWOOD, *Siren Song*

1. Who is speaking in the poem, and what is her point of view? Can the reader trust her? How can you tell?

2. How does she lure the reader onto her island? What is her trick, and why is it fatal? Why can we be so easily deceived by the idea that we are exclusive, unique, and intriguing?

3. Should women be blamed for men's attraction to them? Should women be blamed for using their allure dishonestly?

4. The line, "I don't enjoy it here" is very significant in "Siren Song" How does the poem change with this line? why does the siren speak disparagingly of her fellow sirens? How does the poem draw the reader in with this device?

5. What do the last lines tell the reader about the speaker? Why is she willing to use even a "boring song" to control and capture someone else?

6. Why has the myth of the Sirens continued to catch the imaginations of writers for centuries? What is a "siren song"? What attitude toward women does the story of the Sirens imply? Write about this issue.

7. How and why do people continue in boring and self-destructive patterns? What satisfaction do they get from these patterns? Describe someone caught in such a pattern, or perhaps a boring job you stayed in too long. Write about why you stayed, or why others stay, when they should leave.

Martín Espada

[1957–   ]

MARTÍN ESPADA *has been called* "the *Latino poet of his generation.*" *Born in Brooklyn, New York, Espada, in addition to being a poet and an educator, has worked as a tenant's rights attorney and supervisor of a legal services program. Much has been made of this dual career, but Espada sees no conflict between these roles, thinking of his writing as a "poetry of advocacy." Critic David Charlton echoes Espada's understanding of that close connection, describing him as "a strong adversary for supporters of a status quo that thrives on keeping a class of people as victims. Most of all, the poems kindle the hope that comes from an act of resistance." Author Marge Piercy has written of Espada's most recent collection of poems that, through them, "you can grasp how powerful a poet Martín Espada is—his range, his compassion, his astonishing images, his sense of history," and writer Sandra Cisneros has called Martín Espada, "the Pablo Neruda of North-American authors."*

Espada's seventh collection, Alabanza: New and Selected Poems *(2003), received the Paterson Award for Sustained Literary Acheivement and was named an American Library Association Notable Book of the year. His earlier work includes the volumes of poetry* A Mayan Astronomer in Hell's Kitchen: Poems *(2000);* Imagine the Angels of Bread *(1996), which won an American Book Award and was a finalist for the National Book Critics Circle Award;* City of Coughing and Dead Radiators *(1993); the bilingual collection* Rebellion Is the Circle of a Lover's Hands *(1990), which received the Paterson Poetry Prize and a PEN/Revson Fellowship;* Trumpets from the Islands of Their Eviction *(1987); and a collection of essays,* Zapata's Disciple *(1998). He has edited several anthologies, including* El Coro: A Chorus of Latino and Latina Poets *(1997) and* Poetry Like Bread: Poets of the Political Imagination *(1994). Espada lives with his wife and son in Amherst, Massachusetts, where he is an associate professor of English at the University of Massachusetts-Amherst.*

Espada's writing focuses largely on the experiences of immigrant and working class populations in the United States; as he said in a 2000 interview, "There are many who share my experiences, who might think my same words, but who never have the opportunity to express them . . . to be able to write the poem, get it published, read it to an audience. I get to do that. And it's part of my responsibility as a poet to do that, for those who do not get the chance to speak."

Latin Night at the Pawnshop

MARTÍN ESPADA

Chelsea, Massachusetts
Christmas, 1987

The apparition of a salsa band
gleaming in the Liberty Loan
pawnshop window:

Golden trumpet,
silver trombone,   5
congas, maracas, tambourine,
all with price tags dangling
like the city morgue ticket
on a dead man's toe.

[1987]

QUESTIONS

MARTÍN ESPADA, *Latin Night at the Pawnshop*

1. In what tone does the poem begin? What images create that tone? How do the last two lines affect the poem's tone? How is that shift hinted at in the poem's first line?

2. What effect does the poem's epigraph have on your reading of the poem?

3. What makes this particular night at the pawnshop "Latin"? How does the meaning of that Latin-ness change over the course of the poem?